Dearest Katie

This is to celebrate our 4th wed
and our 1st with Rebeca
Hopefully this book will help us
future years together (especially when your mother not
around). Not just with Rebeca but the rest of
the family!
With things being so hectic over the last month I
know it has been difficult to convey my feelings.
All I can say is that as we enter our 5th year
together, with Rebeca I am the happiest / proudest
husband / father alive
You really have been terrific and I appreciate you more
than ever (even if I don't always show it) and I look
forward to all the years ahead for us all!

lots of love

Bill, Jones Carino
xxx
16/8/95

COMPLETE
BABY AND
CHILD CARE

COMPLETE
BABY AND
CHILD CARE

Dr. Miriam Stoppard

DORLING KINDERSLEY

London • New York • Stuttgart

For Will and Ed

A DORLING KINDERSLEY BOOK

Created and produced by
CARROLL & BROWN LIMITED
5 Lonsdale Road
London NW6 6RA

Project Editor Theresa Reynolds
Assistant Editors Laura Price
  Melanie Halton

Art Editors Mike Snell
  Sally Powell
Designers James Arnold
  Gemma Pearl

Photography Jules Selmes

Production Wendy Rogers
  Amanda Mackie

First published in Great Britain in 1995
by Dorling Kindersley Limited
9 Henrietta Street, London WC2E 8PS

A CIP catalogue record for this book is available
from the British Library.

ISBN 0 7513 0159 0

Reproduced by Colourscan, Singapore
Printed and bound in Great Britain by Butler and Tanner

PREFACE

There would hardly seem to be room for another baby book. Having worked on this subject for over twenty years, however, I've always felt that even the best baby books have gaps. Very few, for instance, deal with three- to five-year-olds. I also feel sure that women who have children with special needs or children with chronic ailments and disabilities feel short-changed by most baby books, including mine, because their babies aren't given enough space or emphasis. Fathers continue to be neglected group, and there's a tendency to overlook the impact of a new addition on the family as a whole. With more and more mothers in the 1990's going out to work, choosing child care is a more universal problem than it once was.

In my previous books there was never enough space to deal with important subjects like caring for twins, to illustrate the treatment of illnesses, from glue ear to hydrocephalus, and to go fully into complicated subjects like baby first aid. Most of all I never felt that I had the freedom to explain how a baby's physical, mental, and social development relates to acquisition of skills. This is a subject that's crucially important to parents. For instance, without the knowledge that a baby cannot hold a bladder full of urine until her nerves and muscles have matured, parents will continue to enforce "toilet training" – a completely outdated and cruel idea.

The scope of this book has given me the chance to plug some of those gaps and to enlarge on those two very important preschool years. Three-year-olds make huge strides in all areas of development when they're introduced to nursery and preschool classes and need a great deal of patience, understanding and support from parents if they're going to realize their full potential – which is every child's birthright, after all.

So as well as dealing with the everyday aspects of baby and child care, this book encompasses the acquisition of skills, your role as teacher, and – something I've longed to write about for two decades – the differences between boy and girl babies, to offer parents guidance on how to treasure and nurture the best parts of being a girl and being a boy.

In twenty years of writing about child care, my aim has always been to help parents feel independent, confident, and free to follow their instincts – which are nearly always right. For the first time I feel I have the space to do so. In this book I've been able to fill out, augment, and introduce the latest research in many areas where previously I felt curbed. While this book is not definitive, it's as near complete as I've ever hoped for.

CONTENTS

Introduction *8*

INTRODUCTION

Whether you are a mother expecting your first baby, have just given birth, or are an expectant or new father, you may be feeling apprehensive about your new role. Don't worry: while parenting may be one of the most responsible and challenging jobs around, it's also one of the most rewarding.

THE NEWBORN BABY

You have just experienced the creation of newborn life. Your baby is probably smaller than you imagined, and she may seem very vulnerable. You may be overwhelmed by feelings of joy, but you will also be anxious to know whether your baby is all right, and whether the sounds and movements she makes are normal. Your midwife or doctor will be able to reassure you, and you will probably be surprised at just how much your baby can do.

EVERYDAY CARE

In the first months of life your child depends on you for everything: you will have to feed, dress, and change him, and carry him around. If it is your first child, you are bound to be nervous. You may wonder whether he is taking enough milk and putting on weight fast enough, whether he is waking too often in the night, or why he seems to cry so much. You'll be surprised at how quickly caring for your baby becomes second nature; in fact, you will hardly believe there was once a time when you didn't know how to change a nappy! You'll be surprised, too, at how quickly the time comes when your child is able to do things for himself: to spoonfeed himself, to walk, to dress himself, to use a potty…. In a few short years he will be able to look after his own basic needs and be ready to go to school.

PLAY AND DEVELOPMENT

Sharing your child's pleasure in new skills and knowledge is one of the great joys of parenthood. It's also the most important thing you can do to promote your child's development: physically, by allowing her to explore her own capabilities in a challenging and safe environment; mentally, by taking time to talk to and play with her; and socially, by providing her with the love and security that will make her a well-adjusted and happy child. In these early years, play is your child's main tool for learning. By understanding how she learns and develops you can help her to get the most from play and from her toys.

FAMILY LIFE

However much getting married or deciding to live with your partner may have changed your life, the birth of your child will change it far more. You need to balance your partner's needs and the needs of your baby with your own. If you've had twins, you will be very much in need of practical help and support. Your extended family may suddenly start to figure more largely in your life. Whether you see this as a good thing will depend on all sorts of personal factors, but your child will undoubtedly benefit from the loving interest of his relations, and this continues to be true even – or rather especially – if the relationship between you and your partner is under strain.

CHILDREN WITH SPECIAL NEEDS

Every mother wants her baby to grow up a happy, well-adjusted adult, and to live a rich and fulfilling life. If your child has special needs – and this applies to a wide variety of children, from those who are very gifted to those born with a chronic physical condition such as cerebral palsy – then achieving this is going to require a lot of extra effort from you. If your child is ill, then at the same time you will have to cope with your own feelings of confusion, anxiety, and perhaps of guilt. Over the months that follow the diagnosis of your child's condition, however, you will learn a lot about what you can do to help your child, and you will almost certainly cope better than you had thought possible. There are many support networks available that offer help to parents of children with special needs; be sure to make use of them.

MEDICINE AND HEALTHCARE

You are responsible for promoting your child's good health, recognising when he is ill, and acting accordingly. Your child can't always tell you what's wrong with him, but you will become sensitive to the signs that tell you something is amiss, and you will learn when you can look after him yourself and when you need to send for a doctor. It is your duty as a parent to learn basic first aid procedures, and you should attend a training course to do this rather than try to learn from a book. (The British Red Cross, St. John Ambulance, and St. Andrew's Ambulance Association run courses; you will find your local branch in the telephone book.) Be sure to learn emergency first aid procedures by heart, and refresh your memory often.

CHAPTER ONE

THE NEWBORN BABY

*Your feelings on the birth of your new baby are likely to be
pride, wonder, and exhilaration mixed with exhaustion. You
may feel fiercely attached to your baby straight away, or
bonding may take a little longer. You will almost certainly be
surprised at his appearance: his oddly shaped head, wrinkled
face, and tiny hands and feet.*

*From the moment of birth your baby will exhibit reflexes and
behaviour that help him survive. In such things as his sleeping patterns and crying bouts you will be able to discern the
beginnings of a personality.*

*The first question in every new mother's mind is "Is he all
right?", and medical staff will carry out tests immediately
after the birth and in the first few days to reassure you on
this score. Your baby will be given all the special attention
that they consider necessary. If he is premature or small for
dates he may need to be kept in a special care unit, but you'll
still be able to bond with him and take part in his care.*

YOUR NEW BABY

Most mothers find they establish a tangible bond with their newborn babies within the first 72 hours, but a "bond" doesn't necessarily mean instantaneous and ecstatic love at first sight.

Attending to the physical needs of your newborn baby is so exhausting that it's easy to forget your baby also has an active emotional life. In the long term the most serious damage to a baby's health may stem from inadequate love and attention – so in the next few weeks and months heap as much upon your baby as you can.

Mother love is partially hormonal, so if you don't feel it immediately it's not your fault. Mother love usually comes in with the milk, 72 hours after the birth of your child, though it may come in later and it may grow quite gradually. One of the hormones that stimulates lactation is also, in part, responsible for mother love.

Some mothers are shocked to find that they lack maternal feelings when they first hold their babies. This may be due to a variety of factors, such as complications with the delivery, unrealistic expectations of childbirth, sheer exhaustion, fluctuating hormone levels, and even the mother's own experience in early childhood. Maternal "indifference" can last from an hour to a week, but rarely much longer.

Bonding
Your baby will be happiest next to your skin, where she can feel your warmth and hear your heartbeat.

Whatever you had expected – bigger, smaller, quieter, less slippery, – your baby will surprise and delight you. Experienced parents discern a personality at birth but first-time parents may think their newborns are oblivious to the world about them. Babies, however, rapidly build up a vocabulary of sensory experiences from birth. When awake, she will be alert and listening. She can respond when spoken to, recognises you by smell, and has an intent gaze. At birth she can recognise a human face, and, she will move her head in response to noise. She is born wanting to talk and will "converse" with you if you talk animatedly about 20–25 centimetres (8–10 inches) from her face where she can see you clearly. She will react to your smile by moving her mouth, nodding, protruding her tongue, or jerking her whole body.

HANDLING YOUR BABY

The need for physical contact throughout childhood is well documented, and this is especially true of the first weeks of life. The majority of newborn babies spend much of their time asleep, so it is important that you're there to hold and mother your baby when she's awake. If your baby is in an incubator, ask to be able to stroke her and change her nappy. One young mother I met recently, whose ten-day-old baby had been in an incubator for the first 48 hours, was too terrified to pick him up because she thought he might "break". Babies are stronger than you think.

BREATHING

After an initial outburst of crying, you may not be able to hear anything more from your baby because it can be difficult to hear a newborn's light breathing. In some cases a baby may even stop breathing entirely for a few seconds, but this isn't abnormal. All babies make strange noises when they breathe – usually a noisy snuffling sound – and their breathing is often irregular.

Your baby's lungs are still weak, which means that her breathing is naturally much shallower than yours or mine. This is nothing to worry about, as her lungs will gradually get stronger each day.

SUCKLING

For the first three days after your baby's birth, your breasts produce not milk, but colostrum, a thin, yellow fluid that contains water, protein, sugar, vitamins, minerals, and antibodies for protection against infectious diseases. During her first 72 hours of life, colostrum helps protect your baby against infections. To stimulate your breasts to produce milk you need to feed her frequently; the sucking action of the baby stimulates hormones that, in turn, stimulate milk production. Even if you do not intend to breastfeed, it is a good idea to suckle your baby as soon as she is born, because the colostrum will be beneficial to her, and the act of suckling will help you bond with your baby.

As soon as your baby is born you can put her to your breast. She will have a natural sucking reflex and the sucking action will encourage the production of the hormone oxytocin. Oxytocin makes the uterus contract and expel the placenta. Touch your baby's cheek on the side nearest your nipple to stimulate her rooting reflex. Rather than just sucking on the nipple, her lips should be on the breast tissue with the whole of the nipple in her mouth.

INVOLVING YOUR PARTNER

Because the experience of childbirth is so focused on the mother it is common for the father to feel neglected or excluded. It is important for father and baby to bond, too: touch, smell, and sound are good ways to do this. Soon after his baby is born her father should hold her against his skin; this way his baby will come into contact with his specific smell and over a period of weeks she will learn to associate this with comfort and reassurance. The father should also speak to his child as she will quickly become familiar with his voice. In fact, if he talks to the baby while she is in the uterus, she will recognise her father's voice when she is born.

It is common for the mother to take prime responsibility for a newborn's care, but the father should be encouraged to take an equal role. He should learn how to hold his baby and should build up a tactile relationship with her. Make sure he becomes involved with day-to-day routines such as bathing and nappy changing. Even if the baby is breastfed, he can learn to bottlefeed her using expressed breastmilk from the mother. Both parents should cuddle her when you and she are naked so that she can feel and smell your skin and hear both of your hearts beating.

YOUR BABY'S FIRST BREATH

Don't be alarmed if your newborn cries vigorously – this is exactly what you want to hear.

In the uterus your baby's lungs are redundant – she gets all the oxygen she needs from the placenta, so the lungs are collapsed.

The very first time your baby takes a breath the lungs expand, and the increased pressure in them shuts a valve just beyond the heart, so that the blood that used to pass to the placenta for oxygenation now goes directly to the lungs. These two crucial steps make her an independent being, able to survive without you, and they happen in an instant.

Nothing should interfere with your baby's ability to take her first breath. That's why doctors and midwives clear air passages immediately and if the first breath is delayed they resuscitate the baby.

Crying
The intake of air that accompanies crying helps your baby to clear her airways at birth.

YOUR BABY'S APPEARANCE

When you are given your baby to hold for the first time you will probably be surprised by his appearance. Although your baby is undoubtedly a bundle of joy, many mothers mistakenly expect a clean and placid bundle, similar to the ones that appear in baby-food commercials. As you now suddenly discover, however, real life is a little bit different.

Skin Your baby's skin may be covered in a whitish, greasy substance called vernix, which is a natural barrier cream to prevent the skin from becoming waterlogged. In some hospitals the vernix will be removed immediately, but in others it may be left on to give your baby some natural protection against minor skin irritations such as flaking and peeling.

Your baby's skin may be rather blotchy in colour; this is because the tiny blood vessels are unstable. Black children are often light-skinned at birth, but the skin begins to get darker as it begins to produce melanin, its natural pigment; it will reach its permanent colour by about six months.

Head Your baby's skull is made up of four large plates that don't fuse, so they can move across each other, especially during labour when your baby's head is compressed by pressure from your vaginal walls. The sliding skull bones enable him to pass through the birth canal without hazard, though his head may become slightly elongated or misshapen in the process. This is entirely normal, and does not affect the brain. There may also be some bruising or swelling, but it will disappear during the first few days or weeks.

The soft spots on the top of your baby's skull where the bones are still not joined are called the fontanelles. In a sense, they are the windows into a baby's body. The skull bones won't fuse completely until your baby is about two. Be careful, especially with a very young baby, not to press the fontanelles.

Eyes Your baby may not be able to open his eyes straight away due to puffiness caused by pressure on his head during birth. This pressure may also have broken some tiny blood vessels in your baby's eyes, causing small, red, triangular marks in the whites of the eyes. Entirely harmless, they require no treatment and will disappear within a couple of weeks. "Sticky eye", which results in a yellow discharge around the eyelids, is quite common. Although this is not a serious condition, it should always be treated by a doctor.

Your baby can see clearly up to a distance of 20–25 centimetres (8–10 inches), but beyond that cannot focus both his eyes at the same time, and this may cause him to squint, or look cross-eyed. Both of these conditions will clear up as his eye muscles grow stronger (usually within a month). If your baby is still squinting (see p.287) at three months you should consult a doctor. You may find it difficult to get your baby to open his eyes at first, but never try to force them open. One of the easiest ways I have found to get a baby to open his eyes is to hold him above my head.

Most newborn babies' eyes are blue regardless of race, and your baby's eye colour is likely to change after birth because it is only then that babies acquire melanin, the body's natural pigment.

Hair Some babies are born with a full head of hair, while others are completely bald. The colour of your baby's hair at birth is not necessarily the permanent colour he will acquire later on in life. The fine downy hair that many babies have on their bodies at birth is called lanugo, and this will often fall off soon after birth.

Genitals Many babies, both male and female, appear to have enlarged genitals shortly after birth, and babies of both genders may have "breasts". This is due to the massive increase in hormone levels that you've experienced just before giving birth, some of which have passed into your baby's bloodstream.

With a baby boy this can lead to an enlarged scrotum and enlarged breasts; he may even produce a little milk. This is not abnormal, and the swelling will gradually subside. A baby girl may have a swollen vulva or clitoris and a small "period" shortly after birth.

Umbilicus The umbilical cord, which is moist and bluish-white at birth, is clamped with forceps and then cut with scissors. Only a short length of cord remains, which dries and becomes almost black within two to four hours. The stump will shrivel up and fall off about seven days after but your baby will feel no pain.

UMBILICAL HERNIA

Some babies develop a small swelling near the navel, called an umbilical hernia. This is caused by weak abdominal muscles, which allow the intestines to push through a little.

Umbilical hernias are most obvious when the abdominal muscles are used for crying. They are very common, and virtually always clears up within a year. If your baby has one and it enlarges or persists, consult your doctor.

Site of swelling
The hernia forms where the umbilical cord entered the baby's abdomen, because there is a gap in the abdominal muscles at that point.

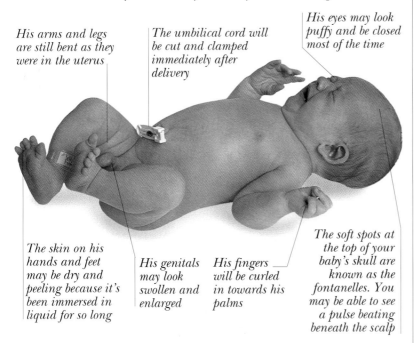

His arms and legs are still bent as they were in the uterus

The umbilical cord will be cut and clamped immediately after delivery

His eyes may look puffy and be closed most of the time

The skin on his hands and feet may be dry and peeling because it's been immersed in liquid for so long

His genitals may look swollen and enlarged

His fingers will be curled in towards his palms

The soft spots at the top of your baby's skull are known as the fontanelles. You may be able to see a pulse beating beneath the scalp

ABOUT BIRTHMARKS

If you haven't found a blemish anywhere on your baby's body, it's probably because you haven't looked long enough.

Virtually every child is born with some type of birthmark, no matter how tiny. Most marks will fade and disappear on their own by the time your child is three years old, although some of them remain and increase in size.

Both my sons had stork bite birthmarks at the back of the neck just under the hairline (which is a very common place to find them). They disappeared, however, by the time they were six months old.

Other likely places are the eyelids, the forehead, and the neck, although one might be found on any part of your baby's skin.

Superficial birthmarks are nothing to worry about. They do no harm and need no treatment.

MEASUREMENTS

Your baby's weight, head circumference, and length will be measured to give an indication of her maturity and development. These measurements can be used as a base-line for her future development if necessary. Although routine measurements are inevitably compared to "the average", don't worry about this too much. An average is just an arithmetical calculation, so the "average child" is only theoretical and doesn't exist.

Weight Newborns differ greatly in weight. Nutritional, placental, and racial factors all have a bearing. The weight range for babies born around their expected time is 2.4–4.8 kilograms (5 pounds 4 ounces to 10 pounds 8 ounces). If you are tall or heavy or if you are diabetic, your baby is likely to be on the heavy side.

Women who suffer from chronic hypertension, vascular or renal disease or pre-eclampsia, and women who smoke during pregnancy are likely to have lighter babies. A woman whose pregnancy is shorter than 40 weeks is also likely to have a lighter baby. Girls generally weigh slightly less than boys, and twins or other multiple births weigh less than singletons.

It is normal for your baby to lose weight in the first few days after birth as her body adjusts to new feeding requirements. She must now process her own food, and it will take a while for her to feed consistently. The usual weight loss at this time is about 115–170 grams (4–6 ounces). After a few days, you can expect your baby's weight to begin increasing.

The significance of a baby's weight gain is what it tells us of her overall physical health. Steady weight gain indicates that her food intake is sufficient and is being absorbed, while poor or erratic weight gain or weight loss signals that food intake is insufficient or that it isn't being absorbed.

Head circumference is an important indicator of healthy development

Head circumference Your baby's head is disproportionately large in comparison to her body size, taking up one quarter of her entire length. The younger a baby is, the larger her head is in proportion to the rest of her body. The average circumference of a newborn's head is about 35 centimetres (14 inches).

Measurements
Your baby's length and head circumference will be measured, and he will also be weighed.

Measuring head circumference is regarded as an essential part of the examination of a baby because the growth of the head reflects the growth of the brain; some experts think there's a relationship between head circumference and intelligence. An unusually large or small head circumference may be an indication of an abnormality of the brain.

Chest and abdomen The circumference of your baby's chest will be smaller than that of her head. Her stomach might appear to be very large, and even distended, but given the weakness in her abdominal muscles, this is to be expected.

THE FIRST NAPPIES

Your baby's stools and urine may not look as you expect them to, and if you have a baby girl there may be some vaginal discharge. None of these necessarily means that something is wrong.

Stools Your baby's first bowel movement will consist of meconium, which is mainly digested mucus and looks blackish green. Some of this is accumulated from swallowing amniotic fluid while inside your uterus. The first meconium stool should be passed within the first 24 hours and it is not unusual for her next bowel movement to be two days later; this is especially true if you are breastfeeding, (check, however, that your baby is wetting her nappy regularly). After the fourth day she may pass four or five motions daily.

You will notice that the colour and composition of her stools change from dark, greenish-black sticky meconium to greenish brown, and then to a yellow semi-solid type. If you are bottle feeding your baby, the stools might resemble scrambled eggs.

Most babies fill their nappies as soon as they have eaten, due to a perfectly healthy gastrocolic reflex, which makes the bowel empty itself as soon as food enters the stomach. Some babies pass motions much more infrequently, but as long as your baby does not have to strain and her motions are a normal colour and soft, there is no need for concern. If her motions are infrequent or hard, it is a good idea to give her a small amount of water (one tablespoon or 15 millilitres) two or three times a day.

Urine A newborn baby passes urine almost continuously because her bladder muscles are underdeveloped. She's unable to hold urine for any length of time – usually no longer than a few minutes – so it's quite normal to find that she wets her nappy up to 20 times in 24 hours. When she does, her urine will contain substances called urates which may stain her nappy dark pink or red. This, too, is normal for a newborn.

Vaginal discharge Newborn girls sometimes produce a clear or white vaginal discharge. In some cases you may notice a small amount of vaginal bleeding, but this is perfectly normal and will clear up naturally after a couple of days. If you are really worried, contact your doctor for reassurance.

TYPES OF BIRTHMARK

Most birthmarks are just abnormal collections of small blood vessels under the skin. They are harmless and do not cause your baby any pain. Here are some of the commonest types:

Strawberry marks These usually first appear as small red dots that are not always obvious. They may grow rather alarmingly during the first months of life into red raised lumps, but during the second year they shrivel and disappear without leaving a scar.

Salmon patches Also called stork's marks or stork bites, these pink discolorations of the skin usually fade with time, often within a few months.

Spider birthmarks (naevi) These small marks appear shortly after birth as a network or a cobweb of dilated vessels. They generally disappear after the first year.

Pigmented naevi These brownish patches can occur anywhere on the body. They are usually pale and nearly always enlarge as the child grows but they seldom become darker.

Port wine stains Found anywhere on the body, these bright red or even purple marks are caused by dilated capillaries in the skin. Although permanent, they can be removed with laser treatment, or easily camouflaged with special make-up.

Mongolian spots It is common for dark-skinned babies to have harmless, dark bluish-black discolorations of the skin, usually on the back or buttocks; these will fade naturally.

NAME *Katharine Winterton*

AGE *31 years*

PAST MEDICAL HISTORY *High blood pressure (140/190)*

FAMILY HISTORY *Several cases of high blood pressure on paternal side*

OBSTETRIC HISTORY *First pregnancy. Mild pre-eclampsia (a condition that causes swelling of the legs, fingers, and face) diagnosed in sixth month. Occasional bleeding gums*

During pregnancy Katharine's whole view of giving birth changed drastically. She had originally decided to do everything naturally, she didn't want any drugs, and the thought of a Caesarean horrified her. When she was told she had high blood pressure, she began to panic. Symptoms that virtually all pregnant women experience at some point, like faintness, headaches, or indigestion, seemed terrifying to her.

NEW PARENTS

Katharine was very concerned that she might develop eclampsia during labour, which can lead to convulsions or fits. In fact, as I explained to her, this is a rare condition that is unlikely to occur even when pre-eclampsia has been diagnosed. Due to her high blood pressure and the weight of the baby (estimated at about 4 kilograms/9 pounds), Katharine agreed to being induced when she was two weeks overdue.

THE LABOUR

In the event, although it was long (17 hours), labour went relatively smoothly for Katharine. She was induced at 9 a.m. on Monday, and at 1 p.m. felt relaxed enough to send her husband Adam to her mother's for lunch… on condition that he bring her back some of her favourite home-made cake.

Katharine used a TENS machine, which is supposed to stimulate natural painkillers through the transmission of electrical impulses. She was put on it late, however, so she's not sure whether it helped or not. At midnight, 15 hours later, she asked for an epidural – something she had sworn not to do – and after that everything was all right. At 1.45 a.m. on Tuesday she was given an episiotomy (which she didn't feel at all), and about ten minutes later the midwife used forceps to pull Natasha out.

FIRST REACTIONS

"I got a bit of a shock when I saw her," recalls Katharine, "because her face was very red and scrunched up, her head looked lopsided and indented because of the forceps, and she seemed to be gasping for air but not making any sound. I kept on asking the midwife 'Is she all right?! Is she all right?!' The midwife turned away for a second and I was absolutely convinced Natasha was dead. That was actually the worst moment during the whole labour, and I started to cry uncontrollably.

"In fact, the midwife was only doing the Apgar scores and, as it turned out, Natasha scored highly. About 30 seconds later we were handed a perfect little baby girl breathing normally.

"I was quite surprised that she had her eyes wide open and seemed to be looking at me and Adam in a very alert, quizzical manner. She just sat staring for about five minutes without crying at all. Natasha is my first child, and so I wasn't prepared for the combination of sheer joy, love, and relief that flooded over me when she was placed in my arms for the first time.

"The placenta came out after only ten minutes, which I'm told is a bit unusual without the use of Syntocinon, and then the midwife clamped the umbilical cord in two places, and Adam cut it."

LOOKING BACK AT THE BIRTH

The one thing Katharine regrets about the whole pregnancy is having had an episiotomy. She is sure she would have dilated enough had she been given another half hour. Although she felt no pain at the time, due to the epidural, she says the episiotomy was the only physical problem associated with the birth that didn't clear up in the first two weeks.

Three months later the episiotomy scar is still sensitive, and she says that the worry of tearing during intercourse has put her off sex completely. I explained to her that, although this fear is genuine, it is almost certain she would have lost her sexual appetite for a time after giving birth, with or without an episiotomy. Although the latest research indicates that tears heal better than episiotomies should the mother not stretch enough naturally, a forceps delivery almost always necessitates an episiotomy.

THE FIRST DAYS

Katharine found that despite her elation after the birth of Natasha, she soon got what are commonly known as the "baby blues", a feeling of deep depression that stayed with her for three days. She found it very difficult to relate to all the people around her, including Adam. She also felt guilty because she had not expected these feelings to accompany the birth of a normal, healthy baby.

"Baby blues" are caused by the huge increase in hormones in a woman's body during childbirth. It takes quite a while, sometimes weeks or months, for the body to readjust, and in the meantime a new mother may have to deal with difficult bouts of depression.

In Katharine's case, things improved when she arrived home from the hospital. Although she was physically exhausted, psychologically she felt much more in control.

"It was only when we walked through our own door with Natasha that I felt the three of us were a proper family. Having said that, Natasha seemed to take up every last second of our time, although I was lucky to have Adam doing about 40 per cent of all the work."

KATHARINE'S TIPS

- Try to be flexible and positive. The only thing to be sure of is that it probably won't turn out as you planned – but that isn't necessarily a bad thing.

- Although I only had my husband with me during labour, a lot of women I spoke to on the ward also had a friend or a relative. I will definitely consider this next time if the hospital allows.

- If you reach the stage where the pain becomes overwhelming, don't be afraid to ask for an epidural – it really did make a difference for me, and after that I enjoyed the birth much more.

- Ask your midwife or doctor to let you stretch naturally rather than attempt too early an episiotomy.

NAME *Adam Winterton*

AGE *30 years*

Because he had done three years' medical training, Adam was sure he would be able to take the birth in his stride. Having his wife as the patient, he admitted, contributed to the loss of a lot of his usual self-composure.

"To begin with, it seemed to be going very slowly, and Kath sent me off to get some lunch. When I got back she was obviously in a lot of pain, and I couldn't believe I had been selfish enough to leave her for two hours. I felt incredibly guilty, and also a bit useless.

"Just before midnight, Kath really started to scream, and that was the worst point for me. All I could do was squeeze her hand tightly, which made me feel terrible.

"I was virtually jumping for joy when they gave her the epidural, something we both decided beforehand we didn't want. After that we knew it was just a matter of waiting, and because Kath was no longer in excessive pain, it was something we could really enjoy together. That was when I felt the most useful, because she needed someone to take her mind off what was going on. We even started planning what we were going to do once we got Natasha home."

NEWBORN BEHAVIOUR

Once your baby is born, it may take you a while to get used to his behaviour. It is worth studying his reactions to various stimuli, and becoming familiar with some of the traits that will mark his personality. Young babies have far more individuality than they're usually credited with, and this is a useful fact to bear in mind as you get to know your child.

REFLEXES

One thing common to all healthy babies is a number of reflexes that can be stimulated from the very first moments after birth. These reflexes are unconscious movements that eventually, at about three months, start to be replaced by conscious movements.

Grasp reflex
If you put something in the palm of your baby's hand, he will clench it surprisingly tightly. The grasp of a baby is often tight enough to support his entire body weight (although you should never try this).

EYE REFLEXES

Your baby will close his eyes, blink, or move them from one side to the other, depending on what is happening around him.

• If light shines in his face, he will blink – usually whether he has his eyes open or not (you should never shine bright light directly in your baby's eyes)

• He will also blink if you tap the bridge of his nose or blow gently across his eyes, or if he is startled by a sudden noise

• If you lift your newborn up and turn him to the left or right, his eyes will not normally move with his head, but will stay fixed in the same position momentarily. This is known as the "doll's-eye response", and will usually disappear after about ten days.

Moro reflex
When your baby's head is allowed to drop back, he will throw his limbs up with fingers outstretched, then let them fall back slowly towards his body.

He will turn to a finger stroking his cheek

The rooting reflex
This is the most basic instinct: the one that helps your newborn baby to find your breast and suck it. If you gently stroke your baby's cheek he will turn his head in the direction of your finger and open his mouth. If you touch the centre of his upper lip, you will also see that his mouth opens.

He instinctively opens his mouth to suck

You might notice that your newborn baby responds in a positive way to your presence by momentarily contracting the whole of his face and body. As he learns to control his movements, you will see that his reactions become more directed and less random. For instance, at six weeks, instead of scrunching up his whole face, he may show you a distinct smile.

TESTING REFLEXES

Until your baby's physical and mental capabilities develop, it will be his instinctive reflexes that provide an indication of his maturity. Doctors can test these reflexes to check your baby's general health and see that his central nervous system is functioning well. Premature babies will not react in the same way as full-term babies.

Although there are more than seventy primitive reflexes that have been identified in newborn babies, your doctor is only likely to test a selected few. The two most commonly recognised reflexes that you can easily test yourself are the rooting and the grasp reflex. Don't try to test the Moro reflex at home, as this could distress your baby and make him cry.

Walking reflex
If you hold your baby under the shoulders so that he is in an upright position and his feet are allowed to touch a firm surface, he'll move his legs in a walking action. This reflex disappears in three to six weeks, and is not what helps your child learn to walk.

Placing reflex
This is quite similar to the walking reflex. If you hold your baby in an upright position and bring the front of his leg into contact with the edge of a table, he will lift his foot as if to step on to the table. The same reflex is present in the arm; if the back of your baby's forearm touches the table edge, he will raise his arm.

Your baby takes up a crawling position when he's placed on his stomach

"Crawling"
When you place your baby on his stomach, he will automatically assume what appears to be a crawling position, with his pelvis high and his knees pulled up under his abdomen. When he kicks his legs he may be able to shuffle in a vague crawling manner. It is not real crawling, however, and this behaviour will disappear as soon as his legs uncurl and he lies flat.

YOUR NEWBORN GIRL

Many behavioural traits that are typical of girls can be observed in your baby as soon as she is born.

• *Hearing in girls is very acute and they can be calmed down with soothing words much more readily than boys*

• *A baby girl cries longer than a boy if she hears another baby crying*

• *Baby girls use their own voice to get their mother's attention earlier and more often than boys*

• *Baby girls can locate the source of a sound without difficulty*

• *Girls respond enthusiastically to visual stimulation from birth*

• *Baby girls are interested in the unusual*

• *Girls prefer the human face to almost anything else. Later in life this trait shows as intuitive reading of facial expression regardless of cultural differences*

CRYING

Assume that your baby will cry a lot and you might be pleasantly surprised if she doesn't. If you think she won't cry and then she does, you may find yourself overwhelmed and disorientated.

Remember that there are really only three states your newborn baby can be in: asleep, awake and quiet, or awake and crying. If she is crying there are a variety of reasons for it. The most likely causes are tiredness, hunger, loneliness, and discomfort – she is too hot or too cold, is in an uncomfortable position, or needs changing. You must accept sometimes, though, that a baby will cry for no discernible reason. This type of crying can be the most stressful for a parent.

Responding to crying Leaving a child to cry on her own is never a good idea, even though you will hear this advice often. If a baby is denied attention and friendship in her early weeks and months, she may grow up to be introverted, shy, and withdrawn. Research on newborns shows that if parents are slow to respond to their baby's crying, the result may be a baby that cries more rather than less. A recent study found that babies whose crying was ignored in their first few weeks tended to cry more frequently and persistently as they grew older.

Often people confuse spoiling a child with loving a child. In my opinion a baby cannot be "spoiled" enough. A six-month-old baby who is picked up, nursed, cuddled, and talked to soothingly and lovingly is not learning about seeking attention; she is learning about love and forming human relationships – and that is one of the most important lessons a child will ever learn in terms of her future emotional and psychological development. What we tend to call spoiling is both a natural response of a mother to a distressed child, and the natural need of the baby.

SLEEP PATTERNS

Once you bring your newborn home, you'll have some sleepless nights unless you are very lucky. Although most newborns usually sleep when they are not feeding – typically spending at least 60 per cent of their time asleep – some will remain active and alert for surprisingly long periods during the day and night.

One young mother was shocked to find that her new baby never dozed for longer than one or two hours at a time until she was four months old. This is a very long time for any parent to survive without a full night's sleep, especially when your body may be in need of rest after an exhausting pregnancy and birth. If you have a very wakeful baby, be consoled by the fact that as long as she isn't left bored on her own, every minute that she's awake she's learning something new – and in the long run you will be rewarded with an eager, bright child.

All babies are different, and their sleep requirements depend on individual physiology. For this reason it's nonsensical to lay down rigid sleeping times that correspond to the average baby. As I've said before, the average baby doesn't exist.

Most newborns fall asleep soon after feeding. At first, a baby's wakefulness is likely to depend on how much feeding she needs, which in turn depends on her weight (see below).

SOUNDS YOUR BABY MAKES

Babies make a variety of strange noises, whether asleep or awake, and this is quite normal. Most of these are due to the immaturity of her respiratory system and will soon disappear.

Snoring Your baby may make some grunting noises when she's asleep. This is not a true snore, and is probably caused by vibrations on the soft palate at the back of her mouth as she breathes.

Snuffling Your baby may snuffle so loudly with each breath that you think she has a cold or that she has catarrh at the back of her throat. In most babies these snuffling noises are harmless and are caused because the bridge of the nose is low, and air is trying to get through very short, narrow nasal passages. As your baby grows older the bridge of her nose will get higher and the snuffling sound will gradually disappear.

Sneezing You may also think your baby has a cold because she sneezes a lot. In fact sneezing is common in newborn babies, particularly if they open their eyes and are exposed to bright light. This sneezing can actually be beneficial – it helps clear out your baby's nasal passages.

Hiccups Newborn babies hiccup a lot, particularly after a feed. This leads some mothers to fear that their baby has indigestion, but this is rarely the case. Hiccups are due to imperfect control of the diaphragm – the sheet of muscle that separates the chest from the abdomen – and they will disappear as your baby's nervous control of the diaphragm matures.

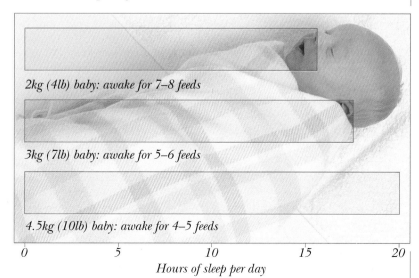

2kg (4lb) baby: awake for 7–8 feeds

3kg (7lb) baby: awake for 5–6 feeds

4.5kg (10lb) baby: awake for 4–5 feeds

| 0 | 5 | 10 | 15 | 20 |

Hours of sleep per day

YOUR NEWBORN BOY

From the moment of birth, baby boys show characteristic male behaviour, some of which will persist throughout life.

• *Hearing in boys is less acute than in girls, so boys are more difficult to calm down*

• *If a newborn boy hears another baby cry, he'll join in but stop crying quite quickly*

• *Baby boys don't make sounds in answer to their mother's voice early on. This hearing response lasts throughout life*

• *Newborn boys have difficulty in locating the source of sounds*

• *Baby boys require more visual stimulation than girls. They quickly lose interest in a design or picture, and lag behind girls in visual maturity up to the age of seven months*

• *Baby boys are interested in the differences between things*

• *Boys are more active, and are interested in things just as much as in people*

• *Boys want to taste everything, touch everything, and move things about more than girls*

Newborn sleep requirements
A newborn's sleep pattern is determined by her weight and feeding requirements. This means that in the first weeks of life, the less your baby weighs, the more often she will need to be fed and the less time she will spend sleeping, and vice versa. The chart is a very rough guide to sleep requirements according to varying birth-weights.

NEWBORN HEALTH

Immediately after birth your baby will undergo five short tests to assess his health

Your baby is given a score of 0, 1 or 2 for each category. If he scores over 7, he is in good condition. If he scores under 4, he needs help and will receive resuscitation. Most low-scoring babies score highly when tested again a few minutes later. The five checks are:

Appearance A pink skin colour shows his lungs are working well.

Pulse This indicates the strength and regularity of the heart beats.

Grimace/crying Facial expressions and responses show how alert he is to stimuli.

Activity This shows the health and tone of your baby's muscles.

Respiration Breathing shows the health of his lungs.

Grimace

Pulse

Respiration

Appearance

Activity

Assessing a newborn
The baby is checked to ensure his lungs and heart are working and his responses are healthy.

Whether your baby is born in hospital or at home, the doctor or midwife will see to it that he is given uninterrupted expert attention until breathing is well established. Any major problems should be identified within a matter of minutes, so that if special care is required it will begin at the earliest possible moment. Immediately after delivery the doctor or midwife will test your baby against the Apgar scale (see left), a series of short tests to determine his general physical well-being. Devised by the late Dr. Virginia Apgar, a renowned anaesthesiologist, they are designed to detect whether your baby is in need of immediate special attention. The doctor or midwife will then examine your baby to assess his general condition. The sort of checks your doctor will do involve:

- Making sure that your baby's facial features and body proportions are normal.

- Turning your baby over to see that his back is normal and there is no spina bifida (see p.28).

- Examining his anus, legs, fingers, and toes.

- Recording the number of blood vessels in the umbilical cord – normally there are two arteries and one vein.

- Weighing your baby.

- Measuring your baby's head and body length.

- Checking your baby's temperature with a rectal thermometer, and warming him if he needs it.

This preliminary examination takes less than a minute when performed by an experienced doctor or midwife. You can then rest easy in the knowledge that your baby is healthy and normal.

THE NEXT DAY

Once the initial tests have been carried out and you've held and suckled him for as long as you and your partner want, your baby will be wrapped up snugly and put in his cot in order to keep warm. He'll be given a thorough examination 24 hours later to ensure that all is well. This takes place when your baby is warm and relaxed. Ask the hospital staff to let you know when the examination is going to take place, so that you can be there. You will have the opportunity to ask your doctor questions and to discuss any worries that you may have.

Your baby is placed on a flat surface in a good light and at a convenient height for the doctor, who may be seated. You can have the examination at your bedside if you are immobile, but should you be absent, never fail to get the results of the examination. Generally your doctor will start examining at the top of the head and work down to the toes.

Head and neck The doctor will look at the skull bones and the fontanelles, and check for any misshaping that occurred when the head passed through the birth canal during delivery. He will look at the eyes, ears, and nose, and check the mouth for any abnormality, such as cleft palate, and for any teeth. Although rare, some newborn babies do have teeth. If they are loose or growing at an unusual angle they will be removed so that there is no risk of their falling out and being swallowed. The doctor will also check your baby's neck for any cysts or swellings.

Chest and heart The heart and lungs are checked with a stethoscope. The lungs should be expanded and working normally. The work-load of a baby's heart increases substantially when he becomes responsible for his own circulation, causing odd sounds that are heard as a heart murmur, but the vast majority of murmurs disappear spontaneously and quickly. Your child will be examined during the post-natal check-up to see if a heart murmur persists.

Arms and hands The doctor will check each arm for a pulse, and for normal movement and strength. He will also check your baby's fingers and palm creases. Nearly all babies have two major creases across each palm; if there is only a single crease your doctor will look for other physical abnormalities.

Abdomen and genitals The doctor will press his hands gently into your baby's abdomen to check the size and shape of the liver and spleen. Both may be slightly enlarged in a newborn baby. He will check the testes to ensure that they are properly descended if your baby is a boy, and check that the labia are not joined and that the clitoris is a normal size for a girl. The doctor will also check the lower spine and anus for congenital abnormalities (see pp. 28–29).

Hips, legs and feet Your doctor will hold both thighs firmly and move each leg to see whether the head of the thigh bone is unstable or lies outside the hip joint, suggesting congenital dislocation of the hip. Testing the hips is not painful, but your baby may cry at the movement. The doctor will examine the legs and feet to make sure they are of equal size and length. If the ankle is still turned inwards as it was in the uterus, your baby may have a club foot. This can be treated with manipulation and perhaps a cast.

Nerves and muscles Your doctor will put your baby's arms and legs through a range of movements to make sure that they are not too stiff or floppy. This will tell him about the health of your baby's nerves and muscles. He will make sure that the normal newborn reflexes, such as the grasp, stepping, and Moro reflexes (see p.20) are present, and check your baby's head control.

JAUNDICE

Jaundice is not a disease and, in the majority of newborn babies, is not dangerous.

Jaundice is likely to occur when a baby is about three days old. It is caused by the breakdown of red blood cells shortly after birth. This breakdown creates an excess in the blood of a pigment called bilirubin, causing a yellowish tinge to the baby's skin.

A newborn is unable to excrete the bilirubin sufficiently rapidly to prevent jaundice until his liver is more mature, at about one week. Treatment for jaundice is usually just a short spell under an ultraviolet light, but even without this, the condition should clear up by itself within a week.

If there is an incompatibility between the blood types of mother and baby (usually a Rhesus-negative mother with a Rhesus-positive baby) a more serious type of jaundice can appear; this requires treatment within the first two days. All your medical staff will have taken preventive steps before you give birth. Other, less common, causes of jaundice are hepatitis and biliary atresia, a rare condition in which the bile duct fails to develop properly.

Phototherapy
Jaundice in a newborn is easily treated by exposure to ultraviolet light for about 12 hours.

SPECIAL CARE BABIES

You should make every effort to establish bonds with your premature baby as soon as possible through your smell, your voice, and your touch.

Much research has been done to illustrate the positive effects of physical human contact on young babies, and this applies equally to those that are premature.

If you are a new mother expecting to have your baby in your arms right after birth, it is obviously distressing to find that he will be kept behind a glass screen, and be surrounded by many machines.

Mothers who do not have early contact with their babies may start to feel cheated of motherhood. They are likely to blame themselves for having "failed" their babies, and these feelings of guilt are intensified because they are unable to comfort their babies, who are obviously in need of help.

It is important to realize, though, that effective bonding can take place with your baby in an incubator – indeed, it is essential that it does. No baby is so ill that you can't place your hand inside the incubator and stroke him gently. Try not to be intimidated by all the machinery; ask the hospital staff to show you what to do.

Incubators
A premature baby will be placed in a closed, thermostatically controlled cabinet to maintain his body temperature, and given oxygen if necessary. His temperature and breathing will be constantly monitored.

One in 18 babies born in Britain today is premature. The medical definition of a premature baby is one that is born at less than 37 weeks. All premature babies need special care.

When we say a baby is premature we mean that he has not yet matured to the point where he can cope easily outside the security of his mother's uterus. Although the chances today of a premature baby surviving and thriving are vastly improved in comparison to our mothers' generation, it's still a worrying experience to see your baby being taken away to a special care or intensive care unit immediately after the delivery. Understanding why a baby needs special treatment for a few days or weeks will help lessen your anxiety. Premature babies have very weak muscle tone and don't move much. They often have calcium and iron deficiencies, as well as low blood-sugar levels. If they are very premature their eyes may still be sealed. They have very red and wrinkled skin. Their heads are disproportionately large in comparison to the rest of the body, and the bones in their skull are soft. They are more than usually prone to jaundice (see p.25).

SPECIAL NEEDS

A premature baby needs to be fed more frequently than a full-term baby because he burns calories more quickly. You can understand why he needs to be fed so often if you think of a tiny hummingbird; it never stops feeding since its weight is so low compared to its volume that it needs constant food to stoke up the metabolic burners and keep the temperature normal. The smaller the baby, therefore, the more often he needs to feed and the less time he spends asleep (see p.22). For premature babies the challenge of living outside the uterus is clearly an exhausting one. The lack of stimulation from being in an incubator and the inability to move very much means that, apart from frequent feeding, premature babies spend most of their time sleeping.

BREATHING PROBLEMS

If a baby has respiratory distress syndrome (RDS) he may stop breathing for a short time; this is called apnoea. Although it sounds very frightening, apnoea is not uncommon, and most babies start breathing again after gentle stimulation such as a tap or a stroke.

Other respiratory problems can arise from fluid inhaled into the lungs, or a lack of surfactant – a substance produced in the lungs which stops the lungs collapsing inwards. If a baby's lungs do not have enough surfactant coating them, they do not expand as well as they should. This can cause the smaller air sacs to collapse inwards, leading to a condition common in babies born before 31 weeks, known as hyaline membrane disease.

Babies suffering from any of these complications can be given oxygen either by way of a face mask or by a small tube inserted directly into the windpipe.

TUBE FEEDING

Most premature babies do not have the strength to suck milk from a teat or bottle, and their intestines may be too weak to absorb food. There are three alternative ways of feeding:

- Intravenous feeding is used for babies who are very ill or so premature that they cannot swallow or digest food for themselves. It may continue for weeks and subsequent feeding will be through a stomach tube.

- With naso-gastric feeding a tube is passed through the baby's nose and into the stomach or intestine. Because the tube is very fine and soft your baby hardly knows that it's there, and it's a very comfortable way to feed.

- When your baby is older, a combination of breast or bottle and tube feeding will suffice; the baby feeds as much as he can from breast or bottle, and then tube feeding supplies the rest. Combination feeding can be used once the rooting and sucking reflexes (see p.20) are established and will continue until your baby is strong enough to feed from breast or bottle only.

PROGRESS

The development of a premature baby can be slow and erratic. It is often a great shock to see just how tiny your premature baby is but he will have a great will to live.

For a premature baby every day can be an uphill battle. Periods of improvement may be followed by setbacks, and this constant uncertainty can make you and your partner feel anxious, moody, and restless. It is encouraging to know, however, that most babies born after 32 weeks will develop normally. of those babies born at 27 weeks (three months early), six out of seven will survive.

HEALTH RISKS

Premature babies are ill-prepared for life outside the uterus, and can have the problems listed below.

Breathing *Due to the immaturity of their lungs, most premature babies experience difficulty in breathing, known as respiratory distress syndrome (RDS).*

Immune system *An underdeveloped immune system and a body that is too weak to defend itself properly means there is a greater risk of infection than with a full-term baby.*

Temperature regulation *A premature baby's temperature control is inefficient and he is likely to be too cold or too hot. He has less heat insulation than a full-term baby, as he lacks sufficient body fat underneath the skin.*

Reflexes *Inadequate development of his reflexes, particularly his sucking reflex, creates difficulties in feeding. Premature babies usually need tube feeding.*

Digestion *A premature baby's stomach is small and sensitive, which means he is less able to hold food down, and so is more likely to vomit. The immaturity of his digestive system makes it difficult for him to digest essential proteins, so they have to be given in a pre-digested form.*

SPINA BIFIDA

When the neural tube (the developing spine) doesn't fuse properly at around four to six weeks in the developing fetus, the meninges (the coverings of the brain and spinal cord) are left exposed.

The affected part of the spine may be covered by skin and marked only by a dimple or a tuft of hair (spina bifida occulta); the meninges may protrude and the bulge may be covered with skin (meningocele); or in the most serious form the spinal cord itself may protrude as a raw swelling over the spine (myelocele). Eighty per cent of all spina bifida babies have some degree of hydrocephalus (see opposite). Women with a family history of neural tube defects are at particularly high risk of successive infants being affected.

Immediate surgery is no longer advocated for spina bifida babies. As long as the back, if it does not heal spontaneously, is repaired in a reasonable time then the prognosis is not affected. In babies with severe defects problems may include complete paralysis of the legs, double incontinence, and mental retardation. Urinary incontinence can be helped by the use of a catheter (a sterile tube that is inserted into the bladder), and physiotherapy is important to encourage mobility.

Spina bifida can be detected in pregnancy by amniocentesis. About 2,000 cases are detected per year in the UK. Of these, 1,600 couples opt for termination after counselling. Seventy-five per cent of spina bifida births could be prevented by taking preconceptional and prenatal folic acid supplements as 400-microgram tablets once daily.

CONGENITAL CONDITIONS

Congenital handicaps are rare. Some are genetic, while others are due to the effects on the fetus of drugs, radiation, infections, or metabolic disturbances. The fetal tissues that are most actively growing at the time when the adverse factor operates are the ones most likely to be affected. An increasing number of defects can be detected before birth and successfully treated just after birth.

Talipes (Club foot) Some infants – twice as many boys as girls – are born with the sole of one or both feet facing down and inwards, or up and outwards. The cause of club foot is not fully understood, but it can be inherited. The foot will be manipulated over several months, and braced or splinted in position between manipulations. If surgery is necessary, it can be carried out when the child is as young as 12–16 weeks. Talipes can be a feature of spina bifida.

Dislocated hip In about 0.4 per cent of infants, the ball at the head of the thigh bone does not fit snugly into its socket in the hip bone. In a newborn, this is a potential rather than an actual problem. It is much more common in girls than in boys and following breech births and pregnancies where there is an abnormally small amount of amniotic fluid in the uterus.

Your doctor or midwife will check your baby's hips for excessive mobility as part of routine tests after birth (see p.24). Treatment such as manipulation and splinting can prevent trouble in later infancy. In severe cases, an operation may be needed.

Epispadias and hypospadias In a very small number of male babies – about 0.3 per cent – there is an abnormality in the position of the urethral opening on the penis. In epispadias, the opening is on the upper surface of the penis, and the penis may curve upwards; in hypospadias the opening is on the underside of the glans (head), and the penis may curve downwards. In rare cases the urethral opening lies between the genitals and the anus, and the genitals may appear to be female. Surgery can be carried out in the preschool years to correct the defect allowing normal passage of urine and, in later life, normal sexual intercourse. Neither of these conditions, even in the severe form, causes infertility.

Congenital heart disease The most common form of heart disease in newborns is a hole in the ventricular septum – the thin dividing wall between the right and left ventricles (pumping chambers). About four weeks after birth, blood will "shunt" from left to right through the hole and the oxygenated blood will flow to the lungs instead of to the body. Symptoms include breathlessness, particularly during feeding. In some cases the hole seals spontaneously, but if it doesn't an operation will be necessary.

Cleft lip and cleft palate A cleft is a split or separation of parts. During the early part of pregnancy separate areas of the baby's face and head develop individually, then join together. When joining does not take place or is incomplete the baby can be born with a cleft lip on one or both sides, with or without a cleft palate. Breastfeeding is sometimes possible, perhaps using a nipple shield; if not, special bottles and teats are readily available. Some milk may return down the nose but this doesn't matter.

A cleft lip will be surgically closed soon after birth or some weeks after. The palate will be closed from about six to nine months. Further operations may be necessary for some children.

Affected children are looked after by a cleft team who will monitor speech, hearing, and teeth and will intervene should this be necessary. Support for parents is available through a national network of regional groups.

Down's syndrome This is by far the most common of a range of conditions called trisomies, in which one pair of chromosomes has an extra chromosome, making three. In Down's syndrome there are three number 21 chromosomes. Affected infants characteristically have small features, a tongue that tends to protrude, and slanting eyes with folds of skin at their inner corners. The back of the head is usually flat. They tend to be rather floppy infants and have short, wide hands with a single transverse crease across the palm. They may also suffer from congenital heart disease.

Down's syndrome babies are usually mentally handicapped, though the degree of handicap varies widely; many are near normal. They are usually affectionate and happy children. With early education and careful attention they often do very well, and some manage to live independently as adults.

Pyloric stenosis In this condition the pylorus, the passage that leads from the stomach into the small intestine, is narrow because of a thickening of the muscle. The cause is unknown and it is more common in boys than in girls. Symptoms usually first appear at two to four weeks, though they can appear earlier. The stomach contracts powerfully in an attempt to force a build-up of food through the narrow pylorus. This is impossible however, and the contents of the stomach are vomited up so violently that they may be propelled up to a metre (3 feet) – projectile vomiting. The baby may also suffer constipation and dehydration. A barium meal may be given to confirm the diagnosis. A simple operation to widen the pylorus can be performed, curing the condition completely.

Imperforate anus In rare cases a baby's anus is sealed at birth, either because there is a thin membrane of skin over the opening or because the anal canal, which links the rectum with the anus, has not developed. The rectal pouch may also be connected to the vagina, urethra, or bladder, and the baby must be referred for surgical treatment at once. This condition is routinely checked for at every birth (see p.24), and is treated immediately if present.

HYDROCEPHALUS

Commonly called water on the brain, hydrocephalus often occurs with other neurological defects such as spina bifida.

It is caused by restricted circulation of the cerebrospinal fluid or excessive formation of this fluid, leading to too much fluid within the skull, and is most common following a brain haemorrhage in a preterm baby. The head swells because the skull bones are still soft, and the soft tissues between the skull bones and the fontanelles become wide and bulging.

If hydrocephalus is suspected, frequent ultrasound checks will be performed and your baby's head circumference measured every two to three days. If a child is born with hydrocephalus, a shunt may be inserted to drain off the fluid. Mental development is usually adversely affected in hydrocephalus, but some children with advanced hydrocephalus are of normal intelligence.

A valve controls the rate of flow

The tube runs just beneath the skin

Shunt
A system of tubes with a valve drains off excess cerebrospinal fluid to where it can pass into the bloodstream, usually the abdominal cavity. The entire device is enclosed in the body.

CHAPTER TWO

EVERYDAY CARE

Confronted with a newborn baby, many parents worry that they will not know what to do. Will she start to breastfeed automatically? How much sleep should she have? How much food does she need? What if she refuses food?

Fortunately, looking after a baby does not require specialist skills – just some basic knowledge, common sense, and a willingness to ask for advice. In the space of a few weeks your confidence and experience will increase dramatically, and you will know the best way to change, hold, comfort, and feed your baby. You will learn that if she needs something she will usually find a way of communicating with you.

As your child gets older, she will become more independent. By the age of four she will be able to feed, wash, and dress herself and she may be quite opinionated about the clothes and foods she does and doesn't like. Her physical needs will no longer take up so much of your time. Your role in her everyday care is to keep her strong and healthy by meeting her dietary needs and looking after her health and hygiene.

EQUIPPING THE NURSERY

SAFETY

When planning a nursery bear in mind that your child will be mobile before long.

• *Make sure there are no sharp edges or corners on the furniture.*

• *Choose a non-slip floor covering and consider fitting bars and locks to the windows*

• *The furniture should be stable so your child can't pull it over*

• *Toys should be stored at floor level so your child doesn't have to stretch to reach them*

• *Choose wall-mounted lamps to avoid trailing flexes*

• *Don't overheat the nursery; overheating is a risk factor in cot deaths (see p.122)*

Your baby may have a room of his own or share yours; once he is sleeping through the night, however, he should have his own space. You'll need little special equipment and you can improvise with household items – a sink will do as well as a baby bath, for example, and a folded towel as a changing mat – but many parents do delight in equipping a nursery.

If this is your first child, ask friends with children which items they found most useful, and weigh up their advice against your own lifestyle. If there's anything you're unsure about, shop around and have a look through the catalogues of the major stores before making a final decision. There will often be many things which you can manage without. The only essentials are somewhere for the baby to sleep, his clothes and nappies (see pp.82–83 and 106–107) and feeding equipment.

You don't have to buy everything brand new; look out for secondhand items advertised in local papers or on noticeboards in the local clinic. A carrycot will last only a couple of months, because babies grow so quickly, so it makes sense to borrow one from friends if you can. If you buy secondhand items, check for general wear and tear, and make sure that all surfaces are smooth and free of rust for your baby's safety. Check, too, that they still comply with the latest safety regulations. Beware of painted items; old-fashioned paints may contain lead, which is poisonous. Never buy secondhand car harnesses or chairs.

BASIC EQUIPMENT

Sleeping	*Bathing*
Carrycot, crib or cot	Baby bath
Mattress with waterproof cover	Cotton wool
Fitted cot sheets	Large soft towel
Cellular blanket (for newborn)	Flannel or sponge
Swaddling shawls	Baby brush
Baby alarm	Baby bath lotion
	Blunt-ended scissors
Transport	
Carrycot pram (suitable from birth), buggy, or pushchair	*Other*
Sling	Bouncing chair
Infant car seat	Muslin squares

Cot   Low nursing   Table for   Non-slip rug   Cupboard
chair   feeding
equipment   Bath
on stand

Changing   Storage shelves   Sink near
mat   for nappies   changing area
and bath

ARRANGING A NURSERY

Planning your nursery, like buying equipment, is best done before your baby is born: once you bring him home you'll be far too busy feeding and changing and you're likely to be tired, too.

Try to ensure that the room is as easy as possible to keep clean, with wipable surfaces. Choose furniture without hard edges or corners and make sure that any painted surfaces are non-toxic and lead-free. You will need plenty of storage space, especially near the changing area. This could be a wide-topped chest of drawers with some shelf space above, or you may like to build your own. Be sure the top is wide enough for the changing mat and smooth as well as washable. Cork tiles and haircord carpets are ideal floor coverings for the nursery, as they are warm and hardwearing.

The baby's room does not have to be very warm, but should be kept at a constant temperature. Around 18°C (65°F) is suitable if your baby is covered with three blankets and a sheet; if the room is warmer, he should have fewer blankets (see p.122). If your baby is tucked up snugly in his cot, all-night heating will not be necessary except during very cold weather: a thermostatically controlled room heater is the most suitable. It is a good idea to fit a dimmer switch so that you can gently bring up the lights without startling your baby. If you like, the light can be left on low as an alternative to a night-light.

DECORATING THE NURSERY

Although a newborn's vision is limited, cheerful colours and decorations will provide a stimulating environment.

• *Light, cheerful colours are the most suitable for your baby's room. Yellow, blue, and grassy green – the colours of nature – will be soothing to your baby, and vivid splashes of primary colours will enliven the room*

• *A newborn baby has a very limited range of vision – only 20–25 centimetres (8–10 inches) so hang mobiles above the cot and the changing area. Their colours and movement will make your baby alert to his surroundings*

• *Put an unbreakable mirror on the side of the cot so your baby can see his face; the human face is fascinating to very young babies*

• *Choose fabrics and wallcoverings that are washable*

• *A folding screen may be useful to shelter the cot from bright sunshine or from cold draughts*

• *Carpet is warm and will absorb noise, but can be difficult to keep clean; a good alternative is a vinyl floorcovering with a couple of non-slip rugs*

Mirror made from unbreakable plastic

Visual stimulation
A sturdy mirror placed in the cot will allow your baby to see his own face.

SLEEPING

The best choice for your newborn is a Moses basket or a carrycot pram; some prams convert to pushchairs for use when she's able to support herself sitting up. Your baby will outgrow baby baskets or cradles quite quickly, so don't splash out on an expensive one unless you're sure you can afford it. When your baby outgrows her crib or carrycot, you'll need a full-sized cot. Choose one with side rails that are set closely together – a distance of $2\frac{1}{2}$–6 centimetres (1–$2\frac{1}{2}$ inches) is suitable – and drop sides so you can lift your baby out easily. The mattress should fit snugly, so your baby can't get

SLEEPING EQUIPMENT

Your newborn will spend much of her time asleep, and she'll be able to sleep just about anywhere. A basket or carrycot is best at first, and easily portable, but once she outgrows these she'll need a cot.

The shade protects your baby from draughts and direct sunlight

Airholes in mattress allow your baby to breathe if she rolls over on her front

Make sure the cover is washable

A waterproof cover will keep the rain out

Handles should be near the hood end to take the weight evenly

The gaps between the bars should be in the range of $2\frac{1}{2}$–6 centimetres (1–$2\frac{1}{2}$ inches)

The drop side should have safety locks so your child can't let it down

Castors for manoeuvrability and for "rocking"

Castor locks

her arm or her leg, or even her head, trapped down the side. The cot will last you until your baby is big enough to clamber out, when you'll need to buy a bed – at about two or two-and-a-half years. The cot mattress should be a foam type, with air holes that allow your child to breathe if she turns over on to her front while asleep. Travel cots are very useful for going on holiday or taking your baby out for the evening. They have fabric sides and are collapsible so they can easily be carried.

Because a young baby can't regulate her body temperature effectively you should use a cotton sheet and cellular blankets for the cot so you can easily add one or take one away. Once she is a year old, a cot duvet will be suitable. Make sure that any bedding you buy is flameproof and conforms to current safety standards.

Sleeping temperatures Research into cot death has shown that babies who get too hot are at a greater risk of cot death. While the temperature of the nursery is an important factor, the number of blankets is even more so. If the nursery is at 18°C (65°F), then a sheet and three layers of blankets will keep your baby at an ideal temperature. If it is warmer, you should use correspondingly fewer blankets (see p.122). Lambswool fleeces and baby nests are such good insulators that they carry a risk of overheating, so don't leave your baby in one all night. Similarly, cot bumpers and pillows can make your baby too hot. Babies lose heat through their heads, so if your baby's head is buried in a pillow or bumper, heat loss will be reduced.

BABY LISTENERS

A baby listener will allow you to keep in touch with your baby, even when she's in another room.

• *Baby listeners are available in different versions: battery, mains, or rechargeable*

• *Lights indicating whether the batteries are low, or the baby unit is out of range, are useful*

Keeping in touch Listeners come in two parts – the baby's transmitter, and the parent's receiver

SLEEPING ACCESSORIES

Cot duvet (not for babies under twelve months)

Cotton sheets

Cotton cellular blanket

Fleecy blanket

Tie-on waterproof sheet to protect mattress

Safety foam mattress with airholes

Lambswool fleece (not for all-night use)

WALKING AND CARRYING

Your baby will spend most of her time being carried, wheeled, or secured in some way, and there is a wide variety of prams and carriers available. When choosing equipment of this kind, safety and portability will be your main considerations.

Slings are the most popular way of transporting a newborn; they're light and comfortable, and allow you to carry your baby close while keeping both hands free. Try one on with your baby in before you buy it, and make sure it has a head support for your baby. Backpacks, which have supportive frames that make it easier to bear a larger baby's weight, are suitable once your baby can sit up by herself.

For longer journeys you will need a pram or pushchair in which your baby can sit or lie down. One in which your baby can lie flat should be used for the first three months, until she has head control. The pram you choose will depend on your budget and lifestyle. Consider where you will keep it and whether you will need to take it on buses and trains or up stairs. Whatever pram you choose, it should have a safety harness or rings to fix one in place.

CHOOSING A PRAM

For the first three months, your baby must be able to lie flat. Reclining pushchairs are available, but a carrycot pram is more versatile. Some models can be converted to pushchairs.

A hood shield will protect your baby from rain

The top lifts off and can be used as a carrycot

Safety locks prevent the frame from collapsing when the pushchair is in use

A safety harness will keep your baby securely strapped in

Make sure the brakes are easy to use

A basket is useful for carrying changing equipment or shopping

Locks allow the wheels to swivel or lock for greater manoeuvrability

CARRYING YOUR BABY

A sturdy frame takes the strain off your back

The sling should have a support for your baby's head

Using a backpack
You can carry your baby in a backpack once he becomes too heavy for a sling. Make sure that he is comfortable and is not restricted by the leg openings.

Using a sling
Your baby will feel safe and secure inside a sling, and it leaves your arms free.

BOUNCING CHAIR

Your baby can be propped up so that she can look around her in a purpose-made chair. When she's on solids, you can sit her in the chair and feed her, but ensure that she is safely strapped in to prevent her slipping.

Put the chair on the floor, never on a table or worktop

SAFETY HARNESSES

Your young baby has no fear of falling, so wherever she sits she will have to be strapped in for her own safety.

• *A five-point harness, which has straps for the shoulders as well as the waist and crotch, is safest*

• *Your baby's pram should have a built-in harness, or fixing points so that you can attach one*

• *High chairs often have a built-in crotch strap, and should also have rings to take a safety harness which you can buy separately*

• *Many harnesses come with reins that can be attached when your baby is old enough to walk*

37

FEEDING AND NUTRITION

MILK: THE IDEAL FOOD

In the first few months of life, your baby will get all the nutrients she requires from breast or formula milk.

Calories *The energy content of food is measured in calories. Infants require about two-and-a-half to three times more calories than adults for their body weight.*

Protein *Vital for building body cells and tissues, a baby's protein needs are three times as great as an adult's on a body-weight basis.*

Fats *Minute traces of fatty acids are needed for growth and repair.*

Carbohydrates *These are the major source of calories.*

Your baby depends on you for the provision of adequate nutrition, and for a newborn, breast or bottled milk will provide all she needs. Breast milk is the ideal food for a baby (see below), but if you choose to bottlefeed, rest assured that your baby will still thrive. Feeding takes a great deal of a parent's time, so it's important to choose a method that is suitable for both parent and baby. Well before delivery you should decide whether you are going to breastfeed or bottlefeed and prepare for whichever you choose.

It's quite normal for all babies, breastfed or bottlefed, not to take much colostrum (see p.40), at first, for they take a while to get the hang of feeding. Your baby will cry when she is hungry, and you should take your lead from her in setting the pattern of feeds.

Babies grow most rapidly during the first six months of life – most babies double their birth weight in around four to five months. Your baby's nutritional needs reflect this tremendous growth. A healthy baby's food has to contain adequate amounts of calories, protein, fats, carbohydrates, vitamins, and minerals (see left and opposite), and until she's at least four months old, your baby will receive all these nutrients from breast or formula milk.

WHY BREAST IS BEST

Human breast milk is the perfect food for babies. Because it doesn't look as rich and creamy as cows' milk, you may think that it is not good enough, but don't be put off. It contains all the nutrients your baby needs, and in just the right amounts.

Breast milk has many benefits for your baby. Breastfed babies tend to suffer less than bottlefed babies from such illnesses as gastroenteritis and chest infections. This is because antibodies from the colostrum and the mother's milk are absorbed into the bloodstream, where they act to protect the baby against infections. In the first few days of life, they also protect the intestine, reducing the chances of intestinal upsets.

Breast milk has other advantages for a baby's digestion. Breastfed babies don't get constipated, since breast milk is more easily digestible than cows' milk, although they pass few stools because the milk is so completely digested that there is little waste. They are less prone to ammoniacal nappy rash (see p.110), too. From a mother's point of view, breastfeeding is far more convenient than bottlefeeding: there is no need for the milk to be warmed up, there are no bottles to sterilize, no formula to be made

Breastfeeding
Suckling helps to form a very strong bond between you and your new baby.

up, and no equipment to buy. Breastfed babies usually sleep longer, suffer less from wind, and posset – that is, regurgitate food – less, and the posset smells less unpleasant. It is difficult to overfeed a breastfed baby, so don't worry if your baby seems fatter than other babies of her age. Each baby has its own appetite and metabolic rate, and yours will be the right weight for her own body.

Some women worry that breastfeeding will make their breasts sag. This is not the case: breasts may change in size or sag after a baby is born, but these changes are due to being pregnant, not to breastfeeding itself. In fact, breastfeeding is good for your figure, as it promotes the loss of any weight gained during pregnancy. While you are breastfeeding, the hormone oxytocin (see p.40), which stimulates milk flow, also encourages the uterus to return to its pre-pregnant state. Your pelvis and waistline will also get back to normal more quickly.

Studies have shown that breast cancer is rarer in those parts of the world where breastfeeding is the norm, and it is possible that breastfeeding may provide some protection against the disease.

BOTTLEFEEDING

Every woman is capable of breastfeeding her baby, and you should try to do so. Many women feel that they must breastfeed to be a good mother, and feel guilty if they decide not to. On the other hand, some women find it emotionally or psychologically difficult to breastfeed; others find that, however much they try, they cannot master breastfeeding. If this is the case, then you should forget about it and concentrate on giving your baby a good bottlefed diet: she will still thrive. If you decide not to breastfeed at all, you will probably be prescribed hormones to suppress your milk supply.

You may consider bottlefeeding because you feel that breast-feeding will tie you down, particularly if you intend to return to work very soon after the birth. This may be the best solution for you, but remember that it is also possible to express enough milk so that your partner or a child-minder can feed your baby in your absence. That way your baby can have the benefits of your milk, and you can still have the flexibility of bottlefeeding and the free-dom that this gives you.

One of the benefits of bottlefeeding is that your partner can be involved with feeding the new baby. He should try to do this as soon as possible after the birth, so that he can learn to handle the baby confidently, and if possible he should share the feed-ing equally with you. Encourage him to hold the baby close and talk to her while feeding, so that the baby gets used to the feel of his skin, his smell, and the sound of his voice.

Bottlefeeding
Make feeding a time of closeness and intimacy for you and your baby.

VITAMIN AND MINERAL NEEDS

As well as the basic nutrients (see opposite page), milk will supply your baby with necessary vita-mins and minerals.

Vitamins *Vitamins are essential to health. Formula milks contain all your baby's vitamin require-ments, but breast milk does not contain as much vitamin D, which is manufactured by the skin when stimulated by light, as formula milk. You should ask your health visitor whether your baby needs vitamin supplements.*

Minerals *Calcium, phosphorus, and magnesium, which are neces-sary for the growth of bone and muscle, are contained in breast and formula milk. Babies are born with a reserve of iron that will last about four months; after this they have to be given iron, either in solids or as supplements.*

Trace elements *Minerals like zinc, copper, and fluoride are essential to your baby's health. The first two are present in breast and formula milk, but fluoride, which protects against dental decay, is not. Never give fluoride supple-ments without checking with your midwife or doctor, as excessive amounts can cause fluorosis (discoloration of the tooth enamel).*

Looking after yourself properly is the key to a good milk supply. If you stay relaxed, eat well, and drink enough fluids, you will have plenty of milk for your baby.

- *Rest as much as you can, particularly during the first weeks, and try to get plenty of sleep*

- *You produce most milk in the morning when you are rested. If you become tense during the day, your supply could be poor by evening. Go through your ante-natal relaxation routines and have a lie-down every day*

- *Let the housework go; do only what is absolutely necessary*

- *Try to give yourself a few treats; relax with a glass of wine at the end of the day*

- *Eat a well-balanced diet that is fairly rich in protein. Avoid highly refined carbohydrates (cakes, biscuits, sweets, and so on)*

- *Ask your doctor about iron and possibly vitamin supplements*

- *Drink about three litres of fluid a day; some women even find that they need to keep a drink by them while they are feeding*

- *Express any milk your baby doesn't take in the early feeds of the day to encourage your breasts to keep on producing milk*

- *The combined contraceptive pill decreases your supply, so avoid it for five months after delivery. Discuss alternative methods of contraception with your doctor*

- *Avoid spicy foods, which could affect your milk and upset your baby's stomach*

ALL ABOUT BREASTFEEDING

Breastfeeding has to be learned, and you should seek support and advice from your family, from friends with babies, and from your midwife or health visitor. Above all you will learn from your baby, by understanding his signals and discovering how to respond to them. No special action is required to prepare the breasts for feeding unless you have an inverted nipple. If you do, use a breast shell to make your nipple protrude so that the baby will be able to latch on to it. If you are having your baby in hospital, make sure the nursing staff know that you intend to breastfeed, and don't be afraid to ask for help. Suckle your baby as soon as he is born – in the delivery room, if you are in hospital – to form a bond with him as early as possible and let him get used to suckling.

COLOSTRUM AND BREAST MILK

During the 72 hours after delivery, the breasts produce a thin, yellow fluid called colostrum, made up of water, protein, and minerals. Colostrum contains antibodies that protect the baby against a range of intestinal and respiratory infections. In the first few days, your baby should be put regularly to the breast, both to feed on the colostrum and to get used to fixing on the breast (see p.42).

Once your breasts start to produce milk, you may be surprised by its watery appearance. When your baby sucks, the first milk that he gets – the foremilk – is thin, watery, and thirst-quenching. Then comes the hindmilk, which is richer in fat and protein.

THE LET-DOWN REFLEX

Pituitary gland
Hypothalamus

The sucking action of your baby at the breast sends messages to the hypothalamus, which in turn stimulates the pituitary gland in your brain to release two hormones: prolactin, which is responsible for the manufacture of milk in the milk glands, and oxytocin, which causes milk to be passed from the glands to the milk reservoirs behind the areola. This transfer is known as the let-down reflex.

BREASTFEEDING POSITIONS

Lying down is ideal for night feeds; when your baby is very small you may need to lay him on a pillow so that he can reach your nipple. You may find a lying position the most suitable if you have had an episiotomy and sitting is uncomfortable. If you've had a Caesarean section and your stomach is still tender, try lying with your baby's feet tucked under your arm.

Both you and your baby should be comfortable

Lying positions
Breastfeeding positions that allow you to lie down are a restful alternative and can keep a wriggling baby off a tender Caesarean incision.

Sitting position
Make sure that your arms and back are supported and you are relaxed.

NURSING BRAS

You should always wear a supportive nursing bra when you are breastfeeding.

Try it on in the store before you buy, and look for one with front fastenings and wide straps that won't cut into your shoulders. Drop-front or zip-fastening bras are easy to undo with one hand while you hold your baby. A good bra will minimize discomfort if your breasts become sore.

SUPPLY AND DEMAND

Milk is produced in glands that are deeply buried in the breast, not in the fatty tissue, so breast size is no indication of how much milk you can produce; even small breasts are perfectly adequate milk producers.

Milk is produced according to demand – you supply what your baby needs, so don't worry that you'll run out of milk if your baby feeds very often. Your breasts are stimulated to produce milk by your baby's sucking, so the more eagerly he feeds, the more milk they will produce, and vice versa. During the time that you breastfeed, the amount of milk available will fluctuate according to your baby's needs, and once he becomes established on solids, the breasts will produce less milk.

	2-week-old baby	2-month-old baby	
12	✓	✓	2 am
am 4	✓	✓	6
8	✓	✓	10
12	✓	✓	
	✓	✓	2 pm
pm 4	✓	✓	6
8	✓	✓	
	✓	✓	10
12	✓		

Frequency of feeds
At first your baby will feed little and often. By about two months he will be feeding roughly every four hours and will take more at each feed than before.

HOW LONG ON
EACH BREAST?

You should keep your baby on the breast for as long as he shows interest in sucking.

• *If your baby continues to suck after your breasts have emptied, it may be that he is just enjoying the sensation; this is fine if it's not making your breasts sore*

• *When your baby has finished feeding from one breast, gently take him off your nipple (see below right) and put him on to the other breast. He may not suck for so long on the second breast*

• *Alternate the first breast you offer at each feed. To remind you which breast was last suckled, put a safety pin on your bra*

Encourage intimacy by talking or singing to your baby

BREASTFEEDING YOUR BABY

Breastfeeding creates a strong bond between mother and baby if feeding time is relaxed and pleasurable for both. Make sure your baby can see you, and smile and talk to him while he is suckling. He will come to associate the pleasure of feeding with the sight of your face, the sound of your voice, and the smell of your skin. Make sure you are both comfortable before you start (see **Breastfeeding positions,** p.41). You should feed your baby from both breasts, and you may like to wind him before changing over (see p.55).

GIVING A BREAST FEED

With an open mouth, your baby feels for your nipple

The rooting reflex
Prompt your baby to look for the breast by gently stroking the cheek nearest to it. Your baby will immediately turn towards your breast, open-mouthed.

Latching on
Your baby should take the nipple and a good proportion of the areola into his mouth. The milk is drawn out by a combination of sucking and squeezing the tongue on to the hard palate.

Releasing the nipple
To break the suction, slip your little finger into the corner of the baby's mouth. Your breast will slip out easily instead of being dragged out.

Your baby presses the elongated nipple against the roof of his mouth as he draws out milk

POSSIBLE PROBLEMS

It is perfectly normal for breastfeeding not to go smoothly at first, so don't get worked up about minor setbacks such as your baby refusing a feed. Remember that he too is learning and that it will take time for you to get used to each other, so persevere, and ask your midwife or health visitor for advice and suggestions.

Refusing the breast It is quite usual for a newborn not to suck very vigorously or for very long during his first 24 to 36 hours. If this occurs later, however, there may be a problem that needs to be addressed. Breathing difficulties are the most likely cause of a baby's having problems taking the breast. It may be that your breast is covering his nostrils; if so, gently pull the breast back from the baby's face, just above the areola. If he seems to have a snuffly or blocked nose, consult your doctor; he will probably prescribe nose drops to clear the nostrils.

If there is no obvious cause for your baby's refusal to feed, he may simply be fretful. A baby who has been crying with hunger, or has been changed or fussed over when he's hungry, can become too distressed to take the breast. You will need to soothe him by holding him firmly and talking or singing; there is no point in trying to feed him until he's calmed down.

If there has been some delay in starting to breastfeed – as with a premature baby who has had to be fed by bottle – your baby may find it more difficult to take the breast, and you will have to be patient and persevering. Your midwife or health visitor will advise you if you need to give expressed milk from a special cup until the baby can take all he needs from the breast. Supplementary bottles are rarely necessary, and they may cause mothers to give up breastfeeding. Giving expressed milk is a better alternative.

Comfort sucking Most babies enjoy sucking on their mothers' breasts for its own sake just as much as feeding. You will learn to tell the difference between actual feeding and comfort sucking. During a feed you may notice that your baby is sucking strongly without actually swallowing. There is no reason why your baby shouldn't suck as long as he wants, provided your nipples are not sore, though he takes most of his feed in the first 3–5 minutes.

Sleeping through feeds If your baby doesn't seem very interested in food during the first few days, make sure that he takes as much as he wants from one breast. If he sleeps at the breast, it means he is contented and doing well, though premature babies should be woken and fed regularly, as they tend to sleep a lot. If your baby does fall asleep at the breast, wake him gently half an hour later and offer a feed; if he is hungry he will perk up.

Fretful feeding If your baby doesn't settle down to feed, or appears not to be satisfied, he is probably sucking on the nipple alone and not getting enough milk. This may also lead to sore nipples. Check that your baby is positioned correctly on the breast.

UNDERFEEDING

You may feel anxious that you can't see how much the baby has taken, but it is rare for a breast-fed baby not to get enough milk.

• *If your baby wants to continue sucking even though he's finished feeding from both breasts, it doesn't always signify hunger; he may just enjoy sucking*

• *Thirst may cause your baby to go on on sucking after he's emptied your breasts. Try giving about 30 millilitres of cooled, boiled water from a special cup*

• *If he seems fretful and hungry, have him weighed at your clinic to check if he is gaining weight as quickly as expected. If not, then your milk supply has been reduced – perhaps because you are tired and run down. You may be advised to give supplementary feeds (see p.45) from a special cup until your supply is back to normal. If you are at all worried you should contact your doctor*

• *Low-milk syndrome, recently described in the US, is a rare condition when a newborn baby fails to get enough nutrition. This is nearly always due to difficulties in learning how to latch on and suckle. In a very few cases it may be due to a mother's failing to produce enough milk. This doesn't preclude breastfeeding, but supplementary bottles will be needed. I cannot stress enough that mothers and babies must be given time to get the hang of breastfeeding.*

• *One warning sign of low-milk syndrome is in the nappies; if your baby wets fewer than six nappies a day, check with your midwife or doctor.*

EXPRESSING MILK

Expressed milk can be easily stored either in the refrigerator or in the freezer. This will free you from feeling tied down by breast-feeding, and allow your baby to be fed with your milk if you are away. It also allows your partner to share in feeding your baby.

Milk can be expressed from your breasts using either your hands or a breast pump, which may be manual or electric. Although small battery pumps are very easy to use, many women find hand expressing to be easier and more convenient. Before you start, you will need a bowl, a funnel, and a container that can be sealed. All equipment must be sterilized, either in a sterilizing solution, with boiling water, or in a special steam unit.

In the first six weeks hand expressing is nearly always a bit difficult, as the breasts have not reached full production, but don't give up. Because breasts produce milk in response to demand, you may need to express milk in order to keep your supply going – if your baby is premature and can't yet breastfeed, for example. Even if you use a pump, it is worth learning the technique of hand expressing in case you need it. The best time to express milk is in the morning, when you'll have the most milk, although when your baby drops the night feed you may find the evening the best time.

- *If you have to lean over a low surface, expressing may give you backache. Make sure the container is at a convenient height*

- *Expressing milk should be painless. If it hurts, stop immediately. Ask your midwife or health visitor if you are expressing correctly*

- *The more relaxed you are, the easier it will be to express. If the milk won't start to flow, place a warm flannel over your breasts to open the ducts, or try expressing in the bath*

- *If you're concerned that your baby might not go back to breast-feeding after getting used to the bottle, try feeding her milk from a specially designed cup, or spooning the expressed milk from a cup. Make sure that both spoon and cup are sterilized before use*

- *Your hands must be clean, and every piece of equipment and all containers should be sterile*

- *Milk will go off unless it is stored correctly, and could make your baby ill. Refrigerate or freeze your milk as soon as you've collected it. Refrigerated milk will keep for 24 hours; frozen milk for up to six months.*

- *Expressed milk should be put into sterile, sealable containers. Don't use glass containers in the freezer – they might crack. Sterile plastic bottle liners are ideal*

EXPRESSING BY PUMP

All manual pumps work on suction and comprise a funnel or shield, pump mechanism, and container. The assembly and operation of different brands of pump will vary a little, so follow the manufacturer's instructions.

Pump mechanism

Funnel

Container doubles as feeding bottle

Using a pump
Place the shield over your nipple and squeeze and release the handle. Your milk should be drawn into the vacuum created in the bottle. If this causes you any pain, stop immediately; expressing should be painless. Try again a little later.

EXPRESSING BY HAND

Massaging the outer breast
Make sure that your hands are clean. Cup your breast in both hands with the fingers underneath and the thumbs above. Squeeze the outer part of your breast gently and firmly between your fingers and thumbs. Repeat this ten times, moving around the breast as you do so.

Massaging the inner breast
Move your hands closer to the areola and repeat the squeezing procedure as above.

Massaging the breast stimulates milk flow

Press back gently and rhythmically

Make sure the container you use is at a convenient height for you

Starting the flow
Place the thumb and fingers of one hand near the areola, press them back into your ribs, then squeeze gently and rhythmically. If the milk doesn't begin to flow immediately, keep on trying.

Express from each breast alternately

Emptying the breast
Continue for about five minutes, working around the areola, then move on to the second breast. Repeat the whole procedure for both breasts.

SUPPLEMENTARY BOTTLES

Even though you are breastfeeding, there may be occasions when you have to give supplementary bottles of formula milk.

If you have a blocked duct or a particularly sore nipple, you may wish to give supplementary bottles, although many mothers prefer to express milk from the affected breast and use this in the bottle.

A baby who has become used to the nipple may dislike plastic teats. Unfortunately, it can be difficult to tell whether your baby just dislikes the teat, or is not hungry. She'll eventually get used to the bottle if you persist, but you may then find that she doesn't want to go back to the breast. If this happens, try giving the milk from a sterilized spoon or cup.

Relief bottles containing your own expressed milk can be given to your baby if you are unable to breastfeed, or are leaving the baby with someone else.

Although they are not essential, you will find breast pads and shields will help keep your nipples clean and dry.

Breast shells
When you are feeding from one breast, milk may drip or even flow from the other. A shell can be used to collect this excess milk, which can then be stored in the refrigerator for up to 24 hours or frozen.

Plastic breast shell

Fabric pads are washable and absorbent

Breast pads
Disposable and washable pads are available which fit inside your bra and protect your clothes from leaks of milk.

MANAGING BREASTFEEDING

Many mothers find that breastfeeding goes smoothly right from the start, but it is also normal to be a bit clumsy at first, for the baby not to suck for very long, or for your breasts to be a bit sore. Remember that it takes time to learn, so if problems arise, do persevere until things get easier.

CARE OF THE BREASTS
The daily hygiene of your breasts and nipples is very important. You should cleanse them every day with water or baby lotion (not soap, which defats the skin and can aggravate a sore or cracked nipple), and gently pat them dry. Dry them gently after feeding. Wear your bra all the time, as you will need lots of support; but leave the front flaps down with your nipples open to the air. You may like to use a moisturizing cream on your nipples or, if they become sore, an antiseptic spray.

Once your milk flow is established the milk may leak out quite a lot. You can use breast pads or clean handkerchiefs inside your bra to soak it up. Change them frequently for cleanliness. A plastic breast shell with a reservoir will help to keep your nipples dry and catch leaks of milk. Milk can be frozen or refrigerated in a sterile bottle. Wash and sterilize the shell before re-using.

IF YOU ARE ILL
If you are confined to bed, you can express milk so that your partner can feed the baby when you are not feeling up to it. If you are too ill even to express your milk, then your baby can be given formula milk by bottle or by spoon and, although she may not like this at first, she will take the milk as she becomes hungrier.

If you have to go into hospital you can still breastfeed. You should inform the nursing staff as soon as possible that this is what you intend to do so that they can make the necessary arrangements – for example, someone will have to be available to lift and change your baby if you are too tired or ill to do so. If you have an operation, though, you will not be able to breastfeed afterwards because of the anaesthetic – you'll be too groggy and, more importantly, the drugs you have been given will have passed into your milk. If you know you will be having an operation, try to express and freeze your milk so that your baby can be bottlefed until you have recovered. It will take up to ten days for your milk to return; your baby should suck as often as she wishes meanwhile.

DRUGS AND BREASTFEEDING
If you can, avoid all drugs when breastfeeding. Many medications pass into the breast milk and can affect your baby. Always inform your doctor that you are breastfeeding if you are already taking medications, or if you consult her for any new problems; she may

wish to prescribe something more appropriate. If you want to use oral contraceptives, you should take the progestogen-only "mini-pill", as the oestrogen in the combined pill may reduce your milk supply. However, as the effects of progestogen on the baby are not yet fully known, it is best to use some other contraceptive method until your baby has been weaned. Your doctor or family planning clinic can help you choose the method that suits you best.

PROBLEMS

Your breasts will be working hard for the next few months, and problems may arise if, for instance, your baby is not latching on properly or drags on the nipple as she comes off. The best way to prevent this is to keep your breasts clean and dry and make sure your baby always empties them when she feeds. You should also wear a proper nursing bra. If your nipples do become sore or cracked, take action immediately or they will get worse.

Cracked nipple If sore nipples (see right) are not dealt with properly, they may become cracked. If this happens, you will feel a shooting pain as your baby suckles. You should keep the nipples dry with breast pads or clean tissues, and stop feeding from the affected breast until it has healed. You should express the milk by hand instead; it can be fed to your baby by bottle or from a special cup.

Engorgement Towards the end of the first week, before breastfeeding has become fully established, your breasts may become over-full and painful and quite hard to the touch. If this happens, your baby won't be able to latch on successfully. Make sure you wear a good bra to minimize discomfort, and gently express some milk before feeding to relieve the fullness. Having warm baths will also help to relieve the discomfort by promoting milk flow.

Blocked duct Tight clothing or engorgement can cause a blocked milk duct, resulting in a hard red patch on the outside of the breast where the duct lies. You can prevent this by feeding often and encouraging your baby to empty your breasts, and by making sure that your bra fits properly. If you do get a blocked duct, feed often and offer the affected breast first.

Mastitis If a blocked duct is not treated, it can lead to an acute infection known as mastitis. The breast will be inflamed and a red patch will appear on the outside, as with a blocked duct. You should continue to breastfeed because you need to empty the breast. Your doctor may prescribe antibiotics to clear up the infection.

Breast abscess An untreated blocked duct or mastitis can result in a breast abscess. You may feel feverish, and you may have a shiny red patch on your breast which is exquisitely tender. You doctor should prescribe antibiotics; if this fails, the abscess will have to be drained surgically, but you may be able to continue breastfeeding even if you need this minor operation – ask your doctor's advice.

PREVENTING SORE NIPPLES

Suckling your baby can cause soreness around the nipples, especially if you are fair-skinned. To minimize the possibility of any problems:

• *Always make sure that your baby has the nipple and areola well into her mouth*

• *Always take your baby off the breast gently (see p.42)*

• *Keep your nipples as dry as possible between feeds*

• *Make sure your nipples are dry before putting your bra back on after a feed*

If one of your nipples does become sore, give that breast a rest from feeding and comfort sucks for 24 hours, or until the soreness has gone. Express milk from the affected breast and feed your baby from the other one. To prevent the nipple from becoming cracked, apply a camomile or calendula cream two or three times a day.

The shield is very soft and allows for a close fit

Nipple shield
This is made of soft silicone and fits over your nipple; the baby sucks through a small teat on the front. Sterilize before use.

NAME *Petrina Wehrli*

AGE *27 years*

OBSTETRIC HISTORY *Normal pregnancy, Benjamin born prematurely at 28 weeks*

PAST MEDICAL HISTORY *Appendectomy at 15 years*

FAMILY HISTORY *Twins in previous generations*

Petrina was enjoying a career in an estate agency when she gave up work to have a baby. She's a very determined woman, and prepared for her pregnancy by eating well and taking regular exercise. When she became pregnant she read all the baby books she could, and even practised expressing milk manually. Mike, her husband, was very involved in these preparations, attending antenatal classes with Petrina and reading baby books with her.

One night while at the cinema, only 28 weeks into her pregnancy, Petrina felt sudden uterine pains, which quickly escalated to regular, strong contractions. Mike took her directly to hospital, where Benjamin was born.

A CASE STUDY

FEEDING A PRETERM BABY

It was a shock for both Petrina and Mike to have their baby a full three months before they'd planned it; Petrina, who likes to feel in control of everything, was particularly disturbed. It was difficult for her to sit by her new baby so impersonally enclosed in an incubator, unable to cuddle and most of all to breastfeed him, something she longed to do.

MAINTAINING A SUPPLY

I explained to Petrina that although no feeding is straightforward for premature babies, breast milk is especially beneficial to them, as it provides protection against infections in the first few risky weeks of life. Benjamin had to be fed intravenously for several days and then gradually through a stomach tube because he had not had time to develop the rooting and sucking reflexes. Petrina expressed her milk from day one and stored it so that it could be used to feed Benjamin when the stomach tube was in place.

She remained adamant that she wanted to breastfeed Benjamin when she could eventually take him home, and as soon as he could be released from the incubator for short periods, the nurses would encourage Petrina to put him on the breast. I reminded her that breast milk is produced in response to demand. If it's not removed by a nursing infant, then it must be expressed or production stops. This meant Petrina had to express milk to keep up production until Benjamin was able to breastfeed regularly.

LEARNING TO EXPRESS

Expressing milk for a premature baby is difficult because all the natural cues for milk let-down are missing: the baby's hungry cry, lifting him up, putting his mouth to the breast. In order to master the technique of expressing milk (see pp.44–45), Petrina needed persistence and support from Mike; many times she felt like giving up. Her breasts became engorged on day three and she could hardly bear to massage them. She explained her problems to the staff nurse on the unit, who arranged for a rota of nurses to help and encourage her to take off milk every two hours (as a very small baby would) and to store it hygienically (see p.44).

Petrina continued to express milk during the night, every four to six hours. By the second week she'd become quite expert, and was asked to teach other mothers how to express. Now she was feeling useful and competent, her fears about her baby started to wane.

BONDING WITH A PREMATURE BABY

One of Petrina's main concerns was that Benjamin wouldn't bond to her and Mike because he couldn't hear her voice properly, and couldn't smell her skin or enjoy her cuddles. The hospital staff, however, showed her how she could put her clean hand into the incubator to stroke and caress Benjamin gently. Within a week Benjamin was showing signs of loving this contact and responded by wriggling when she touched him. Quite naturally she would talk to him as he did this, and during the second week she saw him flick his eyes in recognition at the sound of her voice. She thought of this as their first conversation and continued to babble to him happily during their time together. The hospital staff encouraged both parents to spend as much time as possible with Benjamin, and to help feed and change him as their confidence grew.

COPING WITH THE DEMANDS

Two and a half weeks after Benjamin's birth, Petrina experienced a crisis. The shock of the premature birth, the anxiety of the first few days, and the loss of sleep because of expressing at night were all having their effect, and she felt that she had no emotional resources left. When one of the nurses found her sobbing, she realized immediately that Petrina herself needed some tender loving care. She suggested that Petrina talk to Mike about her feelings. Mike had thought that Petrina was totally absorbed with Benjamin, but was only too willing for them to have some time alone together each day for cuddles and sharing. Petrina also started to take some time for herself – to have her hair done, for instance – and to spoil herself now and then with nutritious treats like strawberries out of season, or malted wholemeal bread. She drank lots of mineral water to keep herself healthy for breastfeeding.

PREPARING TO GO HOME

Before Benjamin was ready to leave hospital, the staff established him on breast milk from a bottle so that he learned to suck well before he was put on to the breast. In the last week before he was due to go home, he was taking five meals out of eight from Petrina's breast so she got over the tricky stage of getting Benjamin used to the breast in the reassuring environment of the unit. When Benjamin was 38 weeks, and 2.5 kilograms (5 pounds 8 ounces) in weight – ten weeks after he was born – Petrina and Mike took him home and felt like a real family for the first time. At home, Petrina had to continue expressing so that she always had enough milk if ever Benjamin showed signs of being hungry after a feed. A week later Benjamin weighed in at 2.6 kilograms (5 pounds 12 ounces) and was thriving. However, I explained to Petrina that she must age him as if he were still in her womb: he wasn't two months old, but 39 weeks, and she shouldn't expect him to catch up completely with full-term babies of his age till he was two years old.

NAME	Benjamin Wehrli
AGE	39 weeks
BIRTH WEIGHT	1.3 kilograms (2 pounds 13 ounces)
MEDICAL HISTORY	Born prematurely at 28 weeks, and nursed in special care unit in an incubator. Allowed home at 38 weeks

MILK FORMULAS

A variety of milk formulas are available, all carefully formulated to make them as close as possible to breast milk: in fact, formula milk has added vitamin D and iron, levels of which are quite low in breast milk.

Most formulas are based on cows' milk, but you can buy soya-based formulas for a baby who finds cows' milk unsuitable. Some formulas are available both in powder and ready-mixed forms.

Ready-mixed milk comes in cartons or ready-to-feed bottles and is ultra-heat treated (UHT), which means it is sterile and will keep in a cool place until the "best before" date. Once the carton has been opened, the milk will keep for 24 hours in a refrigerator. Ready-mixed milk is more expensive than powdered formula, but it is very convenient, and you may like to use it when you are travelling.

If you use powdered formula, it is essential that you make it up precisely according to the manufacturer's instructions. Some parents are tempted to add extra powder to make the milk "more nourishing", but this will lead to your baby getting too much protein and fat, and not enough water.

If you add too little powder, your baby will not be getting the nutrients he needs for healthy growth.

BOTTLES AND MILK

The majority of babies end up being bottlefed at some stage – if not continuously right from the start, then often after weaning or with supplementary bottles. New infant formulas, bottles, and teats appear on the market regularly, all with the aim of making bottle-feeding as convenient and as similar to breastfeeding as possible.

The one thing you cannot give your baby if you bottlefeed from the start is colostrum (see p.40), so even if you're not intending to breastfeed your baby, you will be giving him a good start if you put him to the breast in the first few days. If you decide not to do this, the hospital staff can take care of your baby's first feeds; he will probably be given glucose water a few hours after delivery.

One of the good things about bottlefeeding is that the new father can be involved at feeding times. Make sure that your partner feeds your baby as soon as possible after the birth. This way he can get used to the technique and won't be afraid to handle him. He should open his shirt so that the baby nestles up to his skin when he feeds, and bonds with his smell.

Disposable bottles
Bottles which take disposable liners are convenient when you are travelling. The liner is collapsible, so air does not enter the bottle as your baby draws the milk and there is less likelihood of wind.

BOTTLES AND TEATS

Bottles (left to right)
Tapered bottle
Waisted bottle
Easy-grip bottle
Disposable bottle with liners

Teats (left to right)
Universal latex teats (2)
Silicone anti-colic teat
Natural-shaped teat
Wide-based teat for disposable bottle

STERILIZING THE BOTTLES

It is wise to practise with your feeding equipment before you go into hospital, so buy it well in advance of your delivery date. Large department stores and chemists sell bottlefeeding packs that have all the essential equipment.

I always found it most convenient to sterilize and make up a full batch of bottles (see p.52), and refrigerate them until needed. After the feed, rinse the bottle in warm water and then put it aside. It is a good idea to continue sterilizing all milk-feeding equipment until your baby is nine months old.

Most sterilizing units usually hold only four to six bottles. Your newborn baby, however, will be taking around seven feeds over 24 hours, so you may have to sterilize and prepare the bottles twice a day – morning and evening – to ensure you have enough feed ready for whenever he is hungry. The number of feeds will decline as your baby grows, so you'll only have to prepare one batch a day.

COLD-WATER STERILIZATION

A bottle brush helps remove all traces of milk

Use salt to remove any trapped milk from the teat

Cleaning the bottles
Use a bottle brush and warm soapy water to remove all traces of milk from the bottles. Rinse them.

Cleaning the teats
Rinse the teats thoroughly. Remove all traces of milk by rubbing them with salt.

Soaking the equipment
Fill the sterilizing unit with cold water up to the guide mark, and dissolve one or two sterilizing tablets in the water (as per the manufacturer's instructions). Put the bottles, teats, measuring jug, and spoon into the unit. Submerge all the equipment and leave for the required time. When you are ready to use the equipment, rinse and drain it.

Fill the bottles with water so they don't bob about

STERILIZING METHODS

Most parents sterilize bottles by using sterilizing solution, as shown, but boiling is also effective. It is as well to be aware of other methods in case you are away from home, or run out of sterilizing tablets.

• *Put all the equipment into a large, covered, plastic container and use sterilizing tablets (or fluid) and water as shown*

• *Steam sterilizing units quickly and effectively destroy bacteria on your equipment*

• *You can sterilize your equipment in the microwave using a specially designed steam unit, as long as the feeding equipment is suitable for microwave use*

• *Wash the equipment and boil it for at least 25 minutes in a large, covered pot*

• *You can wash the bottles, jug, and knife on the normal cycle of the dishwasher. The teats should be placed in a covered pan and boiled separately*

Using a ready-made formula is more straightforward than mixing your own, but strict rules of hygiene should still be observed.

• *Before opening the carton, use a clean brush to scrub the top of the carton, paying particular attention to the cutting line*

• *Cut the corner off the carton with clean scissors. Avoid touching the cut edges, as you could contaminate the milk*

• *If you are not using all of the milk, leave the excess in the carton; it can be stored in the refrigerator for 24 hours*

• *Don't store milk that your baby has left in the bottle; it will have been contaminated with saliva*

THE FLOW OF MILK

The hole in the teat should be large enough to let the milk flow in a stream of several drops per second when the bottle is inverted.

If the hole is too large, your baby will get too much too fast and splutter; if it is too small, your baby will get tired from sucking before she is satisfied. To make the hole in a teat bigger, insert a fine, red-hot needle gently through the hole to melt the rubber (stick one end of the needle into a cork so you can hold it over a flame to heat it).

Sculpted teats, which are shaped to fit the baby's palate and allow her control over the flow, are best.

BOTTLEFEEDING YOUR BABY

When you are bottlefeeding, there are a couple of essential points to bear in mind. The formula should be properly made up so that your baby gets correct amounts of both nutrients and water, and your baby should be able to draw milk at a comfortable rate. You can make up one bottle at a time, mixing it in the bottle according to the manufacturer's instructions, or a batch of several.

MAKING UP A BATCH OF FORMULA

Equipment
The equipment should be rinsed with boiled water and drained before use.
• Bottles and lids
• Plastic knife
• Measuring scoop from formula pack
• Funnel
• Teats
• Caps
• Jug

Level off powder with back of knife

Measuring
Using the measuring scoop provided with the formula, measure out the required amount. Use a knife to level off each scoopful, and do not pack the formula down into the scoop.

Mixing
Put the required amount of formula into the mixing jug with the boiled and cooled water. Never add extra formula or the mixture will be too concentrated and could be dangerous. Stir the formula and water until you are sure that there are no lumps or residue and the mixture is smooth.

Storing
Place the sterilized teats upside-down in the bottles; secure with the screw-on lids and put on the plastic caps. Refrigerate the bottles immediately, putting them on a tray to keep them upright.

Use a sterilized funnel to fill the bottles if needed

GIVING A BOTTLE FEED

Make yourself comfortable and support your arms well. Hold your baby half-sitting with her head in the crook of your elbow and her back along your forearm; this will allow her to swallow safely and easily. Keep your face close to hers and chat to her all the time.

If you prefer, there are other positions that are suitable for feeding. For example, you could try lying down with your baby tucked under your arm – this position is especially comfortable for night feeds. Try different positions until you decide which one suits you best (see **Breastfeeding positions**, p.41).

Before you begin, test the heat of the milk; you should already have tested the flow (see opposite). Slightly loosen the cap of the bottle so that air can get in. If your baby is having difficulty drawing the milk, gently remove the bottle from her mouth so that air can enter the bottle, then continue as before. Hold the bottle at an angle so that your baby does not swallow air with the milk.

BOTTLEFEEDING

Giving the bottle
Gently stroke your baby's nearest cheek to elicit her sucking reflex. Insert the teat carefully into her mouth. If you push the teat too far back she may gag on it.

Feeding
Make feeding times as pleasant as possible by chatting to your baby and smiling at her. Let her pause mid-feed if she likes. Change her on to the other arm at this stage to give her a new view, and your arm a rest.

Removing the bottle
If you want your baby to release the bottle, gently slide your little finger into the corner of her mouth. This will break the suction on the teat.

WARMING THE BOTTLE

Some mothers like to warm the bottle, though it will be perfectly all right if it has simply been brought to room temperature. Don't warm the bottle in a microwave oven; they do not always heat evenly, and may create "hot spots" in the milk that could scald your baby's mouth.

Warming the milk
Place the bottle in a bowl of hot water for a few minutes. You could also run it under the hot tap, shaking it all the time.

Testing milk temperature
Try a few drops on your wrist: it should be neither hot nor cold to the touch.

BOTTLEFEEDING TIPS

Bottlefeeding is straightforward, but you will need to make sure that your baby can swallow properly, and that he is not taking in air with the milk.

• *Never leave your baby with the bottle propped up on a pillow or cushion; it can be dangerous. He could become very uncomfortable if he swallows a lot of air with the feed, and he could choke. Moreover, he will miss the cuddling and affection that he should enjoy while he feeds*

• *Tilt your baby on your arm. It is very difficult for your baby to swallow when he is lying flat so don't feed him in this position; he may gag or even be sick*

• *If your baby has a blocked nose he can't swallow and breathe at the same time. Your doctor can give you nose drops to be used before each feed*

• *Don't change your milk formula without first consulting your midwife or health visitor, even if you think your baby does not like it. It is very unusual for a brand of milk to be responsible for a baby's not feeding well; very rarely cows' milk causes allergies in babies, and your doctor may advise you to use a substitute soya formula*

• *Your baby knows when he's had enough, so don't try to force him to finish the bottle after he has stopped sucking*

BOTTLEFEEDING ROUTINES

Bottlefed babies tend to be fed less frequently than breastfed ones. This is because formula milk takes longer to digest and contains slightly more protein, and therefore delays hunger for longer. A four-hourly regime of six feeds a day seems to suit most bottlefed babies after the first two or three days, whereas breastfed babies will probably take seven feeds a day. When first born, your baby will probably not take much over 60 millilitres (2 fluid ounces) at each feed, but as he grows he will take fewer and larger feeds.

Never feed your baby according to the clock; let him determine when he is to be fed. He will let you know quite clearly with cries when he is hungry. Your baby's appetite will vary, so if he seems satisfied, allow him to leave what he does not want. Don't feel that your baby has to finish the bottle at each feed. He will only get overfull and posset it back (see opposite); or worse, become overfed and fat. On the other hand, if your baby is still hungry, give him some extra from another bottle. If this happens regularly, start to make more milk for every bottle.

NIGHT FEEDS

Your baby will need feeding at least once during the night, and this break in your sleep on top of all the other things that you have to do to take care of her may make you extremely tired and tense. The problem is not so much the number of hours' sleep that you lose, but more the way in which your sleep patterns are broken over long periods. For this reason it is very important that you get adequate rest, day and night, and as you are doing most of the feeding, try to get your partner to take on some of the other jobs.

REDUCING NIGHT FEEDS

At first your baby won't be able to sleep for more than five hours at a time without waking with hunger. Once he reaches a weight of about 5 kilograms (11 pounds) try to stretch the time between feeds until you are getting about six hours of undisturbed sleep at night. Although your baby will have his own routine, it's sensible to try to time his last feed to coincide with your own bedtime, which should be as late as possible. You may find that your baby will still wake up and demand the early morning feed, no matter how much you try. If this happens you'll just have to be patient and look forward to when he drops it.

OVERFEEDING

Chubby babies can be attractive, but fat cells, once produced, can't be removed, and a fat baby may grow into a fat adult, with all the attendant dangers to health. Unfortunately, it is easy to overfeed a bottlefed baby. The reasons for this are twofold; first, it is tempting to put extra formula into the bottle, but you should always follow the instructions precisely (see p.52), otherwise you'll be giving the baby unwanted calories. Second, in your anxiety to feed him "properly" you will want to see your baby finish the last drop of his feed, but you should always let him decide when he's finished. Introducing solids too early and giving sweet, syrupy drinks also cause overfeeding.

UNDERFEEDING

This is rare in bottlefed babies. Your baby should be fed on demand and not at set times; demands may vary from day to day. If you insist on feeding to a schedule, never give extra milk in a bottle, and don't allow any interim feeds even though your baby is crying for them, then he won't get all the milk that he needs.

If your child consistently seems fretful after he drains each bottle, he may well be hungry. Offer him an extra 60 millilitres (2 fluid ounces) of formula. If he takes it, then he needs it.

If your baby demands frequent feeds but doesn't take much, the teat hole may be too small (see p.52); so that he is having difficulty sucking the milk and is tired before he gets enough.

WINDING

Winding releases any air that has been swallowed during feeding. It's unlikely that wind causes your baby discomfort, and many babies are not noticeably happier or more contented for having been winded. Swallowing air is more common in bottlefed babies, but you can prevent it to some extent by tilting the bottle more as your baby empties it so that the teat is full of milk and not air, or by using disposable bottles. The good thing about winding your baby, whether you breast- or bottlefeed, is that it makes you pause, relax, slow down, hold your baby gently, and stroke or pat him, and this is good for both of you.

POSSETTING

If your baby tends to bring food straight back up (some babies never do) you may wonder if he's keeping enough down. My youngest son was a child who had a tendency to posset, and I worried in case he wasn't getting enough to eat. I simply followed my own instinct, which was to offer him more food. If he didn't take it, I assumed that he had possetted an excess which he didn't require. The commonest cause of possetting in very young babies is overfeeding, and this is another reason why you should never insist that your bottlefed baby finishes his feed.

Forcible vomiting, especially if it occurs after several feeds, should be reported immediately to your doctor; vomiting is always very serious in a small baby as it can quickly lead to dehydration.

HYGIENE AND PREPARATION

To protect your baby from bacteria, make sure all feeding equipment is scrupulously clean, and take care with the storage and preparation of formula.

- *Follow all sterilizing instructions carefully*
- *Wash your hands before sterilizing, preparing, or giving feeds*
- *Never add any extra feed; follow the instructions given very closely*
- *Give the milk to your baby as soon as it has been warmed up*
- *When making batches, cool the formula as soon as it is made up. Don't store warm milk in a vacuum flask as germs will easily breed there*
- *Keep all prepared bottles refrigerated until they are needed*
- *Keep any opened packets of ready-mixed formula in the refrigerator*
- *After a feed, throw away any leftover milk*

Winding your baby
Hold your baby close to you and stroke or pat him gently to help him bring up air bubbles.

12kg

10kg

8kg

6kg

4kg

2kg

0kg

0   2   4   6
Mths

Your baby's weight
In the first six months your baby girl will be growing fast and will more than double her birthweight. Any weight within the coloured band is normal.

Growth charts
The charts shown here and on pp.62–63, 66–67, and 318–25 show the wide ranges of weight or height within which a "normal" child may fall. The middle line represents the 50th centile: 50 per cent of babies will fall below this line and 50 per cent above it. The lines at the top and bottom represent extremes outside which only a tiny proportion of children will fall; if your child does you should talk to your doctor.

INTRODUCING SOLIDS

During your baby's first year there will be a time when you will have to start to wean her on to solid foods, although not before she's four months, and possibly quite a bit later than that. Before this, your baby's digestive tract is incapable of digesting and absorbing complex foods. If solids are introduced too early, they'll pass through largely undigested, and will put an increased strain on your baby's immature kidneys.

Breast milk (or its formula equivalent) is the only food that your baby needs in the early months, and if a baby is introduced to solids too young it can lessen her desire to suck. Breastfed babies will take less milk from your breasts, and you will respond by producing less milk. Either way your baby will end up having an unsatisfactory diet for her needs.

WHEN TO WEAN

As your baby grows, she'll need to drink more and more milk to maintain this growth. But your baby's stomach can only hold a certain amount of milk at each feed; eventually, she will reach a point when she's drinking to full capacity at each feed, but still doesn't have enough calories for her needs. Your baby will let you know that she needs more to eat by a change in her feeding habits. She may start to demand more milk and appear very unsatisfied after each feed, or she may start demanding a sixth feed, having previously been quite content on five. A classic case is a baby who has been sleeping through the night starting to wake for a night-time feed. This is the time to introduce solids. Many babies do this at

EXAMPLES OF WEANING STAGES

Feeds	1st week	3rd week
1st feed	Breast or bottle feed.	Breast or bottle feed.
2nd feed	Half breast or bottle feed. Try one or two teaspoons of purée or cereal then give remainder of feed.	Half breast or bottle feed. Two teaspoons of cereal. Remainder of feed.
3rd feed	Breast or bottle feed.	Half breast or bottle feed. Two teaspoons of vegetable or fruit purée. Remainder of feed.
4th feed	Breast or bottle feed.	Breast or bottle feed.
5th feed	Breast or bottle feed.	Breast or bottle feed.

around four months, when their intense desire to suck lessens, though it can be later. You should be aware of the signs that your baby gives you, and follow her lead for the introduction of solids. The first tooth, if it appears at or after six months, definitely indicates the need for solids.

GIVING THE FIRST SOLIDS

Have a small amount of prepared food to hand and then settle in your normal position to feed the baby. Although your baby is ready for the calories that solids provide, she will still prefer what she knows is satisfying – milk. Start by feeding her from one breast or giving half the usual bottle. Then give her one or two teaspoons of food. Begin with the midday meal because your baby will not be ravenous but will be wide awake and more co-operative.

Never force your baby to take more food than she wants. When she's taken the solid food, give her the rest of the milk. Once she becomes used to solids, she may prefer to take them first.

As soon as your baby is having any quantity of solid food she will need water as well as milk to drink. Start her off with 15 millilitres of water or very dilute fruit juice between and after feeds, and whenever she's thirsty during the day. Avoid syrups, cordials, and any sweetened drinks, as these will damage your baby's teeth. Give no more than 120 millilitres of juice and water a day; milk is still your baby's main source of nutrition.

SPOONFEEDING

Giving the food
Sit your baby in an upright position halfway through her feed. Scoop up some food on a small spoon and insert it gently between her lips. Don't push the spoon in too far or your baby may gag. She may take a month or so to get used to using a spoon.

Messy baby
Your baby may push more food out than she takes in. Gently scrape the excess on to her lips; she will turn away once she's had enough.

BOYS' WEIGHT

Your baby's weight
Your baby will put on weight faster during this period than at any time in his life, and is likely to more than double his weight in the first six months. Any weight within the coloured band is normal.

WEANING TIPS

Your baby may be reluctant to try new foods, so give her time to get used to each food and don't persist if she seems to dislike something.

• *Give one new food at a time. Try it once and wait for several days before giving it again to see if there's a reaction*

• *Use dry infant cereals rather than ready-mixed ones; they are more nutritious.*

• *Don't give foods containing gluten, dairy products, or egg for at least six months, to avoid developing allergies later*

NAME *Penny King*

AGE *27 years*

OBSTETRIC *First baby, nor-*
HISTORY *mal delivery, no*
complications

Penny and her husband David are
vegetarians and have been since
they married three years ago.
They know that a vegetarian diet
that excludes meat, poultry, and
fish but contains eggs and milk
can provide all the nutrients
necessary for health and vitality
as long as a proper balance of the
different food groups is
maintained. They want Oona to
be a vegetarian and became
particularly concerned when she
was four months old and ready to
eat a mixed diet.

VEGETARIAN WEANING

Penny was nervous about not giving Oona a really balanced diet with
enough protein, vitamins D and B$_{12}$, calcium, and iron, even though she
knows many vegetarian foods are fortified with extra B$_{12}$ and protein. I
told her that a growing baby can get all the nourishment she needs from a
carefully planned diet, although if she wished to bring up Oona as a vegan
(no animal foods whatsoever, not even dairy produce or eggs) she would
need to see a baby nutritionist for advice.

When Oona was four months old Penny started gradually to wean
her by replacing milk feeds with solid foods so that Oona would
end up on three meals a day.

Penny and I planned a schedule where she would introduce one
food at a time, withdrawing it if it didn't suit Oona and trying it
again ten days later. Oona's diet had to include foods from each
of the major food groups (see p.66).

Oona would get protein, essential for growth in a young baby,
from eggs, pulses, nuts, cheese, and milk as well as sunflower seed
spread, soya yogurt, and grains. I pointed out to Penny that she
shouldn't replace cows' milk with sheep's or goats' milk before
Oona was 12–18 months old and that egg whites should not be
given until Oona was nine to ten months old.

Foods made from cereals and grains provide carbohydrates to
give Oona the energy to grow and develop, while fruit and vegetables supply essential vitamins and minerals. I told Penny that
vegetarian diets tend to be bulky and lower in calories than a diet
including meat. This can be hard for a baby because Oona could
get full before she's taken all that she needs, so Penny should give
her a wide variety of foods that are low in fibre such as eggs, milk,
and cheese. Penny and I drew up a menu plan for Oona together
and I gave her a few tips about how to start.

• Penny should choose a time when Oona was hungry but not very
hungry, such as the middle of the day, to try the first solids.

• Oona's first foods should be smooth in texture and mild in taste.
Baby rice, cooked puréed fruit such as apples and pears, or vegetables such as carrots, or potatoes (with no added salt) are ideal.

• Penny should avoid adding lots of seasoning or sugar.

• Adding a spoonful of Oona's usual milk to the food would help
her recognise the taste.

I also advised Penny that when preparing fruit and vegetables, she shouldn't overcook or keep foods hot for a long time; this destroys their vitamin content. Fresh fruit should always be peeled and have all stones, seeds, or pips removed. Oona sailed through her weaning. She seemed to really enjoy foods without salt and sugar, foods Penny thought she would find too bland. Penny found that Oona adored pease pudding made from lentils, a food she introduced when Oona was five months old. She also relished the white of an egg finely chopped and then mashed with soya yogurt. The more solid food she ate, the more fluid Oona wanted to drink, and a little unsweetened orange juice diluted half and half with water became her standard drink. In hot weather Penny found that Oona could easily drink a half-pint of this favourite drink every day.

Oona is now seven months and very much one of the family, eating more and more family food, which only needs sieving or mashing to suit her. She loves gravies and sauces, and Penny has found that these help her to take almost any new food. Ice cream has become such a favourite that Penny has to limit this treat to once or twice a week so that Oona isn't getting too much sugar and fat. She's gaining weight steadily but she's not fat; Penny is very proud of this, and also of Oona's recent attempts to use the spoon to feed herself – something many seven-month-olds do.

Since Oona clearly enjoys her food, Penny is keen to introduce her to lots of new flavours. She asked if there were any foods she shouldn't give, and I advised her to introduce strongly flavoured vegetables such as broccoli, onions, or peppers only gradually, and not to give wholegrain bread, whole nuts, or unpeeled fruit until Oona is a year old.

NAME *Oona King*

AGE *7 months*

MEDICAL HISTORY *Born at full term. Umbilical hernia cleared up by six months. Breastfed*

VEGETARIAN MENU FOR SEVEN-MONTH-OLD BABY

Breakfast.	Breast or bottle feed. Baby yogurt dessert.	Breast or bottle feed. Breakfast cereal with milk.	Breast or bottle feed. Baby rice.
Lunch.	Diluted unsweetened fruit juice or cooled boiled water. Cooked puréed lentils with vegetables. Puréed fruit.	Diluted unsweetened fruit juice or cooled boiled water. Hard-boiled egg and spinach with bread fingers. Puréed fruit.	Diluted unsweetened fruit juice or cooled boiled water. Cheese or well-ground nuts with vegetable purée. Mashed banana and yogurt.
Tea.	Breast or bottle feed.	Breast or bottle feed.	Breast or bottle feed.
Evening.	Mashed potato with grated cheese and broccoli. Soaked dried fruit, mashed.	Thick lentil soup. Baked apple with rice or wheatgerm.	Puréed cabbage with smooth peanut butter and pitta bread.

Your baby's main source of calories is still breast or formula milk, so give this at each feed, but you should also give drinks of cooled boiled water.

FEEDING AND NUTRITION

INTRODUCING CUPS

You can introduce your baby to drinking from a cup when he is about four months old.

• *Beakers with spouts are best as your baby will have to half suck and half drink to get anything. Soft spouts are the easiest to use*

• *As your baby progresses, he may prefer to move on to a two-handled cup that he can grasp easily. Those with specially slanted lips are excellent because the contents come out with very little tipping*

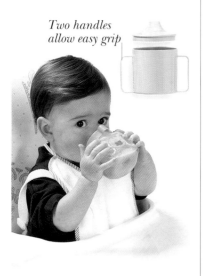

Two handles allow easy grip

Trainer cups
Lunchtime and late afternoon feeds are probably the best times to use the cup; these are times when your baby will be more likely to eat solids.

During her first year, your baby will move on from mere "tastes" of solids with his milk feeds, to three solid meals a day, with drinks of water, diluted fruit juice, or milk.

Once he is happy with a couple of different solids, it is important to introduce a variety of tastes and textures. Not only will he be able to deal with foods that have been puréed, mashed, or chopped, he'll also learn to enjoy chewing and sucking on larger chunks of food (see **Finger foods**, opposite) but it is important to remember that every baby has different requirements and appetites. If you are in any doubt, just feed your baby as much as he will take happily. The amount of milk he requires will lessen as the number of solid meals he takes increases. Since he'll be getting most of his calories from solids rather than from milk, your baby will become thirsty. When he does, give him plain water or diluted fruit juice to drink, rather than milk. Never give your baby a commercial drink containing sugar and colourings.

FEEDING YOUR CHILD

Until he's six months old, you will probably feed your baby on your lap or in an infant chair, but once his neck and back muscles are strong enough to support him, you may consider using a high chair or feeding table. With a feeding table you will have to bend down to feed the baby until he can feed himself and at first you may have to prop up your baby with cushions, so a high chair is probably the better option; make sure your baby is properly strapped in. Your child should always be supervised while he's eating. Almost all children gag on some food at some stage and it is essential that you react quickly in such a situation. A new texture, taken for the first time, may make him gag out of surprise. If he does, pat him firmly on the back and encourage him to cough until the food is dislodged. Talk soothingly and gently rub his back and he'll be more able to swallow the new food. Should your baby's choking happen to be severe, and especially if he loses consciousness, you must know how to administer first aid (see p.326).

Your baby will soon look forward to mealtimes as an opportunity to play as well as to eat, so feeding will become messier. Keep your baby away from the walls and put newspapers on the floor in case he starts throwing food. Within a month or so of starting solids, your baby will be able to take food from the spoon.

SELF-FEEDING

Learning to feed himself is a huge step in your baby's physical and intellectual development and you should encourage all attempts to do so. His manual dexterity and hand–eye co-ordination will

Moulded plastic bib to catch spillages

Self-feeding
Allow your child to spoonfeed himself if he can. Choose foods that are not too runny, such as thick porridge.

Rubber suction pad keeps bowl firmly in place

Wholewheat bread without whole grains is suitable

Pretty shapes will make food look appealing

Cut vegetables into shapes that are easy to grasp

greatly improve with self-feeding, so let him experiment if he shows an interest and be prepared to cope with the mess. Food provides your baby with the perfect motivation for speeding up muscle co-ordination and balance.

It may be several months before your baby becomes proficient at feeding himself. You can help by giving him non-runny foods that will stick to the spoon, such as porridge, scrambled eggs or thick purées. If he finds trying to use a spoon frustrating let him try finger foods. Food will be a plaything, most of which will land on the floor rather than in your baby's stomach, but there's no cause for concern; at the time a baby starts to self-feed, the initial growth spurt is beginning to slacken off, so he needs less food.

The best way to ensure that your baby gets at least some food is for both of you to have a spoon. Use two spoons of the same colour and type so that you can swap your full spoon for his empty one when he has difficulty scooping up the food.

Finger foods
If your baby has difficulty using a spoon he will find finger foods easier to handle; even if the food is hard, he will suck it.

FOOD FOR SELF-FEEDING

FRUIT AND VEGETABLES

Any fresh fruit that is easy to hold, like bananas, cut into slices with the skin or pips removed

Vegetables, particularly carrots, cut into a stick or shape that is easy to grasp. Don't cut vegetables too small

Mashed potato

CEREALS

Small pieces of dried, sugar-free cereal

Boiled rice

Wholemeal bread or rusks (without the complete grains)

Pasta shapes

PROTEIN

Wholemeal bread with smooth peanut butter

Pieces of soft cheese

Toast fingers with cheese

Small pieces of hamburger

Low-fat cheese

Any meat in easily held pieces

Filleted fish in firm chunks

Sliced hard-boiled eggs

YOUR BABY'S NEEDS

Your baby will always take enough food to satisfy her needs. If she doesn't want to eat, then she doesn't need to. This means that there will be days when she will eat hardly anything, but these will be followed by periods of eating a lot.

To eat a balanced diet, your baby should take in foods from all the different foods groups in the correct proportions (see below). This doesn't have to be on a daily basis, though, so when you are considering whether she is eating well, you need to think in the long term: look at what she has eaten in the last week, not just today. Viewed like this, a binge of eating nothing but bread for two days is nothing to worry about, as your baby will probably take in enough fruit and vegetables during the week to balance this out. What is important is that she should be given a wide variety of foods to choose from: she can't eat the foods she requires if they are not made available to her.

Your baby will gradually come to eat many of the same foods as you, prepared in a form that she can manage. It would be wrong, however, to suppose that her needs are the same as yours, or that a diet that is recommended as healthy for you will be good for her. You may aim to reduce your fat intake by using low-fat dairy products, for example, but you should give your child whole milk until she is two years old; after that you can introduce semi-skimmed milk if you wish. The benefits to health of limiting sugar intake, though, apply just as much to babies as to adults. Never add any salt to your baby's feed; her kidneys are too immature to cope.

GIRLS' WEIGHT

Your baby's weight
The rapid weight gain of the first few months slows down, but your baby is still putting on weight steadily. Any weight within the coloured band is normal. (For a full explanation of this chart, see **Growth charts,** p.56.)

The food pyramid
This table shows the proportions in which the main food groups should be eaten in order for your baby to take in the right balance of nutrients. The two most important groups are carbohydrates, and fruit and vegetables, followed by protein-rich foods like meat, pulses, and dairy products. Sugars, fats, and oils should form the smallest part of your baby's diet – in fact, the amounts of these that occur naturally in other foods will be more than enough. By following these guidelines for your baby, you will be helping her form good habits for life.

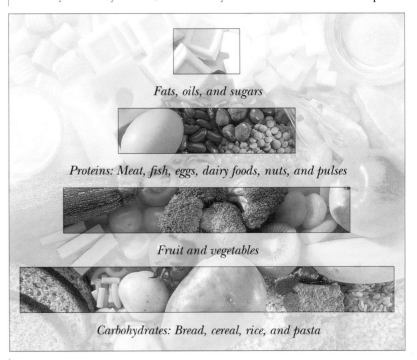

Fats, oils, and sugars

Proteins: Meat, fish, eggs, dairy foods, nuts, and pulses

Fruit and vegetables

Carbohydrates: Bread, cereal, rice, and pasta

SUGGESTED MENUS – AGE 8–10 MONTHS

DAY 1	DAY 2	DAY 3
Breakfast	**Breakfast**	**Breakfast**
Rice cakes	Mashed banana	Cottage cheese or yogurt
Hard-boiled egg	Wholemeal toast fingers	Wholemeal toast fingers
Milk	Milk	Milk
Lunch	**Lunch**	**Lunch**
Strained vegetable and chicken	Mashed potato and cheese	Strained lentils and mixed vegetables
Stewed apple	Pear slices	Banana and fromage frais
Diluted fruit juice	Diluted fruit juice	Diluted fruit juice
Tea	**Tea**	**Tea**
Wholemeal toast fingers	Rice cakes	Home-made rusks
Orange segments	Apple pieces	Fresh fruit
Milk	Milk	Milk
Supper	**Supper**	**Supper**
Cauliflower cheese	Pasta and tomato sauce	Tuna and mashed potato with steamed courgettes
Semolina and fruit purée	Yogurt with fruit purée	Rice pudding
Diluted fruit juice	Diluted fruit juice	Diluted fruit juice

BOYS' WEIGHT

Your baby's weight
The rapid weight gain of the first few months is past, but your little boy is still getting steadily heavier. Any weight that falls within the coloured band is normal. (For a full explanation of this chart, see **Growth charts,** p.56.)

A FLEXIBLE ATTITUDE

The sample menus shown above are intended as a guide to your baby's main meals. Remember, a baby's stomach can't hold very much, and she will need to eat more often than an adult; so don't insist she finishes her meals, and be prepared to give snacks in between times. Of course you should encourage your baby to have regular feeding times, but if you try to make her eat at mealtimes only, they will become battlegrounds, and she may end up not getting the food she needs when she needs it. If she shows that she's had enough, don't try to make her eat more.

Of course it is frustrating if you have spent a lot of time preparing a meal and your baby refuses it, or it ends up on the floor. The answer is to make feeding times as easy on yourself as possible: don't spend a lot of time preparing complicated dishes, and take precautions to protect the walls and the floor from thrown food.

FOOD PREPARATION

Once your baby is on solids, it is no longer necessary to sterilize all feeding utensils, though bottles and teats used for milk should still be sterilized until your baby is about nine months old. Cups, bowls, and cutlery can be washed in hot, soapy water and rinsed with hot water. Now that your baby's diet includes a range of foods, however, you need to take sensible precautions to protect him from the effects of harmful bacteria – salmonella and listeria poisoning, for example – so you should be well informed about the safe preparation, storage, and cooking of food.

BUYING AND STORING

The most important thing to look for when buying food is freshness. Shop often, and use food as quickly as possible. Bruised or damaged fruit and vegetables deteriorate quickly, so don't buy them. Always wash fruit if the skin is to be eaten, as there may be a residue of insecticides or other chemicals. Most packaged foods now carry a "sell by" or "best before" date, so check this and make sure that there are no signs of damage to packets, cans, or jars.

Food stored in the refrigerator should be in clean, covered containers. Store cooked and raw foods on separate shelves, and put raw meat and fish on a plate or the juices could drip on to food on the shelf below. Check the packaging to see if food is suitable for freezing, and never freeze foods for longer than the time recommended by the manufacturer; this will depend on the star rating of your freezer. Always defrost frozen foods thoroughly before using, and never refreeze food once it has been defrosted.

KITCHEN HYGIENE

Scares about food-poisoning in recent years have made parents much more conscious of the dangers of poor food hygiene. The following commonsense precautions will protect your baby.

• *Always wash your hands with soap before handling food, especially after using the toilet or changing a nappy, and after playing with pets. Make sure your family does the same*

• *Be scrupulous about keeping the kitchen clean, especially work surfaces, chopping boards, and utensils used in food preparation. Never use wooden utensils; they harbour millions of germs*

• *Always use a clean tea-towel or paper towels to dry dishes, or let them dry in a rack after rinsing them with hot water*

• *Keep the kitchen bin covered. Empty it often, and rinse it out with hot water and a little disinfectant each time you empty it*

• *Cover any food which is left out of the cupboard*

• *Any leftover food in your baby's dish should be thrown away*

Preparation methods
At first you will need to purée or grate foods for your baby. Steaming is a fast method of cooking which helps to preserve nutrients.

Coarse grater

Hand-held blender

Steamer

COOKING AND REHEATING

Always cook your baby's food thoroughly; this applies especially to meat, poultry, and eggs. You should never give raw or soft-cooked eggs to your baby, nor should you give liver pâté or soft cheeses. It is best not to give your baby reheated leftovers or chilled or frozen foods. If you're preparing food in bulk quantities, don't leave it to cool before putting it into the refrigerator, as this will just give the bacteria a chance to multiply; put it in a cold dish, cover it and put it straight into the refrigerator or freezer.

PREPARATION

At first you'll have to purée all your baby's food, but this stage won't last very long, so if you don't have a blender or liquidizer it's probably best just to get a cheap hand-operated food mill. At first a sieve will be perfectly adequate. As your baby gets older you can feed him coarser foods. By the time he is six months old he will be able to take a thicker purée, and at nine months he will enjoy a mash with chunks of meat or vegetables in it.

You can use a variety of liquids to thin down home-prepared foods: the water you've used to steam fruit or vegetables is ideal. To thicken foods, you can use ground, wholegrain cereals like wheatgerm, cottage cheese, yogurt, or mashed potato. If you feel you need to sweeten food, use naturally sweet fruit juice or dextrose rather than refined sugar.

PREPARATION TIPS

DO	DON'T
• Use fruit and vegetables as soon as possible after buying	• Buy bruised or wrinkled fruit and vegetables
• Peel tough-skinned fruit and vegetables if the skin is likely to cause your baby problems	• Prepare vegetables a long time in advance or soak them in water, as this destroys the vitamins
• Cook soft-skinned fruit and vegetables in their skins; this helps to retain the vitamins and provides additional fibre	• Crush or bruise fruit and vegetables; this destroys vitamin C
• Cook fruit and vegetables in a steamer or tightly covered pan with as little water as possible. This helps to retain the vitamins normally lost in cooking	• Give red meat more than twice a week as it has a high saturated fat content
• Give your baby cooked and puréed meat or fish. The purée can be thinned with vegetable water or soup	• Overcook tinned foods, as this destroys the vitamins
	• Add salt or sugar to your child's food; his immature kidneys can't handle a lot of salt, and giving him sweet foods will encourage a sweet tooth
• Use sunflower or corn oil. Never cook with butter or saturated fats	• Leave prepared food to cool at room temperature; refrigerate it straight away

USING PACKAGED FOODS

Packaged foods are more expensive than home-made ones, but they are convenient, especially if you are in a hurry or travelling. Always observe the following guidelines when using them.

• Check the ingredients listed on the tin or jar. They are listed in order of quantity, so anything that has water near the top of the list will not be very nutritious

• Avoid foods with added sugar or modified starch. It is illegal for baby foods to contain added salt or monosodium glutamate (MSG)

• Make sure that the seal is intact; if it is damaged, the food could be contaminated

• Don't heat the food up in the jar – the glass might crack

• Don't feed your baby from the jar if you intend to keep some of the food, as the leftovers will become contaminated with saliva. You can feed him from the jar if he's likely to eat the whole lot

• Don't keep opened jars in the refrigerator for longer than two days, and never beyond the "best before" date

• Never store food in an opened tin; transfer it to a dish, cover, and refrigerate

• Check the ingredients lists carefully if you are introducing food types gradually – many contain eggs, gluten, and dairy products

FEEDING AND NUTRITION

GIRLS' WEIGHT

20kg

18kg

16kg

14kg

12kg

10kg

8kg

18   24   30   36
Mths

Your toddler's weight
Weight gain may be irregular during spurts of growth, but any weight within the coloured band is normal. (See **Growth charts**, p.56.)

A balanced diet
Variety is the key to a good diet. Choose foods from each of the groups in the chart.

As your child grows his nutritional needs increase proportionately; greater quantities are needed during growth spurts, and when he's learning to walk. Your child should have a diet containing sufficient amounts of protein, carbohydrate, fats, vitamins, and minerals, and he will get all of these as long as you provide a wide variety of foods. Because he is growing, he still needs more protein and calories for his body weight than an adult.

Although, broadly speaking, a variety of foods from three of the four food groups (see p.62) – carbohydrates, fruit and vegetables (fibre), and protein-rich foods – will fulfil your child's needs, some foods within the groups have particular nutritional value. All fruit

FOOD GROUPS	NUTRIENTS
Breads and cereals *Wholemeal bread, noodles, pasta, rice*	*Protein, carbohydrates, B vitamins, iron, and calcium*
Citrus fruits *Oranges, grapefruits, lemons, limes*	*Vitamins A and C*
Fats *Butter, margarine, vegetable oils, fish oils, nut oils*	*Vitamins A and D, essential fatty acids*
Green and yellow vegetables *Cabbage, sprouts, spinach, kale, green beans, squash, lettuce, celery, courgettes*	*Minerals, including calcium, chlorine, fluorine, chromium, cobalt, copper, zinc, manganese, potassium, sodium, and magnesium*
High protein *Chicken, fish, lamb, beef, pork, offal, eggs, cheese, nuts, legumes*	*Protein, fat, iron, vitamins A and D, B vitamins, especially B12 (naturally present in animal proteins only)*
Milk and dairy products *Milk, cream, yogurt, fromage frais, ice cream, cheese*	*Protein, fat, calcium, vitamins A and D, B vitamins*
Other vegetables and fruits *Potatoes, beetroot, corn, carrots, cauliflower, pineapples, apricots, nectarines, strawberries, plums, apples, bananas*	*Carbohydrates, vitamins A, B, and C*

and vegetables provide carbohydrates and fibre, for instance, but leafy vegetables are particularly high in minerals, while citrus fruits are a good source of vitamins A and C (see chart opposite).

SNACKS

Until the age of four or five your child will prefer to eat frequently throughout the day. His stomach still can't cope with three adult-sized meals a day, so he is not ready to adopt an adult eating pattern. He may want to eat between three and fourteen times a day, but the typical range is five to seven times. What he eats is more important than how often he eats. As a rule, the more meals he has, the smaller they will be.

You may be accustomed to thinking of snacks as "extras", but they are an integral part of any child's diet so should not be refused. As long as the snacks do not reduce your child's daily nutrition, and are not being used as substitutes for "meals", snacks can be wonderfully useful for introducing new foods gradually without disrupting your child's eating patterns. Avoid giving your child highly refined and processed foods like biscuits, sweets, cakes, and ice cream, which contain a lot of calories and very few nutrients. Fresh fruits and vegetables, cubes of cheese, peanut butter and cheese sandwiches with wholemeal bread, and fruit juice all make good, nutritious snacks.

Planning snacks Snack foods should contribute to the whole day's nutrition, so don't leave them to chance; plan them carefully, and co-ordinate meals and snacks so that you serve different foods in the snacks and in the meals.

- Milk and milk-based drinks make very good snacks, and contain protein, calcium, and many of the B vitamins. You should use whole milk until your child is at least two years old; then you can use semi-skimmed but not skimmed milk unless your child is overweight (see p.70). Raw fruit juice drinks are also very nutritious, and contain a lot of vitamin C. If you buy fruit juices, avoid those with added sugar.

- Your child may become bored with certain kinds of food, so try to give him plenty of variety, and make snacks amusing if you can: you could use biscuit cutters to cut cheese or bread into interesting shapes, or make a smiling face by arranging pieces of fruit on a slice of bread.

- A food which your child rejects in one form may be acceptable in another: yogurt can be frozen so that it becomes more like ice cream, and a child who rejects cheese sandwiches might enjoy eating cheese and tomato pieces out of an ice-cream cone.

- You can also increase your child's interest in food by involving him in planning or even preparing part of a snack. He will take great pride in eating a sandwich if he has helped you wash or tear the lettuce, for example, or if you allow him to assemble the bread and filling himself.

BOYS' WEIGHT

20kg
18kg
16kg
14kg
12kg
10kg
8kg

18   24   30   36
Mths

Your toddler's weight
Your child may have spurts of growth, but these will balance out with periods of slower weight gain. Any weight within the coloured band is normal. (For a full explanation of the chart, see **Growth charts**, p.56.)

Little and often
Your child will need more snacks than you do, as he can't eat large meals.

*Your child can eat at table in
her usual high chair, but there
are other types of seat available
which are more portable and will
give her greater independence.*

Clip-on chairs
These light collapsible chairs
are suitable for babies over six
months of age. Some will grip
the table when your toddler sits
in the chair; others are attached
to the table by clamps. These
are not necessarily suitable for
all tables, so be sure to read the
manufacturer's recommenda-
tions carefully before buying.

Booster seat
Help your child reach table
height with a purpose-made
seat, suitable for children
over 18 months. It is more
stable than a cushion, and
can be strapped to a chair.

FEEDING YOUR TODDLER

By the age of 18 months your baby will already be eating more or
less the same foods as you, and she will probably take about one
third to half an adult portion at meals. You should ensure that she
has at least one protein food at each meal, and four servings of
fruit and vegetables a day. Aim to give a good mixture of foods
from the different food groups in the chart on p.66.

Don't give your child highly seasoned or sugary foods – fresh
fruit or yogurt rather than puddings should be offered. You also
should avoid any small, hard pieces of food which your child could
choke on, like whole nuts or popcorn, fruits with stones or pips,
or very small pieces of raw fruit or vegetables.

FAMILY EATING

Now that your toddler is feeding herself, she will enjoy sitting at
the table during family mealtimes. Although she's eating the same
food as everyone else, you may need to mash or chop it so that
she can eat it without much help. A very messy eater can be fed
beforehand, then allowed to sit at the table with some finger foods.
Difficult eaters feel encouraged to eat more at family meals.

It will be some time, however, before your child is ready to sit
still during mealtimes. If she wants to get down from the table, let
her go, and don't try to make her come back to finish her food if
she has obviously lost interest in it; she will make up for it by eating more at the next meal.

MESSY EATERS

Your child may regard mealtimes as just another game, and will
see nothing wrong in getting food everywhere. Although it may
seem that she is doing it on purpose, it's just a phase, and her co-
ordination will improve eventually. Make
mealtimes easier on yourself by surrounding
the high chair with newspaper,
which can be gathered up after
each meal. Being tidy can be
turned into a game: you could
draw a circle on the tray of the
high chair to show your toddler where her mug should go;
if she keeps it there, reward her.

Keeping clean
Bibs and easy-to-wash
plastic equipment help
to keep messy mealtimes
manageable.

MENU PLANNING

The menus below assume that your toddler will eat three meals a day and several snacks. If you find in practice that she eats fewer meals and more snacks, just make sure you choose snack foods that you would have served at mealtimes.

SUGGESTED MENUS AGE 18 MONTHS

DAY 1	DAY 2	DAY 3
Breakfast	*Breakfast*	*Breakfast*
¹/₂ slice wholemeal toast	25g cereal plus ¹/₂ cup milk	1 cup diluted fruit juice
1 chopped hard-boiled egg	1 cup diluted fruit juice	1 tablespoon baby muesli with 50ml of milk
1 cup diluted fruit juice	1 sliced pear, without skin	¹/₂ mashed banana
	¹/₂ slice wholemeal toast	small tub of fruit yogurt
Lunch	*Lunch*	*Lunch*
50g white fish	1 beefburger in a wholemeal roll	1 cheese sandwich with wholemeal bread
50g brown rice (dry weight)	30g steamed broccoli	pieces of raw carrot
1 tablespoon sweetcorn	1 medium tomato	1 sliced apple, without skin
1 cup diluted fruit juice	1 cup diluted fruit juice	1 cup milk
Snacks	*Snacks*	*Snacks*
1 cup water	1 cup milk	1 orange in pieces
1 small yogurt	1 unsweetened wholemeal biscuit	1 fromage frais
1 banana	1 cup water	1 cup diluted fresh fruit juice
1 wholemeal bread roll	1 rice cake	1 packet unsalted crisps
Dinner	*Dinner*	*Dinner*
50–75g cauliflower with 50g grated cheese	¹/₂ wholemeal roll	2 sardines (not in oil)
50g broad beans	50g broad beans	50g baked beans
50g chicken pieces, without skin	50g chopped liver	1 medium tomato
¹/₂ banana blended with 1 cup milk	50g wholemeal pasta (dry weight)	1 cup milk
1 small wholemeal roll	1 cup water	

MAKING FOOD FUN

Making mealtimes exciting for your toddler will encourage her to try new foods. Fun foods do not have to be difficult or time-consuming; a little imagination is all it takes.

Smiley pizza face
Cheese, vegetables, and fresh fruit decoratively arranged on top of a plain pizza can be very appealing, and makes a highly nutritious child's meal.

69

OVERWEIGHT

Obesity is one of the most common nutritional problems among children in prosperous western societies. Most plump children, however, are not medically overweight and no special action is needed as long as they are healthy and active.

If you think your child is overweight – that is, markedly fatter than her friends – consult your doctor who will be able to tell you if your child's weight is above the normal range for her height.

The commonest causes of overweight are a poor diet and lack of exercise. The best way to help the child is often for the whole family to adopt a healthier diet: less fat and sugar, more fresh fruit and vegetables, and more unrefined carbohydrates.

You should never aim to make your child actually lose weight, but for her weight to remain stable while she grows in height. The following guidelines may help:

• Bake, grill, and boil foods rather than roasting or frying

• Give water or diluted fruit juice when your child is thirsty. Never give sweetened drinks

• Give wholemeal bread, raw vegetables, and fruit as snacks

• Wholemeal bread and pasta and brown rice are more filling than their refined equivalents

• Encourage your child to be active by playing lively games with her yourself

• No child needs more than a pint of milk a day. Skimmed or semi-skimmed cows' milk can be used for overweight children over the age of one year if vitamin supplements are also given

FEEDING PROBLEMS

Some young children are "difficult eaters", but in many cases the real difficulty is with a parent who expects the child to conform to an eating pattern that doesn't suit her. If you approach feeding problems with sympathy and a flexible attitude, they will usually just disappear. In some cases there may be a genuine problem, such as intolerance of, or allergy to, certain foodstuffs, and you should consult your doctor. Never try to isolate a food allergy yourself; your child could suffer if you deprive her of particular foods.

FOOD PREFERENCES

In the second year your child will start to show likes and dislikes for certain foods. It is very common for children to go through phases of eating only one kind of food and refusing everything else. For example, she may go for a week eating nothing but yogurt and fruit, then suddenly go right off yogurt and start eating nothing but cheese and mashed potato. Don't get cross with your child about this, and don't insist that she eats certain foods. No one food is essential to your child, and there is always a nutritious substitute for any food she refuses to eat. As long as you offer your child a wide variety of foods, she will get a balanced diet, and it is far better for her to eat something that she likes – even if it's something you disapprove of – than to eat nothing at all. The one thing you must watch out for is your toddler refusing to eat any food from a particular group – refusing any kind of fruit or vegetables, for example. If she does, her diet will become unbalanced, so you will have to think of ways of tempting her to eat fruit and vegetables, perhaps by cooking the food in a different way or presenting it imaginatively (see p.69).

If you spend time cooking food that you know your toddler doesn't want, you will feel annoyed and resentful when she doesn't eat it, so give yourself and her a break by cooking food that you know she will enjoy.

Don't try to camouflage a disliked food by mixing it with something else, or bargain with your child by offering a favourite food if she eats the disliked one; she may very well end up refusing other foods as well. If you are introducing a new food, make sure your child is hungry; that way, she is more likely to take it. Never try to force her to take something she doesn't want; if she thinks it's very important to you, she will just use it as a way of manipulating you.

REFUSAL TO EAT

Not eating is an early indication that your child may be unwell, so observe her carefully. If she looks pale, and seems fretful and more clumsy than usual, check her temperature (see p.278) and speak to your doctor if you're worried.

Occasionally your child may have eaten a lot of snacks or a drink of milk before her meal, and she won't show her usual appetite. As long as the snacks are nutritious, this is nothing to worry about.

If she refuses to eat for no reason that you can see, don't let yourself be bothered by it. Your child will always eat as much food as she really needs, and if you insist on her eating, mealtimes may become a battle which you will always lose.

FOOD INTOLERANCE

The inability to fully digest certain foods has to be distinguished from a true food allergy which is quite different and very rare. Intolerance occurs when the digestive system fails to produce essential enzymes that break down food inside the body. One of the most common forms of food intolerance in children is lactose intolerance – the inability to digest the sugars in milk. The enzyme, in this case lactase, may be absent from birth, or its production may be disrupted by an intestinal disorder such as gastroenteritis. Pale-coloured, bulky, smelly stools are characteristic of the disorder. Sometimes food intolerance occurs for reasons that are not known. If your child habitually has symptoms such as diarrhoea, nausea, or pain after eating a particular food, intolerance may be the cause. The best remedy is to avoid the food concerned, but don't try to identify it yourself; you will need medical advice to pin down the culprit food and to eliminate other causes.

FOOD ALLERGY

Most cases of suspected food allergy turn out to be no more than intolerance, or the combination of a fussy child and a fussy mother. A true food allergy is quite rare, and occurs when the the body's immune system undergoes an exaggerated reaction to a protein or chemical it interprets as "foreign". It is a protective mechanism and symptoms can include headache, nausea, profuse vomiting, a rash, widespread red blotches in the skin, and swelling of the mouth, tongue, face, and eyes.

At first the allergen – the substance that causes the reaction – may produce only mild symptoms, but these may become more severe if the child is repeatedly exposed to the food concerned. Some foods that commonly cause allergic reactions are wheat, shellfish, strawberries, chocolate, eggs, and cows' milk.

In the 1980s food allergies attracted a great deal of attention, and were blamed for behavioural disturbances in children, including hyperactivity. More recent studies have cast doubt on these claims: parents continued to report behavioural disturbance even when, unknown to them, the suspect food had been withdrawn from the child's diet. In a very small number of cases it has been proved that food was responsible for the behaviour, but in very many more cases bad behaviour is a way of seeking love and attention from neglectful parents. I feel very strongly that too many parents have been willing to blame foods for behavioural problems rather than look to their own attitudes as a cause. Meanwhile, many children have been needlessly deprived of nutritious foods.

You should never attempt to isolate a food allergy on your own without medical advice, and never assume an allergy is present without a clear diagnosis from a paediatric allergist.

WHEN YOUR CHILD IS ILL

Loss of appetite is often one of the first signs of illness in a child, but this need not be a cause for concern if the illness is short.

• *Your child must drink plenty of fluid, especially if she has been vomiting or had diarrhoea.*

• *Most doctors recommend that drinks containing milk should be avoided if your child is suffering from gastroenteritis*

• *There is no need for a special invalid diet, though it is sensible to avoid rich or heavy foods if your child has an upset stomach*

• *Offer some of her favourite foods to cheer her up, and give smaller portions than usual. Because your child is resting, she will probably not want much*

Giving drinks
Your child's appetite may be poor when she is ill, but make sure she takes plenty of fluids by offering her favourite drink.

71

FEEDING AND NUTRITION

TREATS AND REWARDS

Every parent knows that there are times when it is important either to reward good behaviour or to offer a bribe in return for some form of co-operation.

Sweets might seem like the most suitable reward, as they are always appreciated by children. However, you may feel that to give sweets routinely as a reward undermines the consistency of your approach to sweet-eating in general. There is no hard and fast rule on this, and there is no reason why you shouldn't occasionally reward your child with sweets as long as you make it clear that it is a one-off gift.

It's worth making an effort, though, to devise other forms of reward: a favourite yogurt flavour, a small toy or a new box of crayons, or a specially extended bath-time or bed-time story.

I don't believe in placing a total ban on sweets, because this can encourage children to be secretive and dishonest.

I do believe in rationing sweets, though, and this always worked with my own children. If you let your child have one sweet after lunch and one after supper, and encourage him to brush his teeth afterwards, you will be encouraging self control, good eating habits, and good oral hygiene.

Your pre-schooler will eat broadly the same diet as you, and his dietary needs should be seen in the context of the eating habits of the whole family: you may even have taken the opportunity to improve your own diet as a result of considering the needs of your child. At this stage you will probably be concerned less about making sure your child is getting the right foods in the right amounts, and more about whether he is learning adult behaviour and manners at mealtimes. This is a good time to teach him table manners that will last into adulthood.

FAMILY AND SOCIAL EATING

For many families, mealtimes are about much more than making sure everyone is fed; they are social occasions when all the members of the family sit down together, exchange news, and enjoy each other's company. For a small child these times form an important part of his learning process; he can appreciate this social aspect of mealtimes and will learn most of his behaviour at table from his experience of family eating rather than from any number of lectures at a later age. Every family has its own accepted standards of behaviour and I am not going to lay down rules about what these should be. What is important, however, is that your child learns to fit in so that the family can enjoy their mealtimes together without repeated disruptions caused by bad manners and arguments about behaviour.

As soon as your child first sat in his high chair at the family dining table he will have been watching and learning. He will want at least to try the foods that you are eating and will often join in the conversation. Try to include your child in family meals as often as possible. Encourage him when he attempts to follow your (good) example. Give praise, for instance, when he asks for something to be passed to him instead of attempting to grab it from the other side of the table. Children learn most naturally and easily by example and will rapidly pick up the norms of behaviour that the rest of the family observe. If yours is a family where everyone leaves the table when it suits them, for example, rather than waiting for the others to finish eating, it will be hard to persuade your child to sit still and wait.

There will be occasions when you want your child to behave especially well at mealtimes – usually because you are having visitors. Allow him to join in the excitement of a special meal by letting him help lay the table, perhaps. If he understands that some occasions demand an extra effort, he will find it easier to understand why you want him to be particularly well behaved and will therefore react better to your wishes.

KEEPING MEALTIMES RELAXED

It is important to prevent meals from becoming a battleground for more generalized family conflict. The association between food and love can be very close, and arguments about food and eating can be associated with tensions over other issues. In such cases food and eating behaviour – for example, refusal to eat – can become a weapon that the child uses either to gain attention or to express anger, distress, and many other emotions. It is best, therefore, to be fairly easy-going about table etiquette with your child, to make mealtimes as relaxed as possible, and not to be drawn into arguments. Insist only on the aspects of table manners that you consider essential; refinements can come later.

EATING AWAY FROM HOME

A small baby can eat only what you give him, but an older child will have pronounced preferences about what he wants to eat, and the opportunity to follow them. There are likely to be more occasions when your child is eating outside the home, and while you obviously can't account for every mouthful he eats, you should try to ensure that the good habits he has learned at home are not undermined once he starts to eat elsewhere.

If your child goes out to playgroup, nursery school, or "proper" school, try to make sure he has a good breakfast before he goes. If he doesn't, he will become hungry again long before lunchtime, and both his temper and his concentration will be affected. A healthy mid-morning snack like a piece of fruit or cereal bar will help tide him over until lunchtime. If food is going to be provided for him, try to find out what will be on offer; if you are not satisfied, or if there are no arrangements to feed your child, then provide him with a nutritious packed lunch instead. Lunch need not always be sandwiches; you could give chicken pieces and potato salad, pieces of raw vegetables with a yogurt dip, or other foods that you child can eat with his fingers.

Children are often encouraged to try new foods because they see their friends eat them, and you may find once your child starts at playgroup or school that he starts to eat foods that he previously rejected at home.

FAST FOODS

Do try not to resort to fast-food restaurants too often when you are out with your child and want to stop for something to eat. Most of the foods available in these restaurants – chips, hamburgers, sausages, and sugary drinks – are high in salt, fats, or sugar, and low in nutrients. If you can, bring a supply of healthy snack foods with you, or choose somewhere that offers more healthy foods, such as sandwiches and salads. If your child particularly asks for hamburgers and chips, however, you may like to indulge him now and again – but make it clear that such foods are a special treat, to be eaten only occasionally. My family used to eat at a hamburger restaurant once a week, for Saturday lunch. This satisfied everyone and is not so frequent as to damage good health.

EATING OUT

There will be many occasions when you'll take your child out to eat. Being prepared will make the experience more enjoyable.

• *Try to find out beforehand what facilities will be available at the restaurant you choose: if you are booking a table, mention that you will be bringing small children, and find out whether there will be room for your child's pushchair, and whether a high chair can be provided if you need one*

• *Many children's menus are very limited and offer just hamburgers, sausages, or fish fingers – all with chips. If you don't want your child to have these foods, ask whether you can order a small portion of a suitable dish from the main menu, and whether you will be charged full price for it*

• *Most children will enjoy the experience of eating out, and you should involve your child fully, allowing him to choose his own meal and to give his own order to the waiter if he is not too shy*

• *Bring along your child's booster seat if he normally uses one. If you think he will have difficulty drinking from a glass, you could also bring along his trainer cup*

• *Many restaurants positively encourage children, and will be happy to provide straws for drinks, bibs and high chairs for young babies, and even small gifts such as paper hats or pictures to colour in*

HOLDING AND HANDLING

PUTTING YOUR BABY DOWN

For the first three months of her life, you should always lay your baby on her back.

Research in recent years has shown that babies who sleep on their fronts are at greater risk from cot death than those placed on their backs, and publicity in the UK about this finding has resulted in a significant drop in cot death; it has been reduced by almost 50 per cent in 5 years.

A newborn baby may appear very vulnerable and fragile, but she is more robust than you imagine. With this knowledge uppermost in your mind, you will be able to inspire confidence in your child rather than uncertainty. For the baby's comfort, and for your own peace of mind, it's important to feel at ease when you handle her; you must be able to hold your baby confidently in order to bathe, dress, and feed her successfully.

HANDLING YOUR BABY

When you move your baby, the action must be as slow, gentle, and quiet as possible. You'll find that you instinctively hold your baby close, look into her eyes, and talk soothingly to her. Not surprisingly it has been proven that all children benefit from intimate physical contact, particularly being in a position to hear the familiar sound of your heartbeat. Premature babies, for example, gain more weight when they are laid on fleecy sheets, which give them the sensation of being touched, than when they are laid on smooth ones. Your newborn baby will find comfort in any kind of skin-to-skin contact, but the best way to give her this is for both of you to lie naked in bed. Here she can smell and feel your skin, and hear your heart beating. In this way, too, you can make sure that she becomes familiar with the smell of her father's skin.

PICKING UP YOUR BABY

Lifting your baby
Slide one hand under your baby's neck and the other under her back and bottom to support her lower half securely. Pick her up gently and smoothly and transfer her to a carrying position.

Whenever you pick your baby up and put her down, do it in a way that supports her head; until she is about four weeks old she'll have little control over it. If her head flops back, she will think that she is going to fall, her body will jerk, and she'll stretch out both arms and legs in the Moro, or "startle", reflex (see p.20).

Put your baby down and pick her up with your whole arm supporting her spine, neck, and head. You may like to try swaddling your baby: wrap her firmly in a shawl or blanket so that her head is supported and her arms held close against her body. Once she lies down in the cot, you can gently unwrap her. Swaddling your baby tightly makes her feel secure, so it's a useful way of comforting and calming a distressed baby.

CARRYING YOUR BABY

One way to carry your baby in your arms is to cradle her head in the crook of either arm, which is slightly inclined. The rest of her body will rest on the lower part of your arm, encircled by your wrist and hand which support her back and bottom. Your other arm will provide additional support to her bottom and legs and your baby can see your face as you talk to her and smile at her.

The second way to carry your baby is to hold her against the upper part of your chest with her head on your shoulder. Your forearm should be placed across her back and your hand should support her resting head, leaving your other hand free. This can be used to provide support for your baby's bottom, or to help you balance. Your sense of balance will change at first as you get used to carrying your new baby.

SLINGS

Newborns are best carried in slings worn on the chest, where they feel close to you and secure.

• *Look for a sling in a washable fabric, for it will get rather dirty as you carry your baby around*

• *It must be easy to put on and comfortable to wear for both you and your partner. Try it out with your baby before you buy it*

• *Your sling should support your baby's head and neck, and keep her secure; she must not be able to slip out of the sides*

• *The shoulder straps must be wide enough to support your growing baby's weight. Wide shoulder straps will also make carrying more comfortable*

• *It has been said that a baby shouldn't be carried in a sling until she can support her own head. This is not true. Use a sling as soon as you and your baby are happy about it*

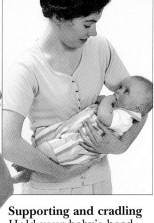

Supporting and cradling
Hold your baby's head and support the length of her body when carrying her. Holding her close will make your baby feel secure and relaxed, especially if she can see your face.

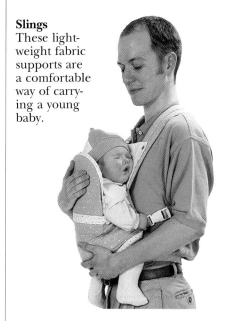

Slings
These light-weight fabric supports are a comfortable way of carrying a young baby.

75

BABY MASSAGE

Massage can have all the benefits for a baby that it has for an adult: it is soothing and can calm a fretful baby and is a marvellous way of showing love. If you massage your baby every day he will learn to recognise the routine and will show pleasure as you begin. You can continue to massage your baby as he gets older; a massage is often the ideal way to calm an excited toddler.

Provide a relaxed atmosphere before you start. As this will be a new experience for you both, any distractions can spoil the mood and upset your baby so choose a time when there is no-one else around and unplug the phone. Make sure the room is nice and warm and lay your baby on a warm towel or sheepskin, or on your lap. Work from his head down using light, even strokes and ensure that both sides of his body are massaged symmetrically. Make eye contact with your baby throughout the massage and talk quietly, gently and lovingly to him.

GIVING A MASSAGE

Head
Start off by lightly massaging the crown of your baby's head using a circular motion, then stroke down the sides of his face. Gently massage his forehead, working from the centre out and moving over the eyebrows and cheeks to finish around his ears.

Make sure you massage both sides of your baby's body symmetrically

Neck and shoulders
Gently massage your baby's neck from his ears to his shoulders and from his chin to his chest. Then stroke his shoulders from his neck outwards.

Arms
Stroke down his arms to his fingertips. Using your fingers and thumb, gently squeeze all along his arm, starting at the top.

Chest and abdomen
Gently stroke down your baby's chest, following the delicate curves of his ribs. Rub his abdomen in a circular motion, working outwards from the navel.

Feet and toes
Rub your baby's ankles and feet, stroking from heel to toe, and then concentrate on each toe individually. End your massage with some long, light strokes running the whole length of the front of your baby's body.

Legs
Now you can massage your baby's legs, working from his thighs down to his knees. Stroke down the shins, and move around to his calves and ankles. Gently squeeze all the way down.

Back
Once you have massaged your baby on the front, turn him over and work on his back.

OLDER BABY

HOLDING AND HANDLING

HOW WE HANDLE GIRLS

According to research, we start preparing our girl babies from the day they are born to conform to a feminine sexual stereotype. When handling girls, we

• *Coo, whisper, and smile gently, and cradle them softly*

• *Don't handle them excitingly so they never know the sensation of flying through the air*

• *Make bathing times for girls much more sedate than for boys*

• *Give them soft, cuddly toys and discourage them from rough, dirty, or dangerous play*

• *Sympathize with slight injuries and make no attempts to stop them from crying, so they grow up thinking shows of helplessness and emotion are all right*

If you would like your daughter to grow up tough, independent, and self-assured, you should adjust your behaviour and treat her more like a boy (see opposite page)

By now you should be quite relaxed about carrying your baby. You will probably settle on a couple of favourite ways of carrying him, depending on whether he wants to be cuddled or to look at what is going on all around him. He is much heavier now, so make sure that you adopt a method of lifting him that won't strain your back.

PICKING UP AND CARRYING YOUR BABY

Your baby now can control his head, so there is no longer any need to support it as you did when he was newborn. Now you can pick him up simply by putting your hands under his armpits and lifting him forward towards you. This is also a very good way of putting him into a high chair: his legs will dangle and he can be slipped into the chair. Alternatively, you can lift him with one hand curled diagonally around his back, and the other supporting his bottom.

You can carry your baby in the crook of your arm, against your shoulder so that he faces you, or with your arm stretched diagonally across his back and holding his thigh as he sits astride one hip. A sling can be used, although for longer journeys a backpack will give you more support.

CARRYING POSITIONS

Your baby enjoys intimacy

Your baby's arms are free to move

On one hip
Your baby can now support himself well enough to sit astride your hip. This allows him to look all around.

Facing forwards
Hold your baby securely around the waist, so he can look around him. You can use your other hand to support him, or keep it free.

Talk to your baby while bouncing him

Rocking
You can make this activity into a boisterous game by swinging your baby quite high, or just doing it gently to soothe him.

Bouncing
Lift your baby up and down on your knees rhythmically. You should always support him so he doesn't slip backwards.

SWINGING AND BOUNCING GAMES

All babies love to be bounced and swung, but just how much they enjoy it will depend on how they're feeling. Being swung up in the air is exciting for your baby, as he can look at his surroundings – and see your face – from a whole new perspective. Sometimes he will prefer to be bounced on your knee or simply gently rocked. Always give your baby a chance to relax after boisterous games by cuddling him quietly for a few minutes.

Swinging
Raise your baby up high then swoop him down between your legs. He will love looking down at your face from a height.

Hold your baby firmly so that he feels safe

Your baby will love the sensation of flying through the air

HOW WE HANDLE BOYS

Experiments have shown that we handle baby boys differently from baby girls, and that we persist in this stereotyping even if we are merely fooled by, say, their wearing pink or blue clothes. When handling boys, we

• *Speak, laugh, even shout out loudly, and grasp them firmly*

• *Swing them about so that they get used to lots of action and physical movement*

• *Encourage them to splash and kick in the bath*

• *Give them tough, hard toys and praise adventurousness, even naughtiness, with encouraging words or phrases*

• *Are efficient rather than tender when a boy grazes his knee, discouraging shows of emotion and applauding independence*

If you want your son to be more in touch with his gentler side, adjust your behaviour so you treat him more like a girl (see opposite page)

79

TODDLER

HOLDING AND HANDLING

LIFTING YOUR TODDLER

Make sure you know how to handle heavy weights in a way that won't strain your back.

Once you have a baby, there are many opportunities for putting a strain on your back. Your child requires constant lifting and carrying, and prams, pushchairs, and other equipment must be shifted. It's important that you learn to lift without injury and strain. Keep your back straight, bend your knees, and, using the powerful thigh muscles to do all the work, lift. Never lift with your legs straight and your back curved forward.

Never refuse your toddler a cuddle; although she will need less holding than when she was a young baby, she will often ask to be carried like she used to when she's been out for a long walk, or when she's generally tired and cranky. She's likely to be clingy when she feels pain or discomfort, when a tooth is coming through, or if she is feeling off colour. You should always respond to her signals and not hesitate to give her a hug for comfort and affection. Your child will make it clear when she has had enough reassurance and will get down and run off. Babies who are given love and cuddles when they need and ask for them usually grow into independent and self-confident individuals.

The desire for physical affection remains with us always. Parents should never scoff at their children's needs, and always respond. When my children were growing up, they liked a cuddle every now and then, especially when they were tired, had had a telling-off from a teacher at school, if they were fearful about my departure or absence, or if the world simply didn't feel right.

"CLINGY" CHILDREN

Older children will still occasionally want to sit on your lap. When they feel ill at ease in strange circumstances, they may even want to eat sitting on your knee, particularly if strangers are present and they feel that they are being watched. Let them do so if it is convenient; you will find that just a few moments of intimacy will give a child the confidence to handle any situation.

Bedtimes are particularly important times for showing affection. In my opinion, a child should never have to go to bed without some cuddling. A cuddle will provide a sense of security and the conviction that you really do care. The rule is that you should always be there with a comforting arm and a kind word when your child is hurt, worried, puzzled, or frightened. Not all children require physical reassurance, so be prepared to provide comfort in the form that your child wants.

THE UNRESPONSIVE CHILD

From a very early age some children stiffen their bodies and cry when you hold them and usually grow up to be children who avoid physical contact – who turn away if you try to kiss them, for example, and make no physical advances themselves. Such children may never enjoy physical affection comfortably, and a parent may find this hard to cope with because it seems like rejection. If your child behaves in this way, don't insist on cuddles that she clearly does not want. Give your physical affection only when she shows you that she wants it and respect her wishes.

SHOWING AFFECTION

By the age of three or four years your child will be much more independent, and you may assume that she needs fewer overt displays of affection. While this may be true, it would be a mistake to think that she wants to go without any physical affection at all. You should pay special attention to boys, who are often expected to give up cuddles and kisses at a very young age because it is not considered to be proper "masculine" behaviour.

It is all too easy to lose the habit of showing affection, so make a resolution to hold and touch your child as often as you can every day, whether it's letting her sit on your knee or putting an arm around her when you look at the paper, or giving her a cuddle when you put her to bed. I made it a rule to tell my children every day that I loved them.

Older children often become self-conscious about being kissed or cuddled in public, so be sensitive to this. Choose private moments when they can enjoy your care, attention, and love.

DIVIDING YOUR ATTENTION

It can be very difficult to divide your time and attention evenly between several young children. A friend of mine, who had twins, adopted a pragmatic approach to this problem: rather than trying to give each twin an equal share of her attention at all times, she decided to attend to whichever twin needed her at any one time, and assumed that it would all even out over the years.

Her example is a good one to follow; for much of the time you will give your children equal attention, so if one of them demands more, you should feel free to give it.

COMFORT AND ENCOURAGEMENT

With any luck your child won't be averse to a cuddle even after she's reached adulthood, but cuddles do change and get more grown-up, and you have to give the kind of cuddles your child needs rather than you want to give. So adapt your style of cuddling to what gives her most comfort.

Preschool children need plenty of cuddles every day, especially congratulatory ones, as when they've mastered something like getting their shoes on the right feet. Comfort cuddles are essential at the first sign of tears. A child responds much better to a cuddle than a reprimand. Therapeutic cuddles reduce the pain of a prick, a knock, or a cut (even a big one) in seconds. Never let your child go to sleep without a huge hug and an "I love you".

As your child gets older, cuddles are transformed into other actions, but they have the same bolstering, encouraging effect. A hand on the shoulder, a small caress, or just taking your child's hand is a sign of love and her confidence will soar. Your child craves your love and approval; never leave her in any doubt that she has both in full measure.

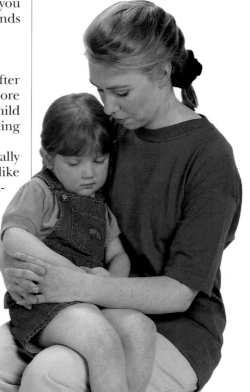

Giving comfort
Many of your child's troubles can be solved with a hug and a few sympathetic words from you.

YOUNG BABY

DRESSING

GIRLS' CLOTHES

Unisex stretch suits and rompers are ideal for everyday wear, but you may prefer more feminine clothes for special occasions.

• *Make sure all clothes are machine washable as they won't stay clean for long*

• *Avoid very fluffy or lacy cardigans. Fluffy ones will irritate your baby's skin, and tiny fingers catch in lacy ones*

• *Hats can be both practical and pretty. Choose one with ties or elastic and a wide brim for sun protection or for warmth in winter*

Dressing up
Your little girl will look very special in a pretty suit and hat. Elasticated arms and legs are comfortable provided they're not too tight.

Everyone loves dressing a baby, and your friends and family will all want to buy clothes for your baby as soon as she is born. You are bound to take great pride in her appearance, and might like to buy some dressy clothes for special occasions, but there's no need to spend a lot of money – she will grow out of clothes very quickly. Remember that as far as your baby is concerned anything goes as long as it's soft and comfortable to wear, and can be put on and taken off without too much disturbance.

Your baby will posset and dribble on her clothes, and there are bound to be accidents and leaks from nappies, so buy only machine-washable, colour-fast clothing, and avoid white – it quickly gets dirty, and frequent washing makes it drab.

Look for soft and comfortable clothes with no hard seams or rough stitching. Towelling, cotton, or pure wool clothes will feel nicer on your baby's skin. If you buy clothes made of synthetic fibres, check that they feel soft.

Always choose clothes that are non-flammable, and avoid open-weave shawls and cardigans, because your baby's fingers could easily get caught in the holes. Check the fastenings, too: poppers in the crotch allow easy access to the nappy area, and poppers at

CHOOSING CLOTHES

Easy-fitting clothes will give your baby the most comfort and warmth. Pay special attention to the cuffs, ankles, and neck where fastenings could cause discomfort.

All babies will feel snug and comfy in an all-in-one suit

Fasteners that snap open and closed are very quick and easy

Loose-fitting shoes with soft soles allow movement

BASIC LAYETTE

6 wide-necked cotton vests or T-shirts	2 nightdresses with drawstring ends
1 hat	2 pairs socks and padders
1 shawl for swaddling	2 pairs mittens (for winter)
8 all-in-one stretch suits	1 padded or fleecy all-in-one pram suit
2 woollen jackets or cardigans (4 in winter)	

the neck mean your baby won't grow out of something quickly just because her head is too big for the neck opening. Babies hate having their faces covered, so look for wide, envelope necks or clothes which fasten down the front. Front fastening clothes also allow you to dress your baby without having to turn her over. This will make dressing more comfortable for her and easier for you.

Take a note of your baby's measurements and bring it with you when you're shopping. Babies of the same age vary a great deal in size, so look at the height and weight given on the label rather than the age. If in doubt, buy the larger size: loose-fitting clothes are warmer and more comfortable than clothes that are too small and your baby will soon grow into them.

BOYS' CLOTHES

Look for clothes that are practical as well as smart to dress your baby boy.

• *Strong primary colours look good on both sexes*

• *A dungaree and T-shirt set is comfortable and looks smart. Look for dungarees with poppers at the crotch so you can get at your baby's nappy easily*

• *Hats with tie-down ear flaps are cosy in winter*

• *Don't think tights are just for girls; babies lose socks and bootees very easily, so tights are practical as well as warm*

• *Tracksuits are very comfortable and allow easy access to the nappy*

Nightdress
Loose-fitting sleeping garments are comfortable for your new-born baby. A drawstring at the end prevents the night-dress from riding up around her body, and gives you easy access to her nappy.

Loose-fitting cuffs give your baby plenty of room to move

An envelope neck allows you to take the nightdress off more easily

A drawstring keeps your baby's feet inside and allows for easy nappy changing

Everyday wear
All-in-one suits with popper fastenings are ideal for your little boy and very versatile. Match them with soft footwear.

DRESSING YOUR BABY

At first you may be nervous about dressing your baby and trying to support him while manipulating the garments. Dressing will become easier with practice, so just be gentle and patient.

You should always dress and undress a young baby on a non-slip flat surface, as this allows you to keep both hands free – a changing mat is ideal. Your baby is very likely to cry as you take off his clothes. This is because young babies hate the feel of the air on their naked bodies; they like to feel snug and secure. It's not because you're hurting him, so don't get flustered by it.

DRESSING

Put vest over head
Lay your baby on a flat, non-slip surface and make sure his nappy is clean. Roll the vest up and pull the neck apart with your thumbs. Put it over the baby's head so that it doesn't touch his face, raising his head slightly as you do so.

Vest armholes
Widen the left sleeve or armhole and gently guide your baby's arm through it. Repeat with the other arm. Pull the vest down.

Gently guide your baby's arms through the sleeves

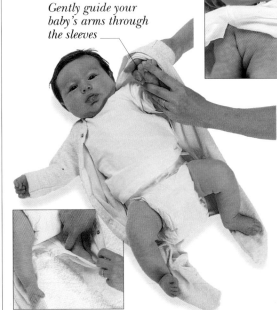

Put on stretch suit
Lay your baby on top of the open suit. Gather up each sleeve and guide his fists through. Open up each leg and guide his feet into the stretch suit. Fasten the suit.

KEEPING YOUR BABY WARM

You may worry that your new baby is not warm enough, but a few common-sense precautions will keep him comfortable and safe. Remember that babies can easily become too hot; this could lead to heat rash, and is also a factor in cot death.

• *A great deal of body heat is lost through a bare head; make sure your baby always wears a hat when you take him outdoors*

• *Very young babies are unable to conserve body heat, and should be undressed only in a well-heated room and out of draughts*

• *The baby's room should be at a constant temperature and the number of blankets he needs will depend on this temperature (see p.122)*

• *If your baby is cold you may need to warm him up. Adding a layer of clothes is not enough in itself; you need to put him in a warmer place first so he can regain his normal body temperature, or hold him close to share your body heat*

• *Never leave your baby to sleep in the sun, or close to a source of direct heat such as a radiator*

• *Wrap your baby up if you take him outdoors, but remove outdoor clothes once you bring him inside again, otherwise he won't be able to cool down efficiently*

UNDRESSING

Undoing the suit
Put your baby on a flat surface and unfasten the suit. If his nappy needs changing, gently pull both legs out of the suit so that his top remains covered while you change him.

Keep your baby's top covered if you need to change his nappy

Bend his knee gently as you ease his foot out of the suit

Taking off the suit
Lift the baby's legs up while you slide the suit underneath his back as far as his shoulders.

Roll the fabric and carefully slide the hand out

Hold the baby's elbow gently

Removing the top
Grasp each sleeve by the cuff and gently slide your baby's hand out. If he's wearing a vest, roll it up towards the neck and gently pull his arms from the sleeves, holding him by each elbow as you do so.

DRESSING ON YOUR LAP

When your baby is three or four months old he will have enough muscle control to sit on your lap while you take off his clothes.

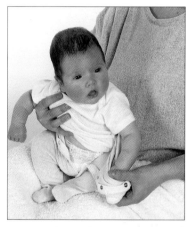

Sit with your legs crossed so that your baby will fit neatly in the hollow of your legs and cradle him with your arm, as his back will still need some support. You may find it easier to deal with the bottom half while he's lying flat.

Taking off the vest
Pull the neck wide open and lift the vest over your baby's head, keeping the fabric off his face.

85

O L D E R   B A B Y

D RESSING

O U T D O O R   C L O T H E S   F O R   G I R L S

Your little girl is more active now, so she won't always be bundled up in her pramsuit when she's outdoors. Look for outdoor clothes that are comfortable and won't restrict her movements.

• Woolly tights are warm and comfortable, and can be bought in colours and patterns to match your daughter's dress

• In very cold weather, a short cape over your little girl's coat will keep her extra warm. A matching muff will add an extra element of "dressing up"

• Gloves can be clipped to sleeves or joined with a tape and slipped through the sleeves

• Sun hats are not just pretty; they are essential if your child spends any length of time in bright sunshine

Once your baby has learned to crawl he'll be far less willing to sit or lie still while you dress him. On the other hand, he is now better able to help you as you put on his clothes. For example, an eleven-month-old baby can make a fist or stretch out an arm, if you ask him to, or hold his arm still while you pull his sleeve into place. If he's very restless you can sing a song to him or distract him with a toy, or involve him in the whole process by naming each item of clothing as you put it on or take it off, and getting him to repeat the names after you, for example. You could also turn dressing into a peek-a-boo game: "Where's your foot gone, then? Oh, look, here it is!"

Here are some tips for dressing your baby if it's difficult to get him to keep still:

• Stand him between your legs so that he's immobilized while you pull up his trousers.

• Sit him in his high chair so that you can put on his shoes.

• You can make a game out of his putting on his shoes by placing them at the bottom of the stairs and getting him to step down into them carefully while you steady him.

C H O O S I N G   C L O T H E S

Now that your baby is more active, you will need to look for clothes that allow easy movement. He will be awake for longer, and moving around, so that his clothes are more likely to get dirty and you'll therefore need more of them. You'll also have to consider whether they are tough enough for the wear and tear that your child will give them: look for sturdy fabrics that last well, and strong fastenings that won't break or fall off. If your baby is crawling, make sure his clothes protect his knees. Once he begins to walk he'll need shoes (see opposite page).

When you're buying clothes, check the label to see what sort of material they are made from. Natural fibres are both strong and comfortable, so look for pure cotton or a fabric with a high cotton content. Towelling, denim, and corduroy are all strong and hardwearing. Look, too, for clothes that can be easily pulled down or up once your child is learning how to use the potty, and avoid zip fasteners or fiddly fastenings; elasticated waists are by far the easiest for him to manage.

Until he's walking, socks or woollen bootees are all your baby needs, even when he's crawling. Fabric bootees with elasticated ankles stay on better. Ensure there's plenty of room for movement; the bones in your baby's feet are so soft and pliable that even tightly-fitting socks could misshape the toes if worn regularly.

Choosing clothes
Ensure the knees are protected if your baby is crawling.

CHOOSING SHOES

When you are buying your child shoes, always go to a reputable shop where the staff have been trained to measure and fit children's shoes. The assistant should measure the length and the width of your child's foot before trying any shoes. Once your child tries on a pair of shoes the assistant should press the joints of the foot to make sure that it is not restricted in any way, and that the fastenings hold the shoe firmly in place and don't let your child's foot slip about. Make sure your child stands up and walks about in the shoes to check that the toe doesn't pinch and hurt when he's walking and to double-check that there's no slipping.

A sturdy, well-made pair of leather shoes is most suitable for general outdoor wear, especially once your child is running about and playing. You should, however, get a pair of wellington boots for wet or muddy conditions. Although leather shoes and sandals are solid and sensible and last well, there is nothing wrong with inexpensive canvas shoes or sneakers as long as you make sure that they fit properly. If your child suddenly becomes less steady on his feet it may be a sign that he is outgrowing his shoes. Well-fitting shoes are essential to ensure that your child has good feet in adult life. You should never try to save money by buying second-hand shoes; they will have moulded themselves to the previous owner's feet.

SHOES FOR HEALTHY FEET

Choose a sturdy leather pair for outdoor wear. Your child's feet must be unrestricted but held firmly in place and unable to slip out. The toes shouldn't curl up or hurt when he walks. Never buy second-hand shoes.

Make sure there are no seams or stitching on the upper which might rub your child's foot

The heel should be no higher than 4 centimetres (1 1/2 inches) from the sole

Wide toes allow your child's toes to fan out. Make sure the box on the toe is high enough so that it doesn't exert pressure on the toenails

Adjustable fastenings hold the foot firmly in the shoe. Buckles and Velcro are easier for young children to manage than laces

The sole should be light and flexible, with a non-slip surface

Surfaces should be easy to clean or polish

There should be space between your child's big toe and the end of the shoe – at least 0.5 centimetre (1/4 inch), but no more than 1.25 centimetres (1/2 inch)

TODDLER

OUTDOOR CLOTHES FOR BOYS

Choose clothes that leave your little boy room for growth and allow him to move freely.

• *Always put a hat on your little boy if he's out in the sun. Cricket or baseball caps worn back to front protect the nape of the neck*

• *Buy outdoor clothes on the large side. This leaves room for extra layers underneath, and allows your little boy to grow into them*

• *Cut the sleeves off an outgrown jacket to make a waistcoat*

DRESSING A GIRL

Your little girl will try to dress herself now, so choose clothes that she can manage easily. She's growing fast, too, so don't spend a lot of money on clothes that she'll quickly outgrow.

• *Buy dresses with fastenings at the front; ones that fasten at the back are too difficult for your little girl to manage*

• *Show her how to get her tights the right way round, and how to roll them up before she tries to put them on*

• *Avoid very fitted clothes; they don't leave much room for growth*

SELF-DRESSING

As your child grows older, she'll develop the co-ordination required to dress successfully. You should encourage her in her attempts at dressing or undressing, however slow or awkward – they're a sign of growing independence and maturity. Learning to manage by herself will improve a child's co-ordination and increase her confidence, so be patient with her first clumsy efforts.

Lay out your child's clothes in such a way that she can manoeuvre them on easily. For instance, you could drape a cardigan on the back of a chair so that she just has to sit down and slide her arms into the sleeves. Let her do as much as she is capable of, and don't step in to help unless it's really necessary, though you will have to deal with most of the fastenings yourself until your child is old enough to manage them.

At 18 months she will already be trying to manage fastenings, and by two-and-a-half she will be able to close a button in a loose buttonhole, and put on her own pants, T–shirt, and sweatshirt. By the age of four she will probably be able to dress or undress herself completely and will have enough dexterity to put her clothes away tidily. There are several things you can do to make getting dressed easier for your child.

• Teach her how to button from the bottom upwards.

• Sew large buttons on to a toddler's clothes so that she can handle them easily.

• Velcro fastenings will be easy for her to manage, but don't use them where they might chafe her skin.

Room for growth
Loose-fitting clothes with adjustable fastenings are suitable now that your child is growing fast.

Dressing himself
By the age of three your toddler may be able to dress himself completely, though it will take him quite a long time. Allow him his independence, and don't step in to help unless you're really needed.

Pinafores or dungarees with ties or buckles can be adjusted to fit your child as she grows

Little hands can grasp a zip fastener more easily if it has a ring attached to the tab

• Buy trousers with elasticated waists to avoid zip fasteners.

• Children find it difficult to put sweaters on the right way round, so explain to her that the label always goes at the back.

Choosing clothes As your child becomes more involved in dressing herself, she will become more conscious of the clothes themselves. Babies are largely unaware of what they are wearing as long as it is comfortable and does not impede their activities, but toddlers gradually begin to notice the colours and type of clothing they put on, and your child may develop preferences. Clothes that seem similar to those worn by mummy or daddy might seem especially attractive. The feel of a garment will also be important to her – whether, for example, it is soft or itchy, tight or stretchy. If she takes a dislike to a garment, it may be because it doesn't fit properly and is therefore uncomfortable to wear..

Your child's concerns should be taken seriously when you are buying her clothing. Once your main requirements, which are practical ones – warmth, durability, washability, and cost – are met, there is no reason why you shouldn't indulge her; the image of a favourite cartoon character or a particular colour may be the deciding factor as far as she is concerned. Allowing her to choose which clothes to wear each day is also important. You may want her to wear trousers on a cold day, but let her choose which pair.

She may develop seemingly irrational likes or dislikes for certain items of clothing – insisting on wearing a particular T-shirt every day, for example, or refusing to wear the hand-knitted pullover that granny gave her for her birthday. The easiest policy is to go along with these preferences as far as possible, though occasionally bribery, or at least negotiation, may be in order: you could offer a special treat in return for wearing that pullover on the afternoon that granny comes to tea.

DRESSING A BOY

Help your little boy to dress himself by making sure his clothes don't have tricky fastenings.

• *Boys are usually slower than girls at learning to use the potty, so it is particularly important to avoid awkward fastenings on your little boy's trousers*

• *Look for adjustable straps on dungarees, or add a button so the straps can be lengthened*

• *Trousers with elasticated waists are easiest but, if he has trousers with zip fasteners, show him how to pull the zip away from him as he closes it to prevent it catching*

• *Show your little boy how to sit down to put his feet into his trouser legs, then stand up to pull them up*

Choosing fastenings
Until your child has enough dexterity to manage fiddly buttons and zips, you need to choose clothes and shoes with manageable fastenings.

Sliding buckles can be adjusted for the best fit

Hooks are easier to manage than buttonholes

Shoes
Velcro fastenings rather than laces or buckles will allow your child to fasten his own shoes very easily.

BATHING AND HYGIENE

WASHING A GIRL

There is no need to open the lips of your baby girl's vulva to clean inside, and you should never try to do so. Just wash the skin of the nappy area and dry it carefully.

When you are washing your baby girl take care to wipe from front to back – that is, towards the anus – when you clean the nappy area. This will avoid soiling the vulva, and minimize the risk of spreading bacteria from the bowels to the bladder or vagina which could cause infection.

Part of your daily routine will be to keep your baby clean. Many new parents worry about handling a very small baby in the baby bath, but you will soon get used to bathtimes and look forward to it as an opportunity to have fun and play with your baby. Instead of feeling apprehensive, set aside half an hour, have everything you need around you, try to relax, and you will enjoy it.

A young baby doesn't need bathing very often because only her bottom, face and neck, and skin creases get dirty, so you only have to bathe her every two or three days, and even then you can top and tail her instead of putting her in the bath (see below). This allows you to wash the parts of your baby that really need washing with the minimum of disturbance and distress to her. You should use cooled boiled water for a newborn, but when your baby is a little older you can use warm water straight from the tap. Do wash your baby's hair frequently to prevent cradle cap forming (see p.93). There is no need to use soap for a newborn; from about six weeks you can use bath lotion, soap, or other baby toiletries.

Babies don't like having their skin exposed to the air, so you should keep your baby undressed for as short a time as possible. Warm a big, fluffy towel on a radiator (not too hot) and have it ready to wrap your baby in as soon as you are finished.

TOPPING AND TAILING

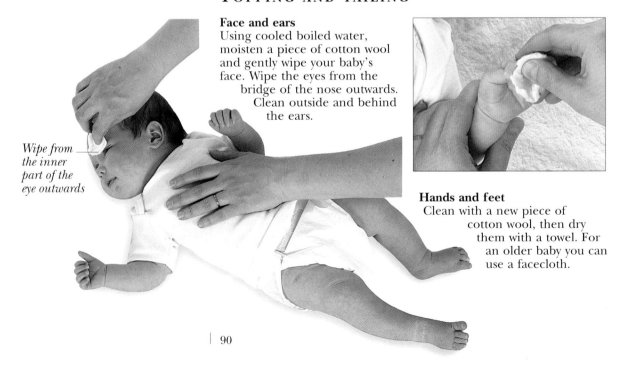

Face and ears
Using cooled boiled water, moisten a piece of cotton wool and gently wipe your baby's face. Wipe the eyes from the bridge of the nose outwards. Clean outside and behind the ears.

Wipe from the inner part of the eye outwards

Hands and feet
Clean with a new piece of cotton wool, then dry them with a towel. For an older baby you can use a facecloth.

BODY CARE

Once you have taken care of your baby's nappy area, and made sure that her skin is kept free from any traces of food or dirt that might cause irritation, the rest will take care of itself.

Eyes, nose, and ears Wash your baby's eyes with cotton-wool balls and some cooled boiled water. Work from the inner part of the eye to the outer, and use a different piece of cotton wool for each eye to avoid spreading any infection that may be present.

Don't poke around inside your baby's nose and ears; they are self-cleaning so don't use nose or ear drops, except on your doctor's advice. Just clean ears using moist cotton wool. If you see wax in your baby's ears, don't try to scrape it out; it is a natural secretion of the canal of the outer ear, is antiseptic and protects the eardrum from dust and grit. Removing it will only cause the ear to produce more. If you are concerned consult your doctor.

Nails Your newborn baby's nails should be kept short; otherwise she may scratch her skin. The best time to cut them is after a bath, when they are soft; use a pair of small, blunt-ended scissors. If you are nervous about it, bite the nails off; your mouth is so sensitive that you will not hurt her.

Navel During the few days after birth, the umbilical stump (see p.15) dries and shrivels, and then drops off. You can bathe your baby before the stump has healed, as long as you dry it thoroughly afterwards. Allow the area to stay open to the air as much as possible to help speed up the shrinking and healing process.

WASHING A BOY

Never pull your baby boy's foreskin back for cleaning; it's quite tight and could get stuck. Wash the whole of the nappy area and dry carefully, particularly the skin creases. By the time your baby is three or four years of age, the foreskin will be loose and can retract without force.

If your baby has just been circumcised, you should watch carefully for any signs of bleeding. A few drops of blood is quite normal; so is swelling and slight inflammation, but this will settle down. If bleeding persists, however, or if there is any sign of infection, consult your doctor. Make sure that you get advice about bathing your baby and special care of the penis, and what to do about the dressing if one has been applied.

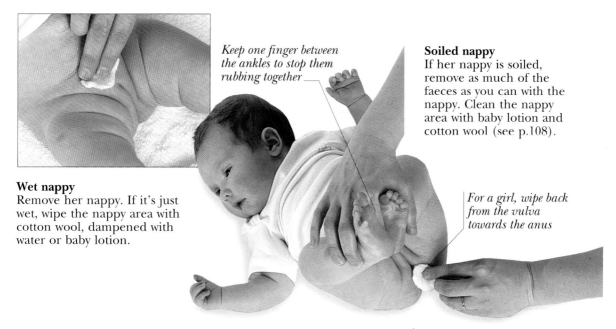

Keep one finger between the ankles to stop them rubbing together

Soiled nappy
If her nappy is soiled, remove as much of the faeces as you can with the nappy. Clean the nappy area with baby lotion and cotton wool (see p.108).

Wet nappy
Remove her nappy. If it's just wet, wipe the nappy area with cotton wool, dampened with water or baby lotion.

For a girl, wipe back from the vulva towards the anus

TOILETRIES

A newborn's skin is delicate. You should not use soap or wipes until your baby is at least six weeks old as it will remove the natural oils from her skin and leave it dry and uncomfortable. Special baby toiletries are mild and won't irritate your baby's skin – many are hypo-allergenic.

• *A little baby oil in your baby's bath water is a good moisturizer for very dry skin*

• *For delicate skin, like the nappy area, baby lotion is an ideal cleanser and moisturizer*

• *Baby powder can be drying to your baby's skin. If you use it, shake it on to your hand first , or it may be inhaled by your baby. Never use powder on the skin creases, where it can cake and cause irritation*

• *Zinc and castor oil cream or petroleum jelly are waterproof and will protect your baby's skin from urine. Medicated nappy creams containing titanium salts are good if your baby has nappy rash (see p.111)*

Use cotton wool and baby lotion to clean your baby's nappy area

GIVING A SPONGE BATH

If your baby really hates being undressed, or if you are a bit daunted by giving him a bath, the best method is to give him a sponge bath. Hold your baby securely on your lap while removing only the minimum amount of clothing at any time. If you find it difficult to manoeuvre your baby while he is on your lap, put him on a changing mat and follow the same sponge bath method, taking care to keep one half covered while you wash the other.

SPONGE BATH

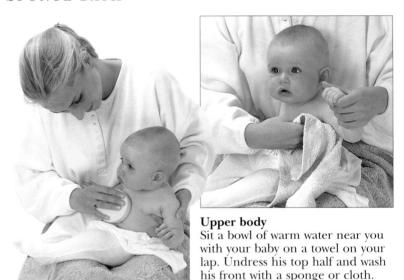

Upper body
Sit a bowl of warm water near you with your baby on a towel on your lap. Undress his top half and wash his front with a sponge or cloth. Pat him dry. Lean him forward over your arm and wash his back.

Nappy area
Either wash your baby's hair at this stage, or put some clean clothes on his top half and remove his lower clothing and nappy. Clean the nappy area (see p.108).

Lower body
Using the sponge or cloth, wash your baby's legs and feet. Gently pat his skin dry, put on barrier cream (if you use it) and a clean nappy, and dress him.

CARE OF THE HAIR

From birth you should wash your baby's hair every day, though not necessarily with shampoo – bath lotion dissolved in water will do. After about 12 to 16 weeks, wash his hair with water daily and once or twice a week with baby shampoo. Make sure that you use a non-sting variety of baby shampoo, but nevertheless take care to avoid getting it near his eyes. You can use a "football carry" (see picture, right) for a small baby, or you can sit on the edge of the bath with the baby across your legs, facing you. (She will feel secure this way, particularly if she's scared of water.) Don't be nervous about the fontanelles (see p.17); the membrane that covers them is very tough, and there is no need to scrub the hair, so you can do no harm as long as you are gentle.

Hair washing
Tuck the legs under your armpit. Support the back and cradle the head.

Apply the shampoo or bath lotion to your baby's hair, and gradually work it in until a lather forms. Wait about fifteen seconds before rinsing it off: there is no need to apply it a second time. To rinse the hair, just use a flannel dipped in warm water to wipe the suds away. Try to remove every trace of soap. When drying your baby's hair, try not to cover his face or he may panic and start to cry. It is best just to use the end of the towel to avoid this.

DISLIKE OF HAIR WASHING

Many babies hate having their hair washed, even if they enjoy having a bath. If this is the case with your baby, it may be best to keep hair washing separate from bathtime; if your child associates the two he may start to fuss about taking baths as well.

The main reason for dislike of hair washing is that babies hate getting water and soap in their eyes, so try to avoid this as far as you can. Specially designed shields are available that fit around the hairline and prevent water and suds running down your baby's face while you rinse his hair. You may also find that your baby will become less distressed of you hold him in your lap while washing his hair, and use a flannel to wet and rinse it rather than pouring water over his head.

Never try to force the issue, and never forcibly hold your baby still while you wash his hair. If hair washing is obviously very distressing for him, give up for two or three weeks before trying again. You can still keep his hair reasonably clean by sponging it to remove any food or dirt, or brushing it out with a soft, damp brush. The hair will probably become greasy, but this will not do any harm.

CRADLE CAP

Occasionally, red, scaly patches may appear on your baby's scalp. Cradle cap is extremely common, and is not caused by a lack of hygiene, or by any shampoo you're using. It usually disappears after a few weeks.

Prevent cradle cap from forming by gently washing your newborn baby's scalp every day with a very soft bristle brush and a little baby shampoo dissolved in warm water. You should comb through the hair, even if he has very little, to stop scales from forming. If cradle cap does appear, smear a little baby oil on his scalp at night to soften and loosen the scales, making them easy to wash away the following morning. Don't be tempted to pick them off with your finger nail as that only encourages more scales to form. If the condition persists or spreads, consult your doctor, who may recommend a special shampoo.

Cradle cap
Scaly patches on a baby's scalp are very common. They are harmless, and usually clear up after a few weeks without any need for special treatment.

Make bath times as pleasant as possible for you and your baby.

• *Before you start, make sure that you have everything that you need to hand*

• *Always put cold water in first. Test the final temperature with your elbow or the inner side of your wrist*

• *Keep the bath water shallow. About 5–8 centimetres (2–3 inches) is deep enough*

• *Keep the time that your baby is undressed to a minimum; small babies quickly become cold*

• *Wear a waterproof apron to protect your clothing; a plastic-backed towelling one will feel nice against your baby's skin*

• *Warm a towel for your baby on a radiator, but don't let it get too hot*

• *Baby bath lotion when added to the bath water is better to use than soap as it is less defatting*

GIVING A BATH

You can bathe your baby in any room that is warm, has no draughts, and has enough space to lay out all that you need. If necessary you can fill the baby's bath in the kitchen or bathroom and then carry it to the chosen room, provided it is not too heavy.

A small baby can be washed in a specially designed plastic baby bath with a non-slip surface. Place the bath on a worktop or table of a convenient height, usually about hip-height, so that you don't have to bend too much. This will protect your back from unnecessary strain. Some baby baths come with their own stands, or are designed to straddle the bath tub, which makes bathing your baby a far more comfortable task.

GIVING YOUR BABY A BATH

Testing the water
Use your elbow or the inner side of your wrist to test the temperature of the water. It should feel neither very hot nor very cold. Until you get the feel of the right temperature, you could use a bath thermometer, which should register 29.4°C (85°F).

Before the bath
Undress your baby, clean his nappy area (see p.109) and wrap him in a towel. Clean his face and ears gently with moistened cotton wool (see p.90).

Washing his head
Holding your baby in a football carry, as shown, lean over the bath and wash his head. Rinse well and pat dry. A gentle brushing is good for cradle cap.

Putting him in the bath
Support your baby's shoulders with one hand, tucking your fingers under his armpit, and support his legs or bottom with the other. Keep smiling and talking to him as you place him in the bath.

Washing
Keep one hand underneath your baby's shoulders so his head and shoulders are kept out of the water, and use your free hand to wash him.

FEAR OF BATHING

Some babies are terrified of having a bath. Should your baby be frightened, don't force him to remain in the water; try again after a couple of days, using only a little water in the bath. You can give sponge baths or top and tail in the meantime.

If your baby continues to be frightened of water, try to introduce it in a play context. Fill a large bowl and place it in a warm room (not the bathroom). Place a towel next to it, and put some toys into the bowl. Undress your baby and encourage him to play with the toys. If he seems happy doing this, encourage him to paddle in the water, keeping a firm grip on him.

After you have done this a couple of times, swap the bowl for a baby bath and continue to let your baby play. When he tries to get into the water with the toys, you'll know he's lost his fear of water, but be patient; let him do this a couple of times before you wash him in the bath as well as letting him play.

Lifting him out
When he is clean and well rinsed, lift him gently on to the towel, supporting him as before.

Drying
Wrap your baby in a towel and dry him thoroughly. Don't use talcum powder on the nappy area; it could gather in the skin creases and cause irritation.

BATHING AND HYGIENE

Between three and six months old your baby will grow too big for a baby bath, so you will have to start using the bathtub. To make the transition easier for your baby, first place the baby bath inside the bathtub so that he becomes used to this larger bath. Once he gets used to it, he will probably spend many happy hours there enjoying his favourite toys.

BATHTIME ROUTINE

Once your baby is mobile, he will get much dirtier than before and baths will become a regular feature of your day. Washing a baby is more awkward in the bathtub than in the baby bath. Spare your back by kneeling next to the bath and make sure that you have everything that you need to hand. Keep the water shallow: no deeper than 10–13 centimetres (4–5 inches) and use a plastic suction mat on the bottom of the bath to prevent your baby sliding about. Keep a close watch on him; it takes only a moment for a baby to slip under the water, so you should never leave him alone, or turn away from him.

By about six months your baby will feel quite secure in the water and will no longer be scared of being undressed. Try to make bathtimes fun and as trouble-free as possible.

FEAR OF THE BATHTUB

If your child finds the bathtub frightening, you'll have to be patient and let him get used to it gradually. You could try filling the baby bath with water and put a few toys

SAFETY CHECKLIST

Be very careful when bathing your child – there are several points to remember.

- *Place a non-slip bath mat in the bottom of the bath*

- *Always check the temperature of the water before putting your baby in the bath. Even older babies need the bath water to be considerably cooler than most adults*

- *Turn the taps off tightly before putting your baby in the bath.*

- *Cover the taps with a flannel so that your baby doesn't scald or hurt herself on the metal*

- *Don't let your baby stand or jump in the water unsupported. A fall, even if he isn't injured, could put him off future bathing*

- *If your child likes toys in the bath, choose light plastic ones with no sharp edges*

- *Don't remove the plug while your baby is still in the bath. Many babies find the noise and the sensation of the water disappearing rather frightening*

- *When you lift your baby out of the bath, make sure that you are standing steadily. Take the strain with your legs, not your back*

- *Make sure you dry your baby well after a bath. Giving him a cuddle wrapped in a warm towel can provide a comforting end to bathtime, even for older children*

The "big bath"
Your child will enjoy splashing around, so always use a non-slip mat.

in; then place it inside the bathtub and put a non-slip bath mat next to it. Put your baby in the bathtub where he can play with the toys and climb into the baby bath if he likes. Once he has got used to this, you could also add a few centimetres of water to the bathtub. Your child can then climb in and out of the baby bath and get used to sitting in the shallow water in the bathtub. You can gradually increase the amount of water that you put in the bathtub; after a while you will probably find that your child doesn't notice whether the baby bath is there or not. If you feel he still needs reassurance, get into the bath with him and play water games with him in your lap.

BATHTIME PLAY

Once your baby is able to sit up, you can give him some extra time in the bath after he's been washed, and let him enjoy splashing and playing with toys. You don't have to provide special toys; sponges, bowls and mugs will keep him entertained. If you have two small children, you could try bathing them together. It will save time for you, and your older child will be able to share games with the baby. Suds are always a great favourite, so you could add lots of bubble bath to the water (careful – it can irritate the vulval area in little girls). Every now and then get into the bath with your baby and have fun together.

BATH TOYS

Your baby will get a great deal of fun out of playing with everyday household objects. Make sure that any bath toys you use are clean and waterproof, without sharp edges, and reasonably light. If you give your baby plastic bottles – for example, old shampoo bottles – make sure that they have been thoroughly washed to remove all traces of their previous contents and remove the lids; your baby will put all these "toys" into his mouth.

Many toys, particularly those made of hard plastic, such as rattles and beakers, are also suitable for the bath. If you want to buy special bath toys, there are lots to choose from. The traditional boats and ducks are always great favourites, but you can also get waterproof books for the older baby, or activity centres that work when water is poured through them.

Traditional plastic ducks are always popular bathtime toys

Bathtime play
Simple floating toys will give your baby added enjoyment at bathtime.

EARLY DENTAL CARE

As early as possible encourage your baby to form good habits with a toothbrushing game.

Let him see you brush your teeth so that he can see how it should be done, then offer him a soft toothbrush to play with. He will try to imitate you by putting the brush in his mouth and moving it about. You don't need to see that he's doing it properly; at this stage it's a game to introduce him to the idea of toothbrushing as something he likes. When you really want to clean his teeth, wet a handkerchief and smear on a pea-sized helping of toothpaste, then gently rub it across the gums and any teeth that your baby has. You should clean the gums even if there are no teeth; it gets rid of the bacteria which cause plaque, and so provides a good environment for milk teeth to grow into.

TAKE CARE

However happy and secure your baby may seem playing with his toys, no baby of this age should be left in the bath unwatched, even for the shortest period of time. Check that the water is not getting too cold; your baby may be distracted from his discomfort by play. Keep your water heater set lower than 54°C (129°F) and never add hot water while your baby's in the bath.

B ATHING AND HYGIENE

*Baths should be carefully super-
vised as a child of this age is still
at risk from slipping and falling
under the water. Although your
child is now old enough to support himself in the bath, much of
what has already been said about
safety still applies (see p.96).*

*Toddlers are generally keen to do
things for themselves – washing
their own face, for example – so
there is the added risk that your
child may turn on the hot tap or
grab the soap or shampoo and get
it in his eyes. Covering the taps
with a towel is a good way to
soften any falls or bangs.*

*A child who has previously been
happy in the bath may take
against it, especially if he gets a
fright while bathing. Providing
plenty of amusements in the bath,
and perhaps getting him to share
the bath with a sibling, can help
reduce this problem. Allowing him
to share a bath with you will
resolve most difficulties.*

Your toddler will probably regard bathtime primarily as playtime,
and you can take advantage of this in teaching him to wash himself by making a game of it. Let him have his own special sponge
for bathtime and show him how to wash his face first, then his arms
and legs, and so on. He won't be able to make a very good job of
it yet, so you'll probably have to go over the same areas yourself
with another facecloth. Soap your child's hands and show him how
to spread the soap over his body and arms; then make a game of
rinsing all the suds off.

WASHING ROUTINES

A child is often hungry when he wakes up, so it's best to leave washing until after breakfast, when your child will be more willing to
stand still to have his face and hands washed, teeth brushed (see
opposite), and hair combed. From the age of about 18 months he
can start learning to rinse his hands under running water and,
later on, he will learn to soap them, though he may make quite a
mess with the soap and water.

CLEANLINESS

The younger you start teaching hygiene the better, and the best
way of teaching is by example. Wash your hands with your child:
get your hands soapy together and wash each other's hands, then
inspect each other's hands to see whose are the cleanest. If he finds
the facecloth rough, let him use a sponge, which is softer.

Make it clear that hands should always be washed after using the
lavatory. You should start this at the potty stage (see p.114) and do
it with your child every single time. Similarly, make sure your child
washes his hands before meals or after handling pets.

Encourage your child to do this for himself. Make sure he can
reach the washbasin and toilet easily by putting a step in the bathroom for him to use, and make sure that he knows which is the
hot tap and which the cold.

HAIR CARE

Your child will probably have a thick head of hair by now, and this
will need regular washing to remove everyday grime. Unfortunately
there are few children who enjoy this process. You can also make
washing as easy as possible for your child by using the following
tips to help to reduce the potential for conflict.

• Keep your child's hair short; it will be easier to brush, too.

• Use a non-sting baby shampoo and get a special halo-like shield
which will keep the water and suds away from his eyes.

- If your child really hates hair washing, try allowing him some control over it: choosing whether he holds his head back for washing or forwards, for example, or holding the shower and wetting his own hair.

- You could also offer incentives to be good, such as the promise of a special game or story once hair washing is successfully completed, or even get in the bath yourself and allow your child to "wash" your hair in return for your doing his.

TOOTHCARE

You will have been brushing your baby's teeth from the time that they first appeared (see p.97) and you should continue to do so at least twice a day. Always brush his teeth after the evening meal so that food particles are not left in the mouth overnight. As your baby gets older, he will probably want to hold the toothbrush and do it himself. While this should be encouraged, he will not be able to clean his own teeth effectively, and you should always follow up his efforts yourself with a thorough brushing.

When brushing your child's teeth, use a small, soft-bristled brush and a toothpaste containing fluoride. You should use only a pea-sized amount of toothpaste, as an excess of fluorine while your child's teeth are growing can cause fluorosis (discoloration or mottling of the enamel). There are many "fun" flavours of toothpaste available which may give your child an incentive to brush his teeth. You should never get a toothpaste containing sugar, though, so always check the ingredients before buying. Sit your child sideways on your knee, holding him securely with one arm, and gently brush the teeth up and down. If he won't keep his head still, try gently resting your free hand on his forehead.

With any luck it will be years before your toddler will need any form of dental treatment. Nonetheless, it is important to get him used to the idea of going to the dentist. Make a point of taking him with you when you go for a check-up. Most dentists are sympathetic to the need to remove any possibility of fear in young patients, and will probably be happy for your child to sit in the "magic" chair and ask him to open his mouth so that his teeth can be checked and counted.

NAILS

Keep your child's fingernails and toenails cut short; it is more hygienic, and helps to prevent him scratching himself or others accidentally. Long toenails may also make his shoes uncomfortable. You will probably still find it easiest to cut his nails when they are soft after a bath, and, as children's nails grow very quickly, it is a good idea to incorporate a nail-cutting session into your bath-time ritual once a week. Use blunt-ended scissors, specially designed to be safe for young children, or nail clippers. You will find it easier to restrain your wriggling child if you sit him on your lap. Follow the natural line of his fingernails and do not cut too close to the quick. Toenails should be cut straight across.

PETS AND HYGIENE

You may be concerned about the possible health risks to your toddler in having a pet. However, if you follow a few simple rules of hygiene, you should have no cause for concern, and the rewards to your child will be well worth the effort.

- *Ringworm (see p.101) is a contagious skin condition which can be caught from pets, and is commonly seen in children. If you suspect ringworm, consult your doctor straight away*

- *Always try to stop your child from kissing his pet, especially near its nose and mouth*

- *Encourage your child to wash his hands after playing with his pet – especially before touching or eating food*

- *Both fleas and worms are easily avoided by regular use of preventive treatments*

- *If infestation occurs, treat is promptly and keep your child away from any pets until the treatment has worked*

BATHING AND HYGIENE

CLEANLINESS IN GIRLS

Most girls are naturally fastidious, and you can take advantage of this in teaching your child to keep herself clean.

- *Encourage good habits in your little girl from an early age by showing her how to wash herself and clean her teeth*

- *Let her brush her own hair; she will prefer it, and it means she can choose her own hairstyle, ribbons, slides, or hairband*

- *Let her have her own special facecloth, soap dish, and towel; she'll be proud of her own things*

- *Allow her to rub baby lotion into her skin after bathing*

- *Teach her to change her underwear and socks daily*

- *Provide her own laundry basket so that she can discard her own dirty clothes*

By the time a child has reached the age of three years, she will have developed her own views on many aspects of her day-to-day life and will want increasing control over her daily routine. This is often expressed negatively in a reluctance or even refusal to co-operate with mundane tasks such as bathtime and hairbrushing, which are often seen as unwelcome interruptions to more exciting forms of play. The best way to avoid arguments is to turn washing and brushing into a game, or incorporate a fun element into the task. Allowing your child to take increasing responsibility for carrying out a task, supervised if necessary, or giving her some element of choice about the activity – choosing which comb or which shampoo to use, for example, can make it more interesting and encourage co-operation. The following hints will make the daily routine easier and more enjoyable for both of you:

- Try not to rush your child to complete a task she is trying to manage by herself. It leads to tension, and may make her less willing to help next time.

- Don't leave bathtime until last thing before bedtime, or your child may be too tired to enjoy it.

- Encourage interest in toothbrushing by using disclosing tablets once a week. The need to brush away the colour is a great way to ensure that your child cleans her teeth really well.

- Make hair washing fun by letting your child see in a mirror all the silly hairstyles she can create from lathered hair.

- Offer the bribe of the use of some "special" grown-up toiletries such as perfumed soap or bubble bath in return for her co-operation at bathtime – I believe in bribes for young children.

EXPLAINING ABOUT HYGIENE

By the age of three your child is capable of understanding, reasoning, and comprehending why something is important. If you give her a reason why she shouldn't do something rather than pulling rank, she's likely to desist and you'll gain her co-operation more readily if you present arguments in favour of certain actions. Explain to your child that if her hands are dirty they're covered in germs that could make her ill; that if she's eaten a sweet it could give her toothache; or that if she's handled the dog she might have germs on her hands that could give her a tummy ache.

Once your child begins to understand the reasons for washing and toothbrushing, you must be consistent. Children are very logical, and if you have persuaded your child that it is essential to

Hair shield
Keep soap and water off your child's face with a specially designed shield.

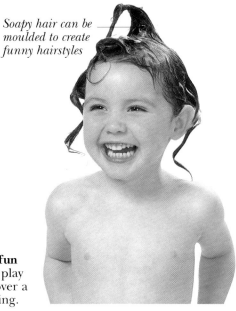

Soapy hair can be moulded to create funny hairstyles

Make hair washing fun
Allow your child to play games to help get over a dislike of hair washing.

CLEANLINESS IN BOYS

Boys are usually quite resistant to washing, and you'll have to spend a lot of time reminding him to wash and brush.

- *Make bathtimes as much fun as possible, with toys, games, and lots of suds*

- *Spend some time showing him how to wash, and do this several times if necessary*

- *Try not to be over fussy about cleanliness; if he's in the middle of a game, let handwashing wait until he's ready*

- *Let him wash himself as soon as he can make an attempt, then clean him thoroughly yourself at the last moment*

- *Encourage a daily change of underpants and socks*

- *Give him his own laundry basket and enourage him to fill it*

wash her hands before meals, and brush her teeth afterwards, she will probably question you if you overlook it. At the same time you should try not to be over-fussy about cleanliness.

CONDITIONS PASSED BETWEEN CHILDREN

As soon as your child starts to socialize with other children, she is at risk from a variety of minor disorders that are commonly passed between children. Don't be unduly upset by these; they are not necessarily a result of poor hygiene, and can all be easily treated. (For more information see **Parasites**, p.296.)

Ringworm A fungal infection affecting the scalp (tinea capitis) or the body (tinea corporis), ringworm appears as small bald areas on the scalp, or round, reddish or grey, scaly patches on the skin. These are usually oval in shape and the edges of the patch remain scaly while the centre clears, leaving rings. Consult your doctor, as the condition is irritating and contagious.

Nits (Head lice) Children are especially prone to nits, which are passed easily from child to child. The insects themselves are difficult to see and most people first notice the pale, oval-shaped eggs which become firmly attached to the hair and become more apparent as the hair grows. Your child's scalp may be very itchy. Consult your doctor, who will recommend an insecticidal shampoo.

Threadworms and roundworms Threadworms are the most common form of intestinal worm in the UK. They live in the bowel and lay eggs around the anus which cause the night-time anal itching. Roundworms are quite rare and are only likely to occur if you have been abroad. Your doctor can prescribe a drug to treat either threadworms or roundworms.

101

EATING FOR DENTAL HEALTH

Taking care that your child is eating the right foods is the most important contribution you can make to her dental health.

• *Never give your baby a bottle of sweetened juice to drink ad lib, as it means your baby's teeth are bathed continuously in sugar and results eventually in "bottle mouth" – a mouth of rotten teeth as early as three years old*

• *Giving sweet foods between meals increases the number of times the teeth are exposed to harmful acids, so give them at the end of a meal instead*

• *If you give sweets, don't choose sticky toffees, as these remain on the teeth for longer*

• *Giving cheese at the end of a meal makes saliva alkaline, and helps counteract the acid which erodes teeth*

• *It is better to give a piece of cake which can be eaten in a few minutes than a packet of sweets which will be eaten all afternoon*

• *Give fruit or sugar-free yogurt as treats to avoid encouraging a sweet tooth*

DENTAL CARE

By the time your child reaches the age of three years, the basic routine of toothcare should be well established (see p.99). Morning and evening toothbrushing sessions need to be carefully supervised by an adult, even though a child of this age will probably be keen to carry out brushing herself. Six-monthly visits to the dentist, to check that the teeth are coming through normally, are also important. These "tooth-counting" sessions are also a good way of letting your child get used to visits to the dentist.

Most people are now aware of the damage caused to teeth by sugar in the diet. Sugary foods produce acids in the mouth that damage the enamel coating of the teeth by removing calcium. Once this has occurred, the underlying tooth is open to decay and cavities will start to form. While fillings can repair cavities, the tooth is inevitably weakened and, if severely affected by decay, may need to be removed and endanger the positioning of second teeth.

PREVENTING CAVITIES

A baby eats only those foods offered by parents and carers. As she gets older and gains in independence, she will begin to express her own food preferences more vigorously and will have increasing opportunities for choosing foods for herself – and sweet foods are often favourites. For this reason good eating habits cannot be started too soon. Above all, try to control your child's intake of sweets. No child needs sugar or sweets and you can easily find less damaging treats in the form of fruit and savoury snacks. Explain to your friends and family that you would prefer that they did not give sweets to your child.

In the real world, of course, children do receive and eat a certain amount of sugary foods. You can limit the damage these do to your child's teeth by incorporating them into mealtimes. Sugary snacks eaten between meals are the most damaging. If your child has eaten something particularly sweet, make sure she brushes her teeth as soon afterwards as possible.

Giving undiluted fruit juice is another common cause of tooth decay even among children who eat few sweets, so you should always dilute fruit juice with water. Eating, or drinking anything other than water at night after the teeth have been brushed, can cause problems. The acids that cause tooth decay will remain in the mouth, allowing the enamel-damaging process to continue for many hours. If your child is greatly attached to having a bottle at night, give it to her before she goes to sleep, then remove it.

Tooth brushing
Give your child a soft toothbrush and encourage her to use it after meals, especially once the molars are through (see p.175).

FIRST FILLINGS

If you are lucky, your child will need little or no dental treatment throughout childhood. Your dentist will notice any signs of decay at your regular six-monthly visits, but make an extra appointment if you notice any unusual tooth discoloration or if your child complains of pain. In cases of slight decay in first teeth, the dentist may decide not to fill the tooth in order to avoid unnecessary upset for your child. Tooth enamel has been shown to be capable of recalcification if the cavity is not too large.

A dentist who is used to treating children will usually have developed techniques for minimizing any fear. Great care will be taken to prevent pain with the use of local anaesthetic sprays and extra-fine needles for injections as appropriate.

ACCIDENTS INVOLVING TEETH

The need for dental treatment other than for cavities in the under fives is rare. An injury to a tooth that damages the nerve can cause it to "die" even if it isn't dislodged. In this case the tooth will become discoloured but no other ill effects will follow and it can be safely left in place until it is replaced by the adult tooth. If a tooth is chipped, you should seek the advice of your dentist. If a milk tooth is knocked out altogether, you will need immediate dental advice; take your child to the nearest emergency dental clinic, bringing the tooth with you. In some cases the tooth can be replaced in the jaw, depending on the child's age and the position of the tooth.

FLUORIDE

Fluoride is a mineral that has been shown to reduce the incidence of tooth decay by strengthening tooth enamel. It is added to many toothpastes and, in some areas, to the water supply.

• *Fluoride can also be taken by mouth in the form of drops or tablets. Dentists recommend toothpastes containing fluoride for both adults and children*

• *Many dentists would argue that fluoride toothpaste alone does not provide sufficient protection against dental decay*

• *If the water in your area is less than 0.7 parts fluoride per million (you can find this out from your local water authority), your child may benefit from fluoride supplements in tablet form*

• *Always consult your dentist or doctor before giving supplements, and follow his advice carefully*

• *It is important to avoid giving excessive fluoride. This can cause a condition known as fluorosis, in which the adult teeth that are developing become mottled*

Be there to hold your child's hand if necessary

You may like to give your child a mirror to hold so that she can see what the dentist is doing

Visiting the dentist
Always stay with your child during any dental treatment, or even a check-up; the reassurance of your presence is vital.

BOWEL AND BLADDER

KIDNEY AND BLADDER FUNCTION

Once food has been absorbed into the bloodstream, waste has to be removed from the blood by the kidneys and eliminated as urine.

Urine production *Waste chemicals in the blood are removed and dissolved in water by the kidneys. The urine then passes down the ureters and into the bladder.*

Voiding *Urine is temporarily stored in the bladder, which is periodically emptied through the urethra. Your baby will not even be aware of passing urine until about 15–18 months (see pp.112–13). The sensation of wanting to pass urine does not come until several months later, because the infant bladder can only hold urine for a few minutes.*

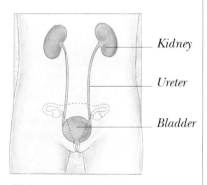

Kidney

Ureter

Bladder

Kidneys and bladder
The urinary and reproductive systems are closely linked; a girl's bladder is next to the uterus.

A newborn baby can need up to ten nappy changes a day and, although the frequency of changes will decrease, most babies don't achieve a degree of bowel and bladder control until the second year. Although you can't speed up this process, your help and support will be very important to your child.

PASSING URINE

A young baby's bladder will empty itself automatically and frequently both day and night. As soon as it contains a little urine, the bladder wall stretches and the emptying action is stimulated. This is absolutely normal, and your baby cannot be expected to behave differently, at least until the bladder has developed sufficiently to hold urine for longer periods of time.

BOWEL MOVEMENTS

When your baby was in the womb, his intestines were filled with a sticky, black substance called meconium. Meconium is passed in the first 24 hours after delivery, and once this has happened normal motions will take over.

Once your baby settles into a regular routine, his stools will become firmer and paler. You don't need to pay much attention to them, and you certainly should never become obsessive or worried about them as long as your baby is content and thriving.

The number of stools a baby passes varies greatly, and initially most bottlefed babies pass a stool for every feed. On the other hand, a breastfed baby may pass only one stool a day or less because there is little waste. The frequency of bowel motions gradually decreases as your baby gets older. It may be that, at the beginning, your baby passes five or six a day, but after three or four weeks he may be having only two movements a day. This is quite normal and should cause you no worry. Similarly, the odd loose, unformed stools or totally green stool are typical of a young baby's bowel movements and are no cause for concern unless looseness persists beyond 24 hours; then seek your doctor's advice.

CHANGES IN BOWEL MOVEMENTS

Don't worry if your baby's stools change in appearance from one day to the next. It is quite normal for a stool to turn green or brown when left exposed to the air. If you are worried, consult your midwife or doctor, who will be able to advise and reassure you. As a rule, loose stools are not an indication of an infection. Watery stools, however, if accompanied by a sudden change in the colour, smell, or frequency of passing stools, should be mentioned to your doctor, especially if your baby is "off colour" (see p.276).

Blood-streaked stools are never normal. The cause may be quite minor – a tiny crack in the skin around the anus, perhaps – but you must consult your doctor. Larger amounts of blood, or the appearance of pus or mucus may indicate an intestinal infection, so contact your doctor immediately.

The breastfed baby By the second day, the light yellow stools typical of the breastfed baby will appear. The stools are rarely hard or smelly and may be no thicker than cream soup. Remember that the food you eat will affect your baby and that anything very spicy or acidic could upset digestion.

The bottlefed baby A baby fed on formula has a tendency to more frequent stools which are firmer, browner, and smellier than those of a breastfed baby. The commonest tendency is for the stools to be rather hard. The easiest way to put this right is to give your baby a little cooled, boiled water to drink in between feeds.

DIARRHOEA

Diarrhoea is a sign of irritation of the intestines resulting in loose, frequent, and watery stools. In small babies diarrhoea is always potentially dangerous because of the risk of dehydration, which can develop very quickly. If your baby refuses food or has any of the following, contact your doctor immediately.

• Repeated watery stools.

• Green and smelly stools.

• A fever of 38°C (100°F) or more.

• Pus or blood in his stools.

• Is listless with dark-ringed eyes.

If you think your baby is dehydrated, look at his fontanelles. If they are depressed, your baby is dehydrated: contact your doctor immediately. If it is treated early, diarrhoea can be cured quickly.

You can start treating your baby immediately yourself if his diarrhoea is mild, and he has no other symptoms. Continue to nurse your baby if you are breastfeeding; diarrhoea usually clears up well on breast milk, but formula should be made up at half-strength, with half the regular formula to the usual amount of water. He may eat only small amounts of food, and will therefore be hungry more often. If mild diarrhoea doesn't improve within two days, consult your doctor.

When you start re-introducing food after a bout of diarrhoea, it is best to start off with small portions of mild, milky ones like jelly or yogurt; diluted fruit juice; stewed fruit; dried cereal with milk; mashed potatoes; white meat and eggs. Begin with less than half the normal amount on the first day, and on the second day, half to two-thirds of the usual amount. Drinks of mineral replacement salts formulated specially for infants are advisable at this stage. If all goes well you can return to your usual servings.

BOWEL FUNCTION

Food passes through the stomach into the small intestine, and from there to the large intestine. The waste products of food are stored in the rectum before finally being eliminated as faeces.

Digestion *The food is broken down by enzymes. Digestion starts in the mouth, then continues in the stomach and the upper part of the small intestine.*

Absorption *Once the food has been reduced to simple molecules, it is absorbed into the bloodstream as it continues its path through the small intestine. It then passes through the large intestine, where any water is absorbed by the body. The waste products pass on to the rectum as faeces.*

Elimination *Faeces are stored in the rectum and expelled through the anus. A baby cannot control the reflex that causes the rectum to empty – even for a second. Young babies generally have bowel movements with each feed, as a result of the gastrocolic reflex which stimulates the rectum to empty every time that food enters the stomach.*

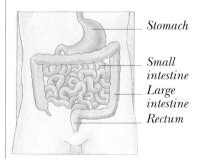

Stomach

Small intestine

Large intestine

Rectum

The bowel system
After food has been digested in the stomach and small intestine, the waste is passed as faeces.

A girl will tend to wet the nappy at the centre, or towards the back if she is lying down.

• *Disposable daytime and night-time nappies are designed differently to take this into account, with the padding at its thickest where it is needed most*

• *You may like to buy decorative or frilly pants to cover fabric nappies; these look pretty under a dress for a special occasion*

NAPPIES

Your first choice in nappies will be between fabric and disposable types. In recent years, the vast majority of parents have opted for disposables, though an increasing consciousness of environmental issues has led many parents to reconsider the virtues of fabric nappies, which create less waste. Yet the issue is not clear cut: the detergents required to clean fabric nappies can be viewed as pollutants to the water supply, and the energy required to wash them might also be regarded as wasteful. While fabric nappies are cheaper than disposables in the long run, you need to consider the increased electricity bills for frequent washing-machine runs, and the cost in your time. What is clear is that providing that the nappy is changed as frequently as necessary, and that the basic rules of hygiene are observed, your baby will be happy whichever option you choose.

DISPOSABLE NAPPIES

Disposable nappies make nappy changing as simple as it can be. They are easy to put on – no folding, no pins, and no plastic pants – and can be discarded when they are wet or dirty. They are convenient when you're travelling as you need fewer nappies and less space to change in, and you don't have to carry wet, smelly nappies home with you to be washed. You will need a constant supply so, to avoid carrying huge loads with your shopping, buy them in large batches. Many shops will deliver nappies.

Never flush disposable nappies down the lavatory as they inevitably get stuck at the S-bend. Instead, put the soiled nappy in a strong plastic bag. The bag should be firmly secured at the neck before you throw it out.

FABRIC NAPPIES

Though fabric nappies are more expensive than disposables at first, they work out cheaper in the long run. Fabric nappies involve much more work than disposables because they have to be rinsed,

DISPOSABLE NAPPIES

Resealable tapes let you check if nappy is clean

Elasticated leakage barriers provide extra protection

Efficient leg elastication gives a good fit with less chance of leaks

Absorbent inner layer has a plastic covering

sterilized, washed, and dried after use. You will need a minimum of 24 nappies to ensure that you always have enough clean ones, but the more nappies you can buy the less often you'll have to do the washing. When buying fabric nappies, choose the best that you can afford. They'll be good value in the long run because they'll last longer; they'll also be more absorbent, and therefore more comfortable for your baby.

Towelling squares can be folded in various ways, depending on your baby's size and needs (see p.109). They are very absorbent – more so than most disposables – so they are good at night.

Shaped terry nappies are T-shaped, made of a softer, finer towelling than squares, and have a triple-layered central panel for added absorbency. Their shape means that they are more straightforward to put on, and fit the baby more neatly.

With fabric nappies you will need nappy liners: choose the "one-way" variety which lets urine pass through but remains dry next to the baby's skin, minimizing the risk of a sore bottom due to friction or moisture. Liners prevent the nappy from getting badly soiled; they can be lifted out with any faeces and flushed away. You will also need at least 12 nappy pins – these have locking heads to protect your baby's skin – and six pairs of plastic pants to prevent wet or dirty nappies soiling the baby's clothes or bedding.

There is a type of fabric nappy on the market which offers all the features of a disposable, but is machine washable: it is shaped to fit, has Velcro closing tabs, elasticated legs, and is made of several layers of absorbent fabric with an anti-leak outer layer.

FABRIC NAPPIES

Pins with self-locking heads are safest

Nappy liners

Plastic pants

Towelling nappies are thick and absorbent and adjust to fit your baby's size

Shaped fabric nappies

BOYS' NAPPIES

Boys tend to wet the front of the nappy, and boy's disposables are designed to cope with this, with extra padding towards the front.

• *Fold fabric nappies in such a way that more of the fabric is at the front, particularly at night*

• *Boys often urinate when they are being changed, so cover the penis with a spare, clean nappy as you take the soiled one off*

• *Always tuck the penis down when putting on a clean nappy to avoid urine escaping from the top of the nappy*

CLEANING A GIRL

Always wipe your baby girl from front to back, and never clean inside the lips of the vulva.

Remove faeces
Clean off as much faeces as possible with the front of the soiled nappy.

Remove urine
Use a wet cloth or cotton wool to clean the genitals and surrounding skin.

Clean bottom
Lift up her legs as shown, and wipe from front to back. Dry thoroughly.

CHANGING A NAPPY

Your baby's nappy will need to be changed whenever it is soiled or wet. The number of changes will vary from one baby to the next. As a rule, though, you will probably change the nappy every morning when your baby wakes, before you put him to bed at night, after a bath, and after every feed, including night feeds.

Changing disposables is straightforward, provided you choose the most appropriate nappy for your baby's size so that it fits him neatly. With fabric nappies you can choose the type of fold that suits you (see opposite). You will need to use nappy liners, too.

DISPOSABLE NAPPY

Positioning your baby
Lay the nappy flat, with the tabs at the back. Slide the nappy under your baby so that the top aligns with her waist.

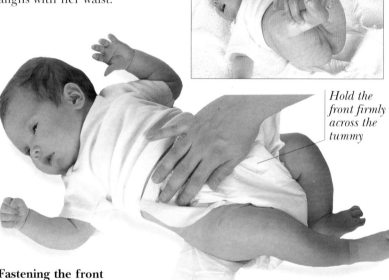

Hold the front firmly across the tummy

Fastening the front
Bring the front up between the legs and tuck it around the tummy. Unpeel the tabs.

Unpeel the adhesive tabs and pull over the front

A comfortable fit
Pull the tabs firmly over the front flap and fasten the nappy. It should fit snugly.

FOLDING FABRIC NAPPIES

Triple absorbent fold

This is the most suitable fold for your newborn; its central panel provides good absorbency and it is very small and neat. It is not suitable for larger babies, however. Start with a square nappy folded in four, with the open edges to the top and right.

Pick up the top layer by the right-hand edge.

Pull it to the left to form an inverted triangle.

Turn the nappy over so the point is at the top right.

Fold in the middle layers twice to form a thick central panel.

Parallel and kite folds

These are suitable for a larger baby. You can adjust the depth of the kite to suit your baby's size. Both start with a nappy laid out in a diamond shape.

Fold the top and bottom points in to the centre.

Pick up the left-hand point and align it to the top edge; do the same with the right.

Fold the sides in to the centre to form a kite shape.

Fold the top point down to the centre. Fold the bottom point up towards the centre, varying the depth to fit.

FABRIC NAPPY

Slide the nappy under your baby so his waist aligns with the top edge. Bring the front of the nappy up between his legs, and hold it in place while you fold the sides in to the centre and fasten with a pin.

CLEANING A BOY

Boys often pass urine when released from their nappy. A tissue laid over the penis will minimize the mess.

Remove faeces
Clean off any faeces with oil or lotion and cotton wool, using a different piece for each wipe.

Remove urine
Wipe with cotton wool, working from the leg creases in towards the penis. Never pull the foreskin back.

Clean bottom
Lift his legs to clean his bottom by holding both ankles as shown. Dry thoroughly.

Washing nappies will take up quite a lot of your time, so make life easy for yourself by being as organized as you can. The following tips are designed to make your washing routine easier.

• *Use plastic tongs or gloves for lifting nappies out of the sterilizing bucket; keep them near by*

• *When you change a nappy at night, keep the dirty nappy in a separate bucket or a plastic bag, and add it to the new sterilizing solution the following morning*

• *If you use a powder sterilant, always put the water in the bucket first; otherwise you run the risk of inhaling the powder*

• *Drying nappies on radiators makes the fabric hard and uncomfortable. Use a tumble drier, an outside line, or a rack which can be placed over the bath*

• *You may like to use an air freshener in the nappy bucket*

Nappy bucket
For sterilization you'll need two buckets: one for soiled nappies, one for wet ones.

NAPPY HYGIENE

It is very important to wash nappies thoroughly; any traces of ammonia will irritate your baby's skin, and faecal bacteria could cause infection. Strong detergents and biological powders could also irritate your baby's skin, so always use pure soap flakes or powders. If you use a fabric conditioner, always make sure it is completely rinsed away, whatever the manufacturer's instructions might say. If you use a sterilizing solution then you will need to wash only soiled nappies, as wet nappies will only need thorough rinsing. There is no need to boil nappies unless they are very stained, or have become rather grey; just use hot water for both rinsing and washing. If your baby's clothing gets soiled, don't add it to the sterilizing solution, as the colour will run. Just remove as much of the mess as you can, rinse the garment and wash it as normal.

WASHING ROUTINE

Establishing a routine of washing will make life easier, especially if you aim to wash the nappies in large loads. To do this, of course, you will need a large supply of nappies – at least 24. You will need two plastic sterilizing bins with lids and strong handles: one for soiled nappies, and one for wet ones. They should be large enough to hold at least six nappies, with plenty of room for solution, but not so large that you can't carry them when full. You can buy special nappy bins, but any good-sized bucket with a lid will do; bins designed for beer-making are ideal.

Fill the bins with sterilizing solution each morning and always rinse a nappy before adding it to the bucket. Wet nappies should be rinsed in cold water, wrung out, and added to the solution. With soiled nappies, remove as much faeces as possible down the lavatory and hold the nappy under the lavatory spray as you flush it. Squeeze out the excess moisture and put the nappy in the "soiled" bucket. When the nappies have been soaking for the required time, wring them out. The urine-soaked ones should be rinsed thoroughly in hot water and then dried; the soiled ones will need to be washed on the hot programme of your machine or in a bath of hot water, then rinsed and dried. Plastic pants will become hard and unusable if you wash them in water that is either too hot or too cold. Wash them in warm water with a little washing-up liquid, then pat them dry and leave them to air before using. If they do become hard them you can soften them in a tumble drier with a load of towels.

NAPPY RASH

If urine is left too long in a nappy or on the skin, it is broken down to ammonia by bacteria from your baby's stools. The ammonia then irritates and burns the skin and this is the commonest cause of nappy rash. A mild nappy rash will appear as small red dots on your baby's bottom, but if it becomes more serious, you will see an inflamed area of broken skin and possibly pus-filled spots.

The bacteria that produce ammonia dermatitis (nappy rash) thrive in an alkaline medium. Breastfed babies are less prone to nappy rash than bottlefed babies. If you follow the guidelines given (right), you will minimize the possibility of nappy rash.

If, despite your precautions, your baby develops a sore bottom, check the chart below to see if she needs treatment. If not, continue your preventive measures (except for the use of barrier cream), as well as the following:

• Change your baby's nappy more often.

• Use a disposable pad inside a towelling nappy for extra absorbency at night, especially if your baby sleeps through the night.

• Once your baby has nappy rash it is important that her skin be aired between nappy changes for say 15–20 minutes.

Not all skin conditions occurring in the nappy area are true nappy rash (see chart below). It is important that you identify a rash correctly so that you can take appropriate action.

PREVENTING NAPPY RASH

The essentials are to keep your baby's skin dry and well aired, and to make sure that nappies are always thoroughly washed and well rinsed.

• *Start using a nappy rash cream at the first sign of broken skin. Ones which include titanium salts are especially good. Stop using plastic pants, too, as they prevent evaporation of urine*

• *Don't wash your baby's bottom with soap and water, as they both defat the skin*

• *Use one-way nappy liners, or disposables with a one-way lining, to keep your baby's skin dry*

• *Use a fairly thick barrier cream, applied generously. Don't use this with one-way liners or disposables, however, as it will clog the one-way fabric*

• *Make sure all traces of ammonia are removed from the nappy by thorough washing and rinsing*

• *Never leave your baby lying in a wet nappy*

• *Leave your baby's bottom open to the air whenever you can*

APPEARANCE OF RASH	CAUSE AND TREATMENT
General redness which starts around the genitals rather than the anus. You will notice a strong smell of ammonia. In severe cases it may spread to the bottom, groin, and thighs, and can lead to ulceration if not attended to.	*Ammonia dermatitis, caused by irritation from ammonia. If the treatment outlined above doesn't work, consult your doctor.*
Small blisters all over the nappy area in addition to a rash elsewhere on the body.	*Heat rash. Stop using plastic pants, and leave your baby's nappy off at every opportunity. Cool your baby down by using fewer clothes and blankets.*
Redness and broken skin in the leg folds.	*Inadequate drying. Dry your baby meticulously and do not use talcum powder.*
Brownish-red, scaly rash on the genitals and skin creases, especially the groin, and anywhere the skin is greasy – the scalp, for instance. It is very rare in babies.	*Seborrhoeic dermatitis. Your doctor will prescribe an ointment for the rash, and perhaps a special lotion if the scalp is affected.*
Spotty rash which starts around the anus and spreads to the buttocks and inner thighs. You may also notice white patches inside your baby's mouth.	*Thrush, caused by a yeast infection. Consult your doctor. She will probably give you anti-fungal treatments.*

Barrier cream
This protects your baby's skin from the irritant effects of ammonia, but should not be used if a nappy rash develops.

BOWEL AND BLADDER

Bowel and bladder control usually start earlier and are complete more quickly in girls. The age ranges given are approximate.

Early stages: 1–1 1/2 years

• *The first sign that the bladder is maturing is when she gestures or makes a sound to indicate she's aware of passing urine*

• *There's usually no sign of bowel control at this stage*

Middle stages: 1 1/2–2 1/2 years

• *One day, between 15 and 18 months, she'll bring the potty to you and if you're quick you may catch her in time*

• *At about 18 months to two years you may find a stool in the potty after a meal. She'll come and tell you when she needs the potty and can wait for it. Once she can wait five minutes or so, try trainer pants during the day*

Later stages: 2 1/2–3 1/2 years

• *Girls achieve bowel control very quickly. She's clean day and night with the odd accident*

• *She's dry all day. Try trainer pants for the afternoon nap; once she's dry for her nap you can try trainer pants at night*

• *She can go dry most nights. Bowel control is virtually complete. She has very few accidents*

Once your baby starts taking solids, you will find that he soils his nappy less often. You will continue to see changes in his bowel movements as his digestive system matures, right up to the age of five or six years. After he's taken solids for a few months, you may feel it is time he used the potty, but don't rush this (see opposite).

CHANGES IN BOWEL MOVEMENTS

In general, you can expect your baby's stools to become firmer and less frequent with age. There are some pretty standard changes at some ages; I give them only to reassure you, not so that you will obsessively examine your child's stools. All dates are approximate.

0–6 months The stools may be almost as frequent as the feeds, and are very soft. They go through colour changes: first greenish black (meconium, see p.104), then yellow, then light brown.

6–12 months After your baby starts on solids the stools become drier, darker in colour, and less frequent, say three times a day. Lots of drinks will keep the stools soft.

1–3 years As soon as your child is on the family diet he will probably only pass two stools a day.

3–5 years The stools are identical to adult stools, except in size, and your child will rarely pass more than one a day.

MALABSORPTION AND COELIAC DISEASE

Malabsorption can occur with allergies (see p.292) or enzyme deficiency, or because of coeliac disease, which is an inflammation of the small bowel due to gluten sensitivity. The inflamed bowel is incapable of absorbing many foods, so your baby can become undernourished. Fortunately, this disease is quite rare.

An early sign of coeliac disease is bulky stools – that is, more in the stools than your baby took in as food. This is because the stools are very fatty. In addition they're a creamy, putty colour. Because of their fat content these stools float on water. It's also said that they're foul-smelling, but I've never found that to be so. If coeliac disease goes undiscovered your baby will not thrive on solids, and his buttocks will be small and slack – a diagnostic sign.

It's extremely important that a baby with coeliac disease is properly diagnosed, otherwise all development could be slowed down. Just as worrying, many dietary deficiencies will develop, and his resistance to infection will be lowered. If you suspect coeliac disease, ask your doctor about it immediately.

Coeliac disease can be treated very simply; your baby will have to eat gluten-free foods. There are lots of gluten-free products available, even in supermarkets. Foods cooked with gluten-free flour are delicious – I once attended the birthday party of a coeliac child where you couldn't tell the difference from the usual party treats.

THE CASE AGAINST "TRAINING"

Babies who are allowed to achieve bowel and bladder control at their own pace learn to use the potty quickly and have few accidents. It's only when parents interfere with their child's steady progress by enforcing timetables or expecting too much too soon that things go awry. Babies are born wanting to be clean and dry; our job is simply to allow them to achieve this milestone happily.

An over-authoritarian parent can do untold harm, even at an earlier stage, and may be responsible for problems in later life. Imagine the scenario: a domineering, insistent mother is bending over her baby telling him that he can't get off his potty until he's performed. He can't understand what she's getting at, because he is unaware of passing urine or stool – his bladder and nervous system are still too primitive. Even if he did understand he has no "control", as you think of it. He can't figure out why something so natural to him is so important to you. And so he has no idea how to please his normally very loving mother. When he gets up to leave you get unusually rough, he can't cope, and he's going to cry. And if you go on like this now he is certainly going to use your obsession with training as a weapon against you later. He sees his stools as something you want and so he will withhold them when he is pitting his will against yours. The answer is to be flexible.

At no point pressure or scold. Praise every success. Let little boys see their fathers passing urine. Children who are pressured into early training tend to be bedwetters, and more engage in pica (eating stools or other non-food substances) and soiling than those children who develop at their own speed.

INTRODUCING THE POTTY

These are the ways you can help your baby to be dry and clean, but only after he indicates to you by sound or gesture that he knows he's passed urine or stool. Allow him to find his own pace, without any pressure from you.

Step 1 *Start by giving him his own "potty" chair, which is like your lavatory. Let him see you or his father using the toilet and let him see the results if he asks.*

Step 2 *Let him sit on the potty chair fully clothed while you read a story to him.*

Step 3 *Gradually let him get used to sitting without a nappy.*

Step 4 *When he soils or wets his nappy sit him gently on the chair after you've cleaned him while you collect fresh things.*

Step 5 *Once he's interested, let him sit two or three times a day.*

DEVELOPMENT IN BOYS

Boys are generally later than girls in developing bowel and bladder control and bedwetting is more frequent in boys. The age ranges given are just a rough guide.

Early stages: 1 1/2–2 1/2 years

• *At this stage your little boy has no "control". His immature bladder cannot hold on to urine for a single second*

• *He still can't wait for you to get the potty after signalling that he's letting go of his urine*

Middle stages: 2 1/2–3 1/2 years

• *Your little boy can bring the potty to you only after he can hold on to urine for a minute or two*

• *He'll come and tell you he needs the potty, but will still have frequent accidents*

• *When he's indicated he can wait several minutes and not before, try trainer pants during the day only*

Later stages: 3 1/2–6 years

• *He may be clean by day, with accidents, but wet at night*

• *He's clean, with accidents, day and night. When he's dry all day try trainer pants during his nap*

• *He's dry all day but needs a nappy at night*

• *He can stay dry through the night with very few accidents*

TODDLER

AIDING A GIRL

Teach your little girl good habits of hygiene, like washing her hands and tidying the bathroom after her. You'll probably find that she responds well to this.

Girls are generally neater than boys, and will enjoy turning a cleanliness routine into a game: "Now we flush the loo ... Now we wash the potty ... Now we wash our hands".

Toilet hygiene
Girls are generally more receptive than boys to being taught good habits of hygiene.

BOWEL AND BLADDER

Once your child shows signs of being ready to use the potty, your aim should be to help and encourage her. If you do this, she is likely to achieve control quite quickly and without much trouble, and will remain happy and confident throughout. If you insist on her using the potty before she is ready, or try to force her, she will be unhappy at first at not being able to please you, and then guilty and resentful. Your relationship with your child will suffer and training will become a battle of nerves, which you can never win.

BOWEL CONTROL

Though a baby is aware first of her bladder emptying, she will probably achieve bowel control first as it's much easier to "hold on" with a full rectum than with a full bladder. You should, therefore, help her use the potty for bowel movements first; this is easier, in any case, because bowel movements are more predictable and take longer than passing urine. When your child indicates that she wants to pass a stool, suggest that she use the potty.

When she's finished, wipe her bottom (front-to-back for girls) then flush the toilet paper and the contents of the potty down the lavatory. Clean off any trace of faeces and rinse out the potty, using disinfectant. Wash your hands afterwards, and encourage your child to do the same. If she doesn't want to use the potty when you suggest it, forget it for the moment and try again a few days later.

CONTROL TIPS

DO	DON'T
• *Praise your child and encourage her to regard control as an accomplishment*	• *Insist that your child sit on the potty, ever*
• *Let your child set the pace. You can help your child along, but you can't speed up the process*	• *Show any disgust for your child's faeces. She will regard using the potty as an achievement and will be proud of them*
• *Suggest that your child sit on the potty, but let her decide*	• *Ask your child to wait once she has asked for the potty, even for a moment – she can only "hold on" for a very short time*
• *Let her be as independent as she likes, going to the lavatory or using the potty, and praise her independence*	• *Scold mistakes and accidents*
• *Use trainer pants to give your child a sense of independence*	

BLADDER CONTROL

The first sign that your child's bladder control is developing is when she becomes aware of the passage of urine, and she may try to attract your attention and point to her nappy. As her bladder matures and is able to contain urine for longer, you may find that her nappy is dry after a nap. Once this is happening regularly, you can leave off the nappy during the nap and encourage her to empty her bladder beforehand. When she can do this and can let you know when she wants to use the potty, you can start leaving off nappies completely during the day, provided she is able to wait for a few minutes while you take down her clothes to let her use the potty. When you are out, you might find it useful to carry a portable potty; these come with disposable liners.

At this stage your child can't hold on to a full bladder for any length of time, and accidents are inevitable, so try to take them in your stride and never scold your toddler for them. Just clean up, change her clothing, and say "Never mind. Better luck next time."

ACHIEVING NIGHT-TIME CONTROL

Control of the bladder during the night is the last to come, as a child of two or three can't hold on to urine for much more than four to five hours. Once your child wakes up regularly with a dry nappy, you can leave off the night-time nappy, but encourage her to empty her bladder before she goes to sleep. It is a good idea to keep a potty beside the bed for your child to use if necessary, but make sure that her nightclothes are easy for her to take down and that you leave a night-light on so that she can see what she's doing. Be patient if she comes and asks for your help; its not easy for her to take responsibility for the potty herself. Try this for a week, but if your child has several wet nights, offer her nappy back for a while – otherwise she will become very tired from disturbed sleep. If she does show signs of becoming more self-reliant, encourage her and boost her confidence. She will still have accidents, so it is a good idea to protect the mattress with a rubber sheet, putting your usual sheet on top. You could also put a small rubber sheet on top of the ordinary one, with a half sheet over that. The half sheet can then be easily removed after an accident, and the undersheet will be protected by the rubber sheet.

USING THE LAVATORY

When your child starts to use the potty regularly throughout the day, encourage her to sit on the lavatory; this will save you having to take a potty with you when you leave the house. Many children are nervous of sitting on the lavatory seat because they feel they'll fall off or even fall in. To make your child more secure on the large lavatory seat, you can use one of the specially designed child-size seats available that fit inside the lavatory rim. Suggest that she holds onto the sides so she feels balanced. You should also stay near by until you are quite sure that she is comfortable on the seat. To help her to get up easily, put a small step or box in front of the lavatory; she can also use this to reach the handbasin.

AIDING A BOY

Boys are often messier than girls in using the potty or the toilet, but there are some things that you can do to help.

Boys are more likely than girls to play with their faeces. If this happens, don't show disgust; just wash your child's hands calmly, as you would if they were dirty with mud or paint.

Show your little boy how to stand in front of the lavatory and teach him to aim at the bowl before he passes any urine. You could put a piece of toilet paper in the bowl for him to aim at. Let him see his father passing urine so that he can imitate him.

Potties
Specially moulded potties provide support and are suitable for both boys and girls.

115

BOWEL AND BLADDER

TRAINER PANTS

Before your child's bladder control is fully developed you may like to use trainer pants.

• *Disposable training pants have easily tearable side seams so that they can be quickly removed in case of accidents*

• *Non-disposable training pants are more absorbent than the disposable kind and can therefore be left on at night. They are also more bulky, however, so some children find them uncomfortable*

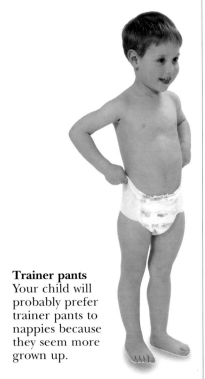

Trainer pants
Your child will probably prefer trainer pants to nappies because they seem more grown up.

By three years of age most children have fairly reliable bladder and bowel control, but accidents will still be common. During the day accidents are most likely to happen when your child ignores the signals of a full bladder because he is engrossed in play or because he is reluctant to use the lavatory in an unfamiliar place. You can help by reminding your child to go to the lavatory at regular intervals and by making a point of accompanying him to the lavatory when you visit new surroundings. Encourage your child to go independently in familiar places as soon as possible, but never insist on his going to a strange lavatory alone.

LATE DEVELOPERS

Some children achieve bowel and bladder control later because brain–bladder connections taken longer than average to form, so it is wrong and cruel to blame your child. Lateness in acquiring control is often hereditary; ask your parents and parents-in-law about this. Few doctors will investigate the problem for a child under three, even if he is wet day and night, or for a child under five who is wet only at night – both fall within the normal range.

ACCIDENTS AND BEDWETTING

When your child does wet himself, remember that however badly you may feel about the inconvenience, it's likely that his embarrassment is much worse. Reassure him that you understand it was an accident and that he hasn't failed you. Being prepared for accidents will reduce anxiety for both of you; always carry spare underwear and trousers on outings.

Bedwetting at night (see p.115) can happen to a child of any age and is very common in children up to the age of five, boys being especially prone. Most children grow out of it after this age without any special help.

You will minimize your child's embarrassment if you keep him in nappies at night until you are confident that he has reached the point where he can stay dry all night. Once you let him go without nappies be prepared for the occasional accident. Concern about the frequency of bedwetting should not be communicated to your child; it only increases his anxiety. Encourage him instead by giving special praise if he has a dry night.

CONSTIPATION

Should your child's stools become infrequent – that is, less often than once every three or four days – and hard enough to cause discomfort or pain, then he is constipated. Constipation without any other signs of illness is nothing to worry about, but if it causes your

116

CONTROL TIPS

DO

- *Remind your child to go to the lavatory at regular intervals*

- *Take a spare set of clothes with you when you go out*

- *Accompany your child to the lavatory in unfamiliar places*

- *Be sympathetic and make light of any accidents*

- *Offer praise when your child has a dry night*

- *If wetting or soiling occurs after a long period of reliable control, look for the cause within the family first. If it persists, consult your doctor*

DON'T

- *Scold or draw attention to any form of accident your child has*

- *Withhold fluids from a child in the evening*

- *Compare your child with others of the same age who may have better control*

- *Make an issue out of any accident in front of friends*

- *Be unsympathetic if your child needs to use the toilet at an inconvenient moment*

REGRESSION

Regression to night- or day-time wetting in a child who has been reliably dry for some time is usually a sign of anxiety.

The arrival of a new baby is a typical reason for your child's regressing to an earlier stage as a way of winning back your attention, but any sort of upset such as a move to a new home or school can cause it. Occasionally regression can be caused by a urinary-tract infection. So when you visit the doctor for any urinary problem, take a sample of your child's urine for testing.

Bowel control, once developed, is usually much more reliable than urinary control. Bowel accidents are uncommon and, if they occur frequently, particularly after control has apparently been reliable for some time, may indicate an underlying problem such as retention of stool or some form of emotional tension. Seek advice from your doctor.

child discomfort, consult your doctor. Most doctors don't recommend using laxatives or purgatives for a small child. (Constipation is rare in very small babies and can nearly always be corrected by giving your baby drinks of water.) You should never try to treat constipation yourself with laxatives, suppositories, or enemas without consulting your doctor.

Once your child is on a varied diet, he shouldn't suffer from constipation if you are giving him enough fresh fruit, vegetables, and wholemeal breads; if he does, just give more of these. The complex carbohydrates in root and green vegetables contain cellulose, which holds water in the stools and makes them more bulky and soft, as do oat cereals like porridge. A few stewed prunes or dried figs can help, too, often producing a soft stool within 24 hours.

A child can become chronically constipated for several reasons: if you are an over-fussy parent and obsessive about the frequency of his bowel motions your child may withhold them as a means of getting attention; if he has experienced pain and discomfort when trying to pass a motion, and holds on to the stools to prevent the pain recurring; or if he dislikes school or other strange lavatories and is unwilling to use them.

Chronic constipation can also cause a condition called encopresis. Hard stools become impacted in the intestine, and loose, watery motions leak out past the blockage, sometimes causing the condition to be mistaken for diarrhoea.

Illness with a high temperature may be followed by a few days of constipation, partly because your child has eaten very little, so there are no waste products to pass, and partly because he has lost water through sweating with the fever. This kind of constipation will correct itself when your child goes back on to a normal diet.

NAME *Fanny Hughes*

AGE *32 years*

OBSTETRIC
HISTORY *Son Will, aged 5; normal delivery*

Daughter Miranda, aged 7 months; normal delivery

PAST
MEDICAL
HISTORY *Usual childhood diseases*

FAMILY
HISTORY *Husband Chris, aged 35, was late in gaining bladder control, and was a bedwetter up to the age of six years*

Fanny had expected Will to be a bit late in mastering bowel and bladder control as she knew boys were often later than girls in accomplishing this stage of development. She'd also read that the fathers of late developers have often been late in gaining full bladder control too, and this turned out to be the case with Chris. She therefore remained very calm and cool when Will was developing control, and never pushed him. Will for his part was very co-operative and eager to please, and was dry and clean by three-and-a-half years.

REGRESSION

When Fanny started to grow big with Miranda, Will couldn't understand at all what was going on. He disowned his baby sister from the start. Fanny did everything she could to reassure him, showing him pictures of babies inside their mother's tummies, letting him feel the baby kick and involving him in all the preparations. A month before the baby was due, Will started having disturbed sleep, when he would babble about the baby, but he remembered nothing in the morning. Miranda was born at home. Will sat outside his mother's bedroom transfixed by all the activity, and refused to go in and see his new sister. That night he wet the bed, which was something he hadn't done for a full year.

FEELING REJECTED

Chris was very angry with Will for not showing more interest in Miranda, scolded him, and sent him straight to bed. That night, because of all the upheaval in the house, Will did not get his usual bedtime story and again in the morning the bed was wet. Chris, who was preoccupied with preparing breakfast for everyone and making Fanny comfortable, lost his temper with Will, who stood in the kitchen and wet himself again. "I don't know what we'll do with you", were Chris's last words to Will as he left for work.

Fanny realized that Will would never wet himself unless he was upset. The midwife immediately saw what the problem was when she arrived to find Will crying in the kitchen. She explained to Fanny that Will was suffering from dethronement. Having been the apple of Fanny's eye for four and a half years, he felt knocked off his throne by Miranda, and Fanny would have to make him feel loved and secure again. She also told Fanny that the doctor should test Will's urine just to make sure an infection wasn't the cause of the bedwetting – the test result was negative.

SEEKING ADVICE

Fanny decided to have a heart-to-heart with her mother, who reminded her of a family rule – dad always carried the new baby so that mum had her arms free for the other children. She pointed out that Will wouldn't have felt left out if Chris had held the new baby so that Fanny's arms were empty for him. Then he'd have known that Fanny still had time for him and that she loved him. She reminded Fanny of a tradition in her own family that the younger children always got a present from the new baby, so that they knew they were loved by her too. She also suggested that on the first night Will should have been allowed to sleep on the couch in Fanny's room, so that he felt special and included.

By now Fanny felt very guilty that she had taken none of these steps to make Will feel important and secure, and she went to her midwife for advice on how to give her son his self-confidence back. The midwife explained that a child who gets upset, for whatever cause, be it a new baby or starting nursery school, will regress to an earlier, more primitive phase of development, exactly as Will had done. She pointed out that Will had no control over this and that, far from punishing Will for future accidents, the whole family must be very relaxed and play them down, saying things like "It doesn't matter, Will. Let me clean you up, then we can play a game if you like." But Will was feeling far too insecure for a quick recovery, and the following morning he regressed even further and refused to feed himself: he demanded to be fed.

A PLAN OF ACTION

Fanny and Chris decided to take immediate positive action and, on the advice of their midwife, started a programme to rebuild Will's confidence.

- They told Will's nursery teacher about the difficulties at home, and asked all the staff to be sympathetic and praise Will's efforts at every opportunity.

- Chris was to spend half an hour with Will when he came home each evening, when he would give Will his full attention and lots of cuddles, and tell Will he loved him as often as he felt like it.

- Fanny would also give Will half an hour of her time when he got home from school, with lots of cuddles and expressions of love and take a deep interest in his nursery school activities.

- Fanny would have regular sit-down breakfasts with Will, putting Miranda out of sight if possible in her cradle. She would never bring Miranda into the room at these special times unless Will suggested it.

- Fanny would point out to Will all the things that he had mastered that Miranda, a tiny baby, couldn't do, and suggest that perhaps Will could teach Miranda, even protect her.

- Will would have his own private bathtime, and Fanny and Chris would take turns to read him a bedtime story each night.

- Fanny and Chris would alternate taking Will out for a treat on his own each week.

Fanny and Chris put this plan into operation immediately, and within three days Will was feeding himself happily. After a couple of weeks he asked to show Miranda his teddy bear, though he wouldn't let her touch him. He had no more daytime accidents after two weeks, and four weeks later he was sleeping dry through the night. Reassured by his parents' loving, caring attention, Will became more accepting of Miranda – in fact, three months later Will said that he'd marry Miranda if he couldn't marry Fanny.

NAME *Will Hughes*

AGE *5 years*

OBSTETRIC HISTORY *Normal birth, no complications*

PAST MEDICAL HISTORY *Minor ear infections in third year, cleared up after treatment*

EVENINGS OUT

Because young babies are easy to carry and sleep a lot they're very portable, so you can still enjoy going out by taking your baby with you.

In the early weeks it's a good thing for new parents, especially mothers, to get out of the house and relax with friends. It's easier to do this while your baby is young because she will sleep anywhere. A car seat that doubles as a free-standing chair is ideal for this; it can be safely strapped in place in the car, then carried indoors when you reach your destination while your baby sleeps.

Take advantage of this flexibility while you can; once your baby starts sleeping through the night you will need to stick to a regular bedtime routine.

Sleeping
Ensure your baby is warm and covered, but not too warm (see p.123). A picture of a face will hold his attention if he's awake.

SLEEP AND WAKEFULNESS

A newborn baby needs a lot of sleep and unless she is hungry, cold, or uncomfortable, it is likely that she will spend at least 60 per cent of her time asleep.

Your baby may fall asleep immediately after – and sometimes during – a feed. She will probably be indifferent to noises such as doors shutting or the radio – in fact, she may find droning noises soothing. Babies' sleeping patterns do vary, though, so if your baby is wakeful after a feed, don't insist that she stays in her cot.

It is important that your baby learns to distinguish between day and night. When it becomes dark outside, close the curtains and turn the lights very low. Make sure that she is warm and covered and, when she wakes during the night, feed her quickly and quietly without turning the lights up, and don't play with her. In time she'll learn the difference between a day- and a night-time feed.

WHERE SHOULD YOUR BABY SLEEP?

You will probably find it easiest to let your baby sleep in something that makes her portable. During the day, a car seat with a carrying handle is ideal if you drive. If you don't have a car, a carrycot is suitable both day and night since it is easily movable and can be clipped on to a wheeled chassis when you go out. When she outgrows a carrycot she will need a proper cot.

Sleeping with you At first some parents will opt to have their newborn baby sleeping with them because night feeds are easier to cope with, and it shouldn't be a difficult habit to break after a couple of weeks. If you do sleep with your baby, let her lie between you and your partner so that she cannot fall out of bed. Don't worry, you won't roll on top of her, provided that you haven't been drinking or taken drugs that make you sleep heavily.

Your baby's bedroom Pay careful attention to the temperature of your baby's room. Babies cannot regulate their body temperatures as well as adults and to maintain the right level of warmth they need a constant temperature and enough blankets to keep them warm – but not too warm (see p.123). A night-light or dimmer switch will mean that you can check your baby during the night without waking her.

Sleeping outdoors Except when it's chilly your baby will sleep quite happily outside, but make sure she's wrapped up and visible at all times and never place her in direct sunlight; choose a shady area or protect her with a canopy. If it's windy, put the hood up on the carrycot so it acts as a windbreak. Put a cat net over the carrycot.

Clothing Your newborn will need to be changed often, and while she is sleeping she should wear something that gives you easy access to her nappy. An all-in-one stretch suit or a nightdress – one with a drawstring at the end so it doesn't ride up her back – is best.

It is important that your baby does not get too hot or too cold. In warm weather a nappy and a vest will be sufficient. In the winter, you can check that your baby is warm enough by touching the back of her neck with your hand. Her skin should feel about the same temperature as yours. If she feels too hot and clammy you should take a blanket off and let her cool down.

PROBLEMS

If your baby wakes you frequently during the night or she cries when you try to go back to bed, you'll be short of sleep and you'll find it difficult to cope. It is essential that you get enough rest and you should share the responsibility of night feeds with your partner – even if you are breastfeeding your partner could bottlefeed your baby with expressed milk on some nights. Alternatively, you can have your partner bring you the baby to feed and then he can change her nappy. If you're exhausted get help from a friend or relative, relax your routine, get up late, and take daytime naps.

Encourage your baby to sleep at night by tiring her out in the day with plenty of stimulation: talk to her, pick her up, and give her lots of different things to look at. If she wakes up a lot in the night because she is wet, use double nappies or nappy liners, and if she cries when you leave her, don't immediately return and pick her up. Rocking her cot, removing a blanket, or changing her position may be sufficient.

Early on swaddling or wrapping your baby may help her to sleep; the sensation of being tightly enclosed gives babies a great feeling of security. It is also a useful way of calming a distressed baby.

SETTLING YOUR BABY

Here are several things you can do to ensure that your baby settles down to sleep.

- *In the first month or so, wrap or swaddle your baby (see below) before you put her down*

- *Give your baby a comfort suck from breast or bottle*

- *Darken the room at night*

- *In cold weather put a hot-water bottle in the cot for a short time before you put your baby down – but never leave it in the cot*

- *Hang a musical mobile over the cot to soothe your baby*

- *If she doesn't seem to be settling down, rock her gently or stroke her back or limbs to soothe her*

- *Try carrying her around in a sling and jogging her up and down: your closeness and heartbeat will help her to settle down*

SWADDLING

Lay baby on shawl
Fold a shawl or small blanket in half to form a triangle and lay your baby on it, aligning his head with the longest edge.

Wrap baby
Fold one point of the shawl across your baby and tuck it firmly behind his back. Do the same with the other point.

Cover his feet
Tuck the bottom of the shawl back underneath your baby's feet to keep them covered.

REDUCING THE RISK

By following these guidelines you will significantly reduce your baby's risk of cot death.

• *Always place your baby on his back to sleep*

• *Don't smoke, don't allow anyone in your house to smoke, and avoid smoky places*

• *Don't let your baby get too hot*

• *When covering your baby allow for room temperature – the higher the temperature, the fewer blankets and bedclothes your baby needs, and vice versa (see chart opposite)*

• *Avoid swaddling and tucking in so your baby can throw off bedclothes if hot*

• *If you think your baby is unwell don't hesitate to contact your doctor*

• *If your baby has a fever don't increase the wrapping – reduce it so he can lose heat*

Protecting your baby
The most important thing you can do is put your baby to sleep on his back. You should also make sure he is not too warm.

PREVENTING COT DEATH

Sudden Infant Death Syndrome (SIDS), known colloquially as cot death, is the sudden and unexpected death of a baby for no obvious reason. The rate for cot deaths in the UK is 3 per 2,000 live births. In actual figures this translates to the deaths of 1,134 babies in 1991. Following a campaign to give parents useful advice about SIDS the death rate was nearly halved to 613 deaths in 1992.

The causes of cot death are unknown, and there is therefore no advice that can guarantee its prevention. There are, however, many ways in which parents can vastly reduce the risk.

SLEEPING POSITION

One of the most crucial risk factors is the position in which you put your baby down to sleep. In most countries, babies have traditionally slept on their backs. In the UK as well, most babies slept on their backs until the 1960s, and the number of cot deaths was low. In 1970, however, special care baby units started to lay preterm babies face down because it seemed this position improved breathing and reduced vomiting, and eventually the practice was extended to full-term babies.

The significance of sleeping position in relation to SIDS was looked at in 1965, but the evidence was not convincing, and it was not until 1986, when SIDS rates in different communities were compared, that it became clear that SIDS was less common where babies slept on their backs. In the UK by this time, 93 per cent of babies were put in their cots to sleep face downwards.

Quite by luck, when my first son was born in 1972, I avoided this risk by laying him down on his side, thinking that if he wanted to suck his thumb it would be easier for him to do so, and I kept him there with small soft pillows placed in front of and behind him. Research in New Zealand since then has shown fewer cot deaths in babies placed on their sides, but without support they can roll on to their tummies. The safest position for your baby, therefore, is on his back. Some people will tell you that this position may allow inhalation of posset, but there is no evidence to support this.

SMOKING

A mother who smokes during pregnancy increases the risk of SIDS. (She also increases the risk of a premature or low birth-weight baby.) What's more, the risk increases with the number of cigarettes smoked. The risk of SIDS in babies born to smokers is twice that for babies born to non-smokers, and with every ten cigarettes a day the risk increases threefold. About 365 cot deaths a year could be avoided in the UK if maternal smoking could be eliminated. Studies carried out in the United States now strongly suggest that exposure of a baby to smoke increases his risk of suffering SIDS by 200 per cent, and if both parents smoke the risk increases more.

TEMPERATURE

There's no doubt that overheating from too many night clothes, too many blankets, and too high a room temperature is a contributory factor, as SIDS is much more common in overheated babies. (The risk of overheating alone, however, is less than that from sleeping position and smoking.) Two-thirds of cot deaths occur in winter, when babies may be wrapped up too warmly.

Many parents increase the amount of bedding when a baby is unwell, but this is not what your baby needs. High temperature plus infection in babies over ten weeks old greatly increases the risk of cot death. If heat loss is prevented, the body temperature of a restless baby with an infection will rise by at least 1°C per hour. A baby loses most heat from its face, chest, and abdomen, so lying on the back allows body temperature to be better controlled.

Baby nests, sheepskins, duvets, and cot bumpers are all heat insulators, and so should not be used for young babies, as they prevent heat loss. There is no need to heat the nursery all night unless the weather is very cold; just make sure that your baby has enough blankets (see below). If you do have a heater in the nursery, use a thermostatically controlled one that will switch off if the room gets too warm, and switch back on again as it cools down.

CONTINUING RESEARCH

Although risk factors have been identified, the causes of cot death are still not understood. Current areas of research include the development of a baby's temperature control mechanisms and respiratory system in the first six months, and the recent discovery that an inherited enzyme deficiency may be responsible for a small number – about 1 per cent – of cot deaths. A recent study in the UK connected cot death with flame-retardant chemicals in cot mattresses, but the connection has not been definitely proven.

GETTING HELP

The unexpected death of an infant is a particularly painful bereavement, but support is available to help parents cope with their feelings of grief, bewilderment, and guilt (see Useful Addresses, p.344).

• *Many parents seek help immediately after the death – sometimes within hours – and telephone support lines are available that can provide information and a sympathetic listener*

• *In the longer term, parents may seek professional help. The continued support of a health visitor, social worker, or religious adviser can be invaluable, so don't be afraid to ask*

• *Parents may be helped by being able to talk to someone who has been through a similar experience, either in support groups or on a one-to-one basis*

• *Befriending schemes exist in some areas that continue long after professional help may have ceased, and these can be invaluable at times of particular grief such as the anniversaries of the baby's birth and death*

• *Parents who have lost one baby through cot death are likely to be extremely anxious when another baby is born. Support schemes exist that involve the parents, midwife, doctor and health visitor in making sure the new baby gets the best possible care*

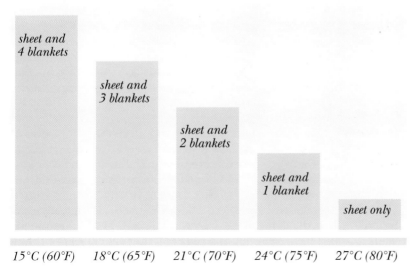

sheet and 4 blankets

sheet and 3 blankets

sheet and 2 blankets

sheet and 1 blanket

sheet only

15°C (60°F)   18°C (65°F)   21°C (70°F)   24°C (75°F)   27°C (80°F)

Controlling the temperature
Keep a thermometer in your baby's room so that you can see how many blankets he needs. At 18°C (65°F), a sheet and three blankets is adequate.

SLEEP AND WAKEFULNESS

CAUSES OF WAKEFULNESS

Here are some of the things you can do if your baby is wakeful through the night.

- *Make sure that your baby is neither too hot nor too cold (see p.123)*

- *Check that your baby isn't in any discomfort from a soiled nappy or nappy rash*

- *Don't keep popping into your baby's room to see if he's asleep*

- *If your child suddenly becomes sleepless, think about the possible causes, such as a change in routine, someone new staying with you, or your going out to work. Whatever the cause, he will need lots of your attention*

Restlessness
Put mirrors and noisy toys on the side of the cot to amuse your restless baby.

Babies usually establish their sleep patterns within the first few months and if you find that yours sleeps a lot in his first year, he will probably do the same in his second. At some time in the first 12 months he'll sleep through the night (though with some babies it can be much later), and once he starts to crawl he'll be using up so much energy during the day that he may sleep for 10 or 11 hours uninterruptedly. Even though he needs sleep, however, he's able to keep himself awake so that he can stay in your company. He may whimper and cry, become hot and bothered, and then so tense and unhappy that sleep becomes impossible. If your baby is clingy and sleepless and appears to be insecure the best treatment for him is you. Stay with him, hold him close to you, rock him, sing to him, soothe him, and walk up and down with him until he feels that you are not going to leave him and is reassured by your closeness. This may take half an hour, but usually he'll fall asleep in your arms after about ten or fifteen minutes, and then you can put him back in his cot.

WAKEFUL BABIES

There's no question that some babies need very little sleep. Wakeful babies, as I like to call them, are usually bright, curious, intelligent, and very affectionate. They quickly latch on to the fact that you're there all through the night and that they can attract your attention with crying or calling out to you. I firmly believe that no baby's crying should be ignored. A baby that's left to cry quickly learns that adults don't respond to his cries for help and love. He will stop asking for attention and may become solitary and withdrawn. Try not to get upset because your baby is wakeful; he's demonstrating his sociability and intelligence because he's learning all the time, and you'll find as he grows up that he's a very rewarding friend. If your baby wakes before your bedtime try carrying him around in a sling or put him in a baby bouncer so that he can tire himself out.

Solutions Wakeful babies very often need diversion, so as soon as your baby can sit up, leave some favourite soft toys or soft books in the cot. Put a mirror on the side of the cot so that he can look in it and talk to himself. A mobile above the cot that makes sounds can fascinate your baby for quite a long time, too.

I had two wakeful babies and I had to resort to extreme measures to get any sleep myself. I erected a camp bed alongside my baby's cot, and when he woke up in the middle of the night I would soothe him so that he went back to sleep without really waking up. This prevented him from getting upset with a crying bout.

If your baby only whimpers, don't get up immediately because he may go back to sleep without any soothing at all. If, however, the whimper becomes true crying then you should go and see him. The first time you go in try soothing talk while patting him on the back. If this doesn't work you'll have to pick him up to soothe him, then put him back in his cot, and leave the room. If he continues to cry, you may decide to go back every five minutes to calm your baby down. (If you do, try to soothe your baby without lifting him up – say by rocking the cot or talking to him.)

BEDTIME ROUTINES

As your baby gets older he'll require more of your attention at bedtime, and probably will have settled into some routine that he needs in order to sleep, such as a story, a song, or some kind of gentle game. Do everything you can to make your baby calm, tranquil, and happy before sleep. If necessary, forego a scolding for a minor misdemeanour; you don't want your child to face bedtime feeling tearful and upset.

There's nothing magical about bedrooms or cots. You are your child's favourite playmate, and he will be happiest if he goes to sleep in your company. If you have the energy, let him run around you until he actually drops asleep at your feet, curl up in the chair next to you, or put a pillow on your knee on the sofa and go to sleep with his head resting in your lap. As soon as he's asleep you can take him to his cot and, instead of a lonely child upstairs becoming upset and calling out to you, you'll have a secure, calm child who in all probability will sleep through the night.

Comfort habits Your child may become attached to a comfort item of some sort: a doll, a small handkerchief, or a tiny piece of torn blanket. Whatever it is don't try to take it from your child and don't try to change it. You may also find that habits such as rocking, thumb-sucking, twisting his hair, or rubbing his top lip will become part of his bedtime routine. There's nothing wrong with any of these bedtime rituals. By using a comforter to help him to go to sleep your baby is using his inner resources and becoming self-reliant. He will give up these habits in his own good time.

HOW NAPS CHANGE

Some babies sleep through the night from early on, some do not. As a rule, the more mobile your baby is and the more energy he uses, the more soundly he sleeps – sleep being divided between daytime naps and night-time.

When your baby grows, night sleep usually becomes unbroken and naps are fairly regular – one in the morning and one in the afternoon for varying lengths of time.

Later, your baby's nap times will change: he may put off his morning nap until after lunch, and then need another nap at around 3.30 or 4 p.m. before sleeping for the night at around 7 p.m. Every day may be different.

Whatever time your baby is disposed to nap, take the lead from him; don't try to impose nap times on him. And try to clear your time so that you are able to take a nap with your baby; both of you will be recharged when you wake up.

Security objects
Your child may use a comforter such as a soft toy or blanket to help him sleep. This is quite normal so don't try to take it away from him.

Cotton vest

Fabric book

Soft cotton blanket

Fleecy fabric rattle

Silk handkerchief

TODDLER

SLEEP AND WAKEFULNESS

AWAY FROM HOME

It's quite reasonable for your child to be scared or refuse to get into a strange bed – when she goes to stay with friends and granny, for instance, and when you go away on holiday.

• *Make the new bed into a play-ground: put lots of toys on the bed, and let your child have drinks and food on the bed, so that she associates it with pleasant experiences*

• *Show your child that you are in easy reach. Get her to call out and then answer her back so that she knows you are close by*

• *If she gets scared and refuses to use the bed don't ridicule her, don't force her into bed, don't leave her alone, and don't lock the door. That will only make her worse, so give it a break.*

• *Try telling her that because she is being so grown-up in using a new bed she can have a treat, such as a new bedtime story or ten minutes' sitting on your knee watching television*

Many two-year-olds periodically wake up during the night. If your child is one of them, this may be distressing for you and your partner, but it is both usual and normal, and you should never deny your child love, comfort, and affection. There may be some obvious problem but often you won't be able to find out a reason for your child's waking up. It could just be that she's a bit afraid of the dark, but she cannot explain to you what is wrong, nor can you reassure her with words. You have to comfort with actions, so give lots of kisses and cuddles to show your child that she is loved.

Daytime napping As your child gets older you will find that she doesn't necessarily want to sleep at nap time, but she does need a rest. Try to make a routine out of nap time whether your child sleeps or not by, say, playing some music or reading. You may find your child goes to sleep at nap time if you allow her to sleep in your bed as a special treat or if you give her some idea of how long the nap time will be; one way of doing this is to put on her favourite tape and say that nap time isn't over until the tape is finished.

COT TO BED

When your child is strong enough and well co-ordinated enough to climb out of her cot and come into your room, it is time for her to start using a bed. Most children will be pleased and excited with their new bed, but if your child seems nervous, there are plenty of things you can do to help (see pp.128–29); the simplest is to let her take naps in the bed until she is ready to sleep in it at night. If you are worried that your child might fall out of the bed, you could fit a bed guard to one or both sides as appropriate.

Naps
During the day watch your child for signs of bad temper or fretfulness and ensure that she rests or plays a quiet game.

PLEASANT BEDTIMES

From the age of three onwards your child may well use delaying tactics in order to put off going to bed. The way you handle this situation really depends on how much energy you have at the end of the day, and what your previous bedtime routine has been.

If you've been looking after your child and managing the household tasks all day, you will be in need of private time and may feel you can insist on her going to bed. On the other hand, if you have been out at work all day you will want to see your child, so you may feel very sympathetic to her pleas for your attention.

If you've always had quite a strict bedtime routine and your child suddenly departs from this, then it's probably best for both of you if you firmly re-institute the bedtime with loving fairness. If, however, you've been flexible about bedtimes then it's probably as well for your child's happiness and your serenity to let her stay with you and make herself comfortable. She will be asleep in a few minutes if she has the reassurance of your presence in the room.

KEEPING BEDTIME PEACEFUL

I'm convinced that bedtimes should be happy times and with my own children I was always prepared to make concessions to this guiding principle. I would do anything to avoid my children going to bed unhappy. I would do my utmost to prevent any crying, and whereas during the day I might punish a small misdemeanour, it would go unmarked at night time to make sure that my child didn't go to sleep with the sound of an angry parent's voice in his ears.

If you have more than one child let them enjoy their bedtimes in the same bedroom. Company is reassuring and seeing a sister or brother in pyjamas at the same time as her makes your child feel that bedtimes are just and fair, even if your older child is allowed to stay up slightly later. Until they get to an age where they need their privacy it's a good idea for them to share a bedroom.

FEAR OF THE DARK

As your child gets older and her imagination becomes more fertile, it's very easy to imagine frightening things in the shadows. A fear of the dark is entirely normal – even adults retain it. Leave a night-light on in the room or leave a light on outside with a dimmer switch so that your child can see her way to the bathroom if she needs it, or to your room if she's frightened. (If you use a night-light make sure it doesn't cast frightening shadows.) Never insist on her bedroom being completely dark, and never ridicule her fear; it's really a sign that your child is growing up and learning about the world around her. Tell her that if she wakes up in the night and is frightened she can always come to you for a cuddle.

PRESCHOOL

PRIVACY

You can teach your child to stay within her own space as early as two years, but certainly by three when she is open to reason. She'll learn that it's her responsibility not to disturb you thoughtlessly just because she feels like it.

Teaching her to respect your privacy is far better than shutting her out of your room, which you should never do. You can encourage mature behaviour by providing her with her own private space, which is hers alone, in which her belongings reside and where she can find her favourite things. Children respond very quickly to the idea of privacy, particularly if they are given a private space of their own that they can tidy up, be proud of, and go to if they want to be quiet and play on their own.

You can affirm this sense of privacy by always pointing out to your child that certain things belong to her: this is her book, her toy, her dress, and they all have a proper place. In this way she will become familiar with her belongings and where she can find them. By about the age of four she's mature enough to realize that if she has her things, you have yours and that just as she doesn't like her possessions being disturbed, neither do you.

127

NAME *Rachel Freiman*

AGE *28 years*

MEDICAL HISTORY *Nothing abnormal*

OBSTETRIC HISTORY *One child, Hella, aged three years. Three months pregnant with second child.*

There are several ways to lure a child from a cot to a bed, but the least tearful always involve a bit of preparation so it's best to plan a few months in advance. Rachel and her husband Zac decided to move three-year-old Hella into a bed when Rachel was three months pregnant with their second child, and their decision was influenced as much by the need for extra space as by Hella's age.

COT TO BED

Rachel and Zac didn't think it was practical to have Hella in the small nursery with the new baby, nor did they want her to feel resentful that she was being pushed out of her own bedroom to make way for a new arrival. They decided to make the switch at the same time – a new bedroom and a new bed – before the baby arrived, so there seemed nothing unnatural about it. "With hindsight," says Rachel, "it may have been too much of a change all at once, because although Hella was excited about her new room, it was still an unfamiliar environment, which meant she was less settled at night."

Rachel and Zac involved Hella as much as possible, letting her choose the colours for her new room, and taking her shopping to buy her choice of Minnie Mouse duvet cover – a clever way of enthusing her about her new bed. If you don't really need a new cover, it's just as effective to get your child a new toy – a teddy bear or a doll – which "lives" in the bed. This will make her feel secure.

LITTLE BY LITTLE

Rachel and Zac allowed Hella a few practice runs in her bed, which is a good idea. "As a treat," says Zac, "we would hide a little toy under the duvet and then let her find it. Two weeks before we planned to move her in, we started letting her take her naps there – a good tip that Rachel picked up at a toddler playgroup. Because Hella had the naps during the day, she got used to her bed without the complication of night-time fears.

"I think it was a good idea to do this gradually, because children can have fears that adults never imagine. One of the new things we bought to go in Hella's room, for instance, was a Mickey Mouse alarm clock, to go with her duvet. On the second night in her new bed, we heard her crying and rushed into her room. She was obviously terrified and said there was a man there. We assured her there wasn't, but she insisted she could hear his footsteps quite clearly. Luckily Rachel took her seriously, and worked out it was the rather loud ticking of the alarm clock she could hear!"

Even though Rachel and Zac took the clock away, Hella refused to spend the rest of the night in her room. The night after was better, although there were several occasions during the following fortnight when she wet the bed. This seems to have been part of the adjustment process, as she hasn't done it since.

"It's difficult to see it from a child's point of view," explains Zac, "but I suppose it must be quite frightening to be put in a big bed in a new room. At first I thought Rachel was being pedantic when she said we should prepare Hella for the move, but in the light of experience I realize she was quite right."

When is the right time?

There are no hard and fast rules for deciding when the time is right to make the switch. In general, it is between the age of two-and-a-half to three-and-a-half years, although this largely depends on your child's temperament and your own personal circumstances; like Rachel and Zac, you may have little choice, or alternatively your child might clearly outgrow her cot and refuse to stay in it. A child who can climb out of her cot can cause herself harm, and it is safer to put her in a low bed than run the risk of her toppling off the edge of a high cot.

Bear in mind that once your child is in a bed, she will be able to get out and investigate the nooks and crannies of her room when she wakes up in the morning. This means it is advisable to reassess safety measures to make sure that an unsupervised child won't come to any harm.

If, like Rachel and Zac, you are expecting another baby, don't move your first child out of her room or cot when the new baby arrives, as this will obviously fuel jealousy. As with everything else, it's best to give your child time to adapt to a new idea and involve her in the preparation wherever possible.

Unless you have to move your child, there is little point in trying to force the issue. While some children want to get out of their cot as soon as possible, others need a little more time and a bit more persuading. If all else fails, entice your child into bed by getting into it yourself – children are usually curious about what their parents are doing, and will quickly imitate you.

Making a smooth transition

Help your child make the switch to a big bed by recreating a secure environment like the one she had in her cot. If your child is scared or unsettled she won't sleep, and that means you won't either, so it's worth preparing your child for the move. Start off, as Rachel and Zac did, by making it a positive and exciting change.

Tell your child that now she's a big girl, she's very lucky to get to sleep in a big bed, "like Mummy and Daddy do". Put lots of her favourite toys there and consider installing a night-light or just leaving the bedroom door open so she can see the landing light. If music helps to soothe her, leave it on while she goes to sleep.

Once you have put your child to bed, don't make the mistake of disappearing suddenly as this will unsettle her, and you might find yourself back at square one. Instead, make sure she is comfortable: sing songs or read a story, leave a drink by the bed, and a potty if necessary, and then say goodbye more than once without closing the door so that she knows you are still there.

If your child is not changing rooms, put the new bed into the nursery for a few months before making the switch so that it's familiar. Some children are scared they will fall out of their new bed because there is no barrier. If this is a problem make a temporary barrier by lining a few chairs up next to the bed, or putting a row of cushions in between your child and the edge of the bed.

NAME *Hella Freiman*

AGE *3 years*

MEDICAL HISTORY *Minor childhood ailments. Bowel and bladder control now almost complete, wears trainer pants at night.*

CRYING AND COMFORTING

The amount of crying, and reasons for crying, are different in boys and girls.

• *Baby girls are less vulnerable to stress at the time of birth than male babies and less likely to cry*

• *An American study has shown that girls are less irritable than boys at the age of three weeks, and therefore cry less*

• *Girls are less likely than boys to cry in new situations*

• *Mothers tend to give extra attention to girls who cry a lot*

All babies cry quite a lot and so will yours, so be prepared for it. There will be times when the reason for her crying is obvious: she's hungry, too hot, too cold, bored, uncomfortable because of a wet or a dirty nappy, or she might simply want your affection and closeness. One reason for crying that parents often fail to recognise is the desire for sleep. I well remember trying to console my newborn son in all kinds of ways before it occurred to me that he just wanted to be left alone to sleep.

Very young babies cry when they are disturbed, when they are roughly handled, such as at bathtimes, or when they get a shock, perhaps from feeling that they are going to be dropped, from a loud noise, or from a bright light. A two-week-old baby always responds to the security of being firmly wrapped in a shawl or held in strong, confident arms. Once you have investigated your baby's crying, don't worry too much about it – crying is practically her only way of communicating.

Recognising different cries Within a few weeks, you can distinguish between the different cries that mean your baby is hungry, is niggling because she is bored, wants to be put down to sleep, or wants a cuddle. Of course your baby is learning about you, too, and how to communicate with you. She cries out of need and you respond by giving her what she wants.

RESPONDING TO YOUR BABY

I believe you should respond quite quickly to your baby's cry. If you don't respond then your baby feels as you would if you were ignored in a conversation. There's quite a lot of research to show that your baby is affected by how you respond to crying. For instance, mothers who respond quickly to crying tend to have children with more advanced communication skills, including speaking and outgoing behaviour. Babies who are ignored cry more often and for longer in the first year than babies who are attended to quickly. It seems that mothers cause their babies to settle into a pattern of crying often and persistently because they fail to respond, and a vicious circle is set up in which the baby cries, the mother fails to respond, the baby cries more, and the mother is even less inclined to act. A sensitive response from

Communication
Your baby can only make his needs known by crying, so always respond

you promotes self-confidence and self-esteem in later life. Some mothers believe that always responding will spoil their babies. A young baby has a limitless capacity for soaking up love and there's no way that you can spoil a baby by attention in her first year.

CRYING SPELLS

Most babies have crying spells. Often crying occurs in the late afternoon or early evening, when your baby may cry for as long as half an hour. If your baby has colic (see p.133), evening crying spells can last up to two hours. At one time mothers used to say that a child required this exercise to help develop healthy lungs and therefore felt they could leave their babies to cry. This is nonsense; you should always try to console your baby during a crying spell.

Once your child establishes a pattern of crying spells they may go on for several weeks. It's understandable – it's your baby's way of becoming adjusted to being in a very different world from that experienced inside your uterus. The more sensitively you respond to her and take your lead from her, the more rapidly she will become acclimatized to her new lifestyle; the sooner you accommodate her likes and dislikes, the sooner crying spells will stop.

NIGHT-TIME CRYING

There is no doubt that every parent finds crying spells difficult to cope with, especially if they occur during the night. Don't get frustrated because your child doesn't respond to your attempts to soothe her. If walking up and down, singing songs, wrapping, or swaddling just don't seem to work, you could take her for a short drive; the gentle swaying motion of a car may send her to sleep.

During the night, crying will almost certainly make you feel impatient at the least, and at the worst, that you will do anything to stop your baby crying. These feelings are normal, so don't become frightened and tense, otherwise the crying will simply get worse. When my five-day-old baby cried persistently during the night, I actually thought that if I threw him against the wall he would be bound to stop. I didn't, of course, but it is quite normal to think such things; it would only have been abnormal if I had done it.

WHY DOES MY BABY CRY SO MUCH?

There is research which shows that your child may cry despite your best efforts to console her, regardless of whether or not she feels any discomfort. For instance, babies of mothers who have a general anaesthetic during labour or who have been delivered by forceps tend to cry more in the first weeks of life. Similarly, babies born after a long labour are likely to sleep in short bursts, and to cry quite a lot in between. There's no question that a mother communicates her mood to her baby, so if you are tense, irritable and impatient your baby will feel it, and cry. There are individual and racial differences between babies. Some cry a different amount even if they're given the same care and attention. For instance, researchers have observed that Chinese-American babies cry less than European-American babies.

CRYING BOYS

Boys differ from girls in their reasons for crying, and in the way they respond to attempts to soothe them.

- *Baby boys tend to benefit from a regular routine early on, and if the routine is disturbed they quite often resort to crying*

- *Boys tend to take longer to adapt to new situations, and may cry if pushed*

- *More boys than girls tend to be labelled as difficult, but studies show that "difficult" baby boys are no more difficult than any other by the age of two years, especially if parents work hard to console them and make them happy*

- *Boys seem to need responsiveness from their parents more than girls in order to be happy, and cry readily if parental attention and love is not forthcoming*

- *Mothers of boys are less likely to give extra attention and cuddles when their baby is crying a lot, because they mistakenly want them to be tough*

Newborn crying
Many newborns cry a lot at first, but then settle down after just a few weeks.

SOOTHING YOUR BABY

DUMMIES

Babies are born with a sucking reflex. Without it they wouldn't suckle and wouldn't nourish themselves. I feel it's important that babies are allowed to indulge their desire to suck.

Some babies are more "sucky" than others; I certainly had one who wanted to suck all the time, whether he was hungry or not. With all four of my sons, I used gently to put their thumbs into their mouths so that they could suck to soothe themselves. But at the same time I see nothing wrong with using dummies as comforters, though very young babies will not take to one readily.

While a baby is young, dummies should be sterilized in exactly the same way as you sterilize feeding bottles and teats. Once your child is being weaned, however, and starts to use his fingers for feeding himself, it is pointless to sterilize dummies. Careful washing and rinsing is all that is needed.

Have several dummies so that they can be interchanged when they get dirty or damaged.

There are lots of remedies you can try to soothe and console your baby if he's crying. As a general rule, most babies respond to movement and sound: hence the effectiveness of taking them out in the car, where the motion of the vehicle and the steady humming sound of the engine will usually quieten them. Your baby will probably find any of the following movements or sounds soothing:

- A movement that rocks him, whether it is you, a swing, a rocking cradle, or a rocking chair.
- Walking or dancing with an emphasis on rhythm, since it reminds him of the time when he was being jogged inside your uterus.
- Bouncing him in your arms or in the cot.
- Putting him in a sling.
- Any form of music as long as it is not too loud but is rhythmic – specially recorded sleeping tapes are available.
- A noisy toy which your baby can shake or rattle.
- A steady household noise such as the washing machine.
- Your own singing voice, especially if you sing a lullaby.

UNDERSTANDING THE CAUSE

You have to learn to read your baby's signals and gain insight into his needs and desires. Once you recognise your baby's cry you have to respond to it, otherwise he's bound to scream even louder. Always be sensitive to your baby's needs. Look, listen, and try to interpret what he is trying to say to you through his behaviour. As you get to know your baby, you will learn to understand what he really wants. If you know, for example, that he's hungry, don't delay his feed by deciding to give him a bath first, simply as a matter of sticking to your routine. Occasionally, you have to ignore routines in order to respond to your baby's crying.

There are all sorts of signs of small discomforts to which you must be alert. When your baby has a cold, for instance, his nose may become blocked, making it impossible for him to breathe and feed at the same time, so he'll become angry and frustrated and almost certainly cry.

Undressing
Many young babies cry when they are having a bath, because they hate having their skin exposed to the air.

CAUSE OF CRYING	WHAT TO DO
Hunger *A hungry cry is nearly always the first cry that a parent recognises and it is the most common reason that young babies cry. They rarely cry after feeding. Babies love the sensation of a full stomach, more than being held or sucking.*	*Feed on demand. If you have a baby who wants to suck all the time you don't need to feed; just give him a drink of boiled water. Use a dummy, holding it in his mouth if necessary, so that he can suck on it.*
Tiredness *Until they're used to their new world, babies cry when they are tired and it takes an observant parent to realize this and put a baby down.*	*Lay your baby down where he is quiet and warm. Wrapping or swaddling him before you put him down to sleep helps, too.*
Lack of contact *Some babies will stop crying as soon as you pick them up, because they want a cuddle. Babies brought up in cultures where they are constantly in a sling or swaddled rarely cry.*	*Always pick up your baby as soon as he cries. Carry him around in a shawl or a sling. Lay your baby tummy down across your lap and gently massage his back.*
Startling *A jerky movement, a sudden noise, or a bright light can upset your baby. If physical games are too rough, he'll cry.*	*Hold your baby close, rock him gently, and sing to him. Avoid sudden jerky movements, noises, and bright lights.*
Undressing *Most babies dislike being undressed as it puts their bodies through movements which are neither familiar nor comforting and they hate the feel of air on their skin. Being jerked suddenly makes them fearful.*	*Undress your baby as little as possible in the first few weeks, and keep him wrapped or covered with a towel as you remove layers of clothing. Keep up a running commentary of reassuring talk as you undress him.*
Temperature *Babies tend to cry if they become too hot or too cold. They may cry if a wet or soiled nappy gets cold or if they are suffering from nappy rash.*	*Keep your baby's room between 20–22°C (68–72°F) with the number of blankets suggested on p.123. Remove blankets and clothing if your baby is too hot; add another layer of clothing and a blanket if he's too cold. Change his nappy if necessary.*
Pain *An ear infection, colic, or some other source of pain may cause your baby to cry. If his ear hurts, he may hit it with his fist; if it's colic his legs may be drawn up to his abdomen.*	*Hold your baby close, cuddle him, and talk soothingly. If you can find the source of pain, such as a nappy pin, remove it immediately. If your baby seems ill seek medical advice.*

COLIC

Crying caused by colic can be distinguished from other forms because it is more of a high-pitched scream than a cry, and usually you'll find that your baby's legs are drawn up to his abdomen and that his face becomes very red.

Colic-related crying usually starts in the early evening between 5 and 6 o'clock, and is not usually pacified by the usual remedies. Colic generally stops by the age of three or four months without your doing anything at all, is rarely serious, and needs no treatment. However, parents find it distressing. It is not known why it happens but it usually starts in the first three weeks of a baby's life. It is well recognised that colicky babies are quite healthy and continue to thrive.

All sorts of causes have been put forward, such as constipation, diarrhoea, overfeeding, underfeeding, wind in the bowel, being picked up too much or too little, indigestion, and tension.

It has always struck me that tension is the most likely cause. You're preoccupied in the evening with bathtime and bedtime for the baby and getting your evening meal. It is likely that your baby picks up on the tension, and quite normal that he should respond with a crying spell.

As your baby is likely to cry every night for 12 weeks I'm against using any kind of medicine to forestall the crying. Of course you should try to soothe your baby but don't expect him to respond readily. Try to take comfort from the fact that these spells come only at night and last for only three months, so there is light at the end of the tunnel.

OLDER BABY

CRYING AND COMFORTING

As your baby grows older and her world becomes more complex, the causes of crying change. In an older baby the cause is nearly always some form of emotional disturbance: mother leaving and the deprivation of her love, fear, anxiety, or separation.

BOREDOM

The older she gets the longer your baby will spend being awake, and there is therefore greater scope for her getting bored. Many children cry out of sheer boredom, especially if left alone with no distractions, nothing to look at, and no-one to play with. Your child of a year old enjoys your company more than anything else, and is constantly interested in what you are doing.

What to do Always leave toys in the cot, especially old colour magazines or cloth books. Mobiles, baby gyms, or strings of interesting objects above the cot will help to amuse and distract your baby. Though it may be tiresome for you, your baby will cry a great deal less from boredom if you keep her with you as much as you can.

FEAR OF SEPARATION

When your baby is about six to eight months, separation from a parent becomes the greatest source of distress to her and nearly always precipitates crying. Try to get your baby accustomed to separation over several months by leaving her for longer and longer periods, say twenty minutes, then an hour, then three hours. If you go out to work, you will find your baby's fear upsetting, but this phase will pass as she gets used to seeing you go and always returning. While it lasts, be very careful about the way you take leave of your baby, and ensure that she's familiar with her surroundings and the people she's with. If she finds separation very unpleasant the first time, she's likely to respond with crying the second time. It's up to you to make separation as easy as possible.

What to do Be sympathetic and supportive and never make fun of your child's fears. She will respond better to reassuring actions than words, so if you make a promise to her that you are coming back, always keep it. If you say that you're only going for five minutes, just leave the room, get on with some small job and come back in exactly that time.

INSECURITY AND ANXIETY

As your baby gets older she becomes increasingly aware of strangers. Those situations which cause her most anxiety are being in a strange place with you, or being with strangers. As long as you're there she

Dealing with anxiety
Unfamiliar people and places make your baby anxious so reassure him with lots of cuddles.

can cope but being left in a strange place with strange people completely unnerves her. Never do it. Any source of anxiety makes your child clingy. She will turn to you for comfort. She may even go off her food. If you become aware that your child is anxious you should respond to her immediately.

As your child searches for comfort she may become attached to an object such as a blanket, or turn to thumb-sucking as consolation when you're not around. Nearly all children require some form of comfort that they control. Very often comfort objects are ones that they suck or stroke in moments of anxiety or stress, to simulate the effect of being stroked or being comforted.

What to do The best thing is extra reassurance, physical contact, cuddles, love, and soothing talk. Your child will grow out of this period of anxiety, but it helps never to force her to go to a stranger if she doesn't really want to. Explain to strangers that she's shy, and needs some time to get used to them. Your presence will help her to cope with new situations and experiences, even though she may feel fearful and uncomfortable at first. Whatever you do, always let your baby have the comforter of her choice, and always give her lots of cuddles to reassure her.

This doesn't mean to say you can't gently encourage your child to be curious and adventurous. To grow up with a feeling of self-confidence, your child requires your approval, love, and praise, so give it every time she shows some independence.

FRUSTRATION

As your baby grows up her desire to do things far outstrips her ability to do them, and so she becomes frustrated. This often results in crying. As she starts to crawl, then cruises along the furniture, then walks, you will almost certainly have to restrain her, which will result in added frustration, and crying every time you do it. By the time she gets to 18 months your baby's spirit of adventure is in excess of her balance, mobility, and co-ordination. She is likely to attempt tasks that are beyond her and she'll become very frustrated as a result. Even though you know she is frustrated you are going to have to stop her doing things simply to protect her.

What to do Make your home as childproof as possible (see pp.306–11): remove precious objects from within her reach, and fit safety plugs and guards around the house to make sure she can't injure herself. Distraction is a good ploy for frustration, so always have a favourite toy to hand or be ready with a game.

Relaxed bedtimes
Spend time with your child just before bedtime in some quiet activity so she goes to bed calm and relaxed.

BEDTIME CRYING

Babies tend to cry at bedtime because they're tired, irritable, and don't wish to be separated from you. You can reassure them by establishing happy bedtime routines (see p.125).

Make the hour before bedtime a really happy one. Sit your child on your lap, read a story or book, or play a quiet game, or sing a song to her.

• *A gentle, playful bathtime will make your baby slightly sleepy, as will a warm drink before being put to bed*

• *Your baby will almost certainly have a favourite game, song, or story and for a baby repetition is happiness, so do as she asks; it makes her feel secure*

TODDLER

INJURIES

Toddlers tend to cry at even the most minor injury such as a small scratch, an abrasion, or a tiny bruise.

In our house, I always had "the magic cream" (a mild antiseptic cream) on hand, and my children responded almost immediately to attention, reassurance, and a thin smear of the magic cream. Sometimes I had to sit down with them, hold them close, give them a big cuddle, and make very sympathetic sounds to show them that I knew how much it was hurting or how frightened they were – many young children are terrified by the sight of blood. Comfort and the magic cream nearly always had a calming effect.

Whenever your child comes to you in distress crying over a small injury, be sympathetic. Say you know how much it's hurting and don't try to make him be brave. In a few moments he'll skip off your knee and return to his play after a kiss to make it better, a cuddle, and a favourite drink or snack.

If necessary, put some interesting idea into your child's mind to distract him from the injury, such as a special treat for tea, a special game with dad, a picnic, or an outing to a favourite place.

CRYING AND COMFORTING

As your baby's thinking becomes more sophisticated, he gains a wider appreciation of what's going on in the world around him, and his reasons for crying become more difficult to sort out. He's starting to understand what you say, not only in terms of facts but of your answers, and he's beginning to use his own reason and respond to reasoned argument. He's becoming very aware of himself and other people, and of the will of others versus his own. His fears are therefore much more related to his daytime activities and any upset arising from them. Emotionally, he's developing very rapidly too. He can feel guilt, shame, jealousy, and dislike, and be so upset that these emotions make him cry.

FEARS

The commonest fears in this age group are of the dark and of thunder. Fear of the dark is so common as to be almost universal. It has no explanation, and reasoning with your child will not help. It's cruel to make fun of his fear and you should never do that. Give your child an exciting night-light – perhaps one with a coloured bulb or one that plays a tune.

Fear of thunder and lightning is also very common, and the best way to deal with it is to distract your child while he can hear it. You can play loud music, turn on the television set, or take him into a quiet room and read him a story. You could also treat him by giving him the toy you had put aside for a rainy day.

DEALING WITH FEARS

One of the best ways to dispel fears is to talk about them, so get your child to be open and frank about what frightens him. Give him your full attention and ask questions, so that he knows that you are taking him seriously. Quite often fears are difficult to put into words, but hear your child out. Help him to explain by supplying a few examples, and confess that you have similar fears too. Never scold or ridicule your child about his fears. Do something simple and reassuring, like demonstrating to your child that it is fun in the swimming pool and the water is nothing to fear. Your child will trust you and his fear will gradually diminish. When he's old enough, try to explain how things work: for instance, that lightning is just like a giant spark.

If your child is afraid of going to a friend's house, talk him through it step by step: "First I'll drive you to Johnny's house, then you'll give Johnny his present and he'll ask you to play with him…" Nearly all children have some irrational fears, such as fear of monsters, ghosts, or dragons. Remember, to your child a fear is serious, so you shouldn't try to tell him that his fears are unreal.

FEAR OF SEPARATION

Even when your child is three years old he will still have fears about losing you. When he was younger, he worried about losing sight of you; now, he is fearful that you will not come back, that you will die while you are away from him, and that he will be deprived of you forever. Again, a very good way to reassure your child is to go step by step through what is going to happen when you leave him. The more details you can give, and the more you can confirm the details, the better. What you might say is, "When Daddy comes home from work, we are both going to get ready to go out to visit Aunt Sarah. I'll have a bath, Daddy will shave, and we'll change our clothes. Then we'll put you to bed and we'll have our usual song, story, and game. Then Mummy will lie on your bed and cuddle you while we talk about your day, and what you are going to do tomorrow. Mummy won't leave you until you are fast asleep, and the next thing you will know is that it is morning and Mummy will be there."

DETHRONEMENT

Your child is bound to feel pretty distressed at the thought of a new baby brother or sister and the "dethronement" that he thinks will follow. Take all the precautions you can to make him feel good about the baby. Refer to the baby as his new sister or brother, and let him feel your tummy as the baby grows and kicks. Show him where the baby is going to sleep, and teach him all kinds of helpful things he can do to look after her. If you are having the baby in hospital, make sure your child is at ease with the person who is going to look after him while you're there. When you come home, have someone else carry the baby; you should have your arms free to scoop your child up and give him a big cuddle. Don't turn to the new baby until he asks to see her. Make sure that you bring home a present from the baby for him. If you have to stay in hospital, let him visit you as often as you like, and when he does, make sure that the baby is not in your arms, but is lying in a cot at your side so you're free to hold your child.

OVER-TIREDNESS

A child of this age very often becomes over-excited and over-tired towards bedtime. He will try to put off his bedtime as long as possible, and simply become more distressed. Your child might become so fragile that any small discomfort or frustration will make him cry inconsolably.

If you are expecting your child to have a late evening, or a special treat such as a party or a school play, make sure he has a nap during the day so that his energy will last. If he does become over-excited and over-tired it is especially important that you remain calm and quiet. Talk to him gently, give him lots of cuddles, be infinitely patient, and take him gently to his bedroom. Sing him a song or read a story until he has become calm and quietened down.

TANTRUMS

Young children nearly always have tantrums out of frustration or because they are pitting their will against that of others.

Older children have tantrums because they can think of no other way of showing their determination. In the privacy of your own home the best way to deal with a tantrum is simply to ignore it and leave the room.

It's slightly more difficult, however, in public, and you can do several things. Don't fuss, shout, or get flustered. Take your child calmly into a quiet place and attempt to calm her down. If you are in a shop take her out into the street, or into your car, or out of the restaurant into the toilet.

Fearful toddler
Always take your child's fears seriously and ask her to explain them if she can.

CRYING AND COMFORTING

FEARS

Three years is a highly anxious age, but by four years your child's fears are more clearly defined.

She will be easily frightened by sounds, for example, especially loud sounds outside, such as a fire engine. She may fear people of a different culture or appearance from herself, old people, "bogey men", the dark, animals, and your leaving her – especially at night. Children of this age may enjoy being mildly frightened by an adult in play, as long as it's clearly pretend.

By five years your child will probably have more concrete, down-to-earth fears, like bodily harm, falling, dogs, sounds, thunder, lightning, rain, storms (especially at night) and that her mother will not return home or be at home when she gets there.

Just as dislike of certain foods is suggested by chance remarks made by adults, fear of animals, motor cars, and thunder are suggested in a similar way. Gruesome tales and stories about ghosts, devils, and such like may terrify a small child and lead to serious sleep disturbance. For this reason, you should choose bedtime stories carefully, don't let your child watch scary television programmes just before bedtime, and never deliberately frighten her with stories of "bogey men" to make her behave.

The four-year-old cries a great deal and may whinge if her wants are not met and there's nothing interesting to play with. By the age of five, a child cries much less, though she may cry if she's angry, tired, or can't have her own way. Crying is now of shorter duration, and your child may be able to control it and hold her tears back. She is rarely moody and may be as right as rain as soon as the crying is over. She may whine occasionally, though a lot less than she did at four years. This phase may pass, however, and give way to temper tantrums with loud angry crying and banging about. There may be a return of moodiness, whining, and expressions of resentment, but you can often get your child to laugh when she's crying by joking with her. Your child may become astonishingly brave about real injuries yet still cry at small hurts.

BAD DREAMS AND NIGHTMARES

Between the ages of three and five years children quite often have bad dreams. Your child may walk or talk in her sleep, or have night terrors. This is normal because while her understanding of the world is growing, she cannot entirely make sense of it, and so she goes to sleep with unresolved questions. She's also getting more in touch with her feelings and she knows what it is to be afraid or feel something is not quite right. These feelings come out at night.

Often a child cannot explain her dreams and has difficulty in going back to sleep. Animals, especially wolves and bears, may chase your child during a nightmare, or she may dream of strange, bad, or odd-looking people, fires, and deep water. Only if your child wakes up should you try to console her and take her in your arms. If she remains asleep, don't do anything to wake her; simply stay by her. If you find that she is sleepwalking periodically you must put a gate across the stairs to prevent falls.

Night terrors Sometimes you will find your child in bed, apparently awake, terrified, and possibly thrashing and screaming. She may be angry or desperately upset. This is a night terror rather than a nightmare, and it can be very alarming. You will feel quite anguished at your child's fear and pain, but all you can do is stay close and wait for the terror to pass. There is no point in trying to reassure your child specifically, because she is beyond reason. Don't leave her or scold her; that would simply make the terror worse.

PRESCHOOL NERVES

A child who goes to nursery school without a backward glance, says goodbye to her mother, and gets straight into play at the sandpit ·is rather unusual. Most children harbour fears of a strange place with strange people and separation from you. You have to give your child both the time and the opportunity to adjust to this quite frightening change in her life.

You can do much to allay your child's fears by familiarizing her with the journey to school, the entrance to the school, her class-room, some of the children who will be in her class, her teacher, where the games are, and what some of the routines are. Most teachers will welcome your taking your child along to the school several times before she starts so that she can feel comfortable in her new surroundings. Make the first visit as casual as possible. Stay for only a few minutes, so that your child does not get bored or frightened and don't make her do anything she doesn't want to.

Making separation easy The first morning is likely to be difficult for both of you. It may be that you have to stay with your child for the whole morning, but this shouldn't happen more than once. Do not forget that it is a great transition for her to make, so be patient. Many nursery schools will welcome your staying to give your child confidence. Eventually, when your child realizes that you are not going to leave, she will be happy to get on with her classroom routines as long as you sit somewhere quiet and discreet.

Maybe during the first morning, but certainly on the second, suggest that you are going out to buy a newspaper, but come back within five minutes, so that your child is reassured. Don't go if your child gets very distressed at the prospect of your leaving. Once she's happy, suggest that you leave again, this time for about half an hour, and come back in exactly the time you said you would. Over the next few days, leave for longer and longer periods according to how your child reacts. You'll find that in a short time you won't need to stay at all. A confident child may want to be self-reliant and suggest that you leave long before you think that she is capa-ble of being separated from you. Sometimes a teacher will advise you when it's time to go.

Starting nursery school
Once your child is engrossed in some activity she may hardly even notice when you leave.

Your child will become very dis-tressed indeed if she thinks that the people dearest in the world to her, her mother and father, no longer love each other, and that there's a danger that they may separate or leave her.

Children are extremely sensitive to atmospheres within the home so if you and your partner are going through a bad time, behave car-ingly and affectionately in front of your child and show that you have concern for each other. Witnessing a row is one of the most harmful experiences you can inflict on your child, so that thought should act as a deterrent.

On the other hand, I don't believe in a united front between parents on every question. Your child should understand that it's all right for mum and dad to have different opinions, as long as they are expressed without acrimony.

Children have to get used to con-flict because they're going to meet it very quickly when they leave home. The best place for them to become familiar with it is in the security of their own home.

Most children will blame them-selves for any conflict between their parents and will go to great lengths to make you friends again. Reassure your child that she is not to blame for any anger you feel towards your partner, and that you love her regardless.

139

You'll need basic changing and feeding equipment, and a toy for your baby.

- *Changing bag or mat*

- *Fabric or disposable nappies*

- *Baby wipes*

- *Nappy cream*

- *A sealable container or plastic bags for dirty nappies*

- *A bottle containing a whole feed if you're bottlefeeding*

- *A change of breast pads if you're breastfeeding*

- *Hat*

- *Cardigan*

- *A couple of favourite toys*

TRAVEL AND OUTINGS

Time spent in planning your outing or travel schedule is never wasted. The younger your baby, the more you will have to plan. In the first few months, your baby's feeding schedule may not necessarily be very predictable, so you will need at least one spare bottle if you're not breastfeeding and, of course, whatever changing equipment you normally use. Lightweight baby-changing bags containing a portable changing mat are widely available. Plan your route so that you know where you can stop, where you can change your baby, and where you can feed him without embarrassment or inconvenience. If you're planning to shop, it is even worth ringing up stores to find out if they have a mother-and-baby changing room, and avoiding those that don't.

With a very young baby it's simply not worth undertaking a very busy outing where you will have to walk a great deal, carry heavy loads, or make lots of changes of transport. Be easy on yourself. Try and take a friend or your partner with you if you can, so there is always an extra pair of hands and someone to help you should you get into a scrape. Your baby can go with you anywhere as long as you're well enough prepared and have something in which to carry him – a sling, pram, or car seat.

USING A PUSHCHAIR

If you do not want to carry your baby in a sling, a pushchair is ideal for a small baby, who will fit comfortably and snugly into its shape. Babies are interested in their surroundings from an early age, so as soon as your baby can sit up, angle the pushchair so that he can see what is going on around him.

You must become adept at collapsing and opening the pushchair within a few seconds without any problems, so practise it at home before your first outing. If you can't fold up the pushchair efficiently, you will find people jostling to get in front of you when you are in a queue, which will only add to your frustration. At the very least, you should be able to open it with only one hand, kick it shut with your feet, and know how to operate the brakes – and don't forget you will have to do all these things while holding your baby. Here are a few safety tips:

- When you open your pushchair, always make sure that it is in the fully extended position with the brakes fully locked.

- Never put your baby in the pushchair without a safety harness.

- Never, ever, leave your baby in a pushchair unattended.

- Should your baby fall asleep in the pushchair, adjust it to the lie-back position so that he can sleep comfortably.

- Don't put shopping on the handles of the pushchair; it can unbalance the pushchair and your baby may be injured.

- When you stop, always put the brakes on because you could inadvertently take your hands off the pushchair and it could run away.

- Check your pushchair regularly to make sure the brakes and catches work well and that the wheels are solid.

PUBLIC TRANSPORT

Using public transport can really be a trial, as neither buses nor trains are equipped or serviced for mothers and young children. Picture yourself with a pushchair, a heavy and wriggling baby, the baby bag, your handbag, a coat, and possibly a toddler in tow, and public transport is the last thing you want to face.

Of course, you can make things easier by never travelling in the rush hour or, with a young baby, carrying him around in a sling. For an older baby, a backpack makes you much more independent, and you can manage everything more easily with your hands free. Always prepare yourself well ahead of time. I simply would not leave home with my children without some distracting toys, a favourite book, and a favourite snack. All your belongings, including the pushchair, should be collected together prior to leaving and in good enough time so that you can check them over to make sure that you have not forgotten anything. The same goes for when you are getting off a bus or train; be ready to get off in plenty of time for your stop. Always ask for help from fellow passengers.

SPECIAL OUTINGS

Your baby is never too young for an outing; indeed, with a young baby you can go just about anywhere and, provided he can look about him, he will enjoy the change of scene even if he doesn't understand much of what's going on. When planning an outing for an older child, always try to consider what your child's personality can cope with best. If you have a quiet child who has a long concentration span, you can take him to a flower show or an antique market, and point out the things around him. If, on the other hand, he is very active, he will need more space to run around in and a trip to the zoo, a playground, or a fair is therefore more appropriate. Wherever you go, you should be prepared to make endless stops to look at anything that catches your child's attention. Always take enough drinks and snacks to keep your child happy for the full duration of the trip. Don't take on a trip of any kind if you or your child are feeling out of sorts; the day is bound to be a disaster, so don't feel guilty about cancelling the outing altogether.

WHAT TO TAKE: OLDER BABY

For an older baby, you'll need solid food, and feeding and changing equipment.

- *Changing mat*
- *Fabric or disposable nappies*
- *Baby wipes*
- *Nappy cream*
- *Plastic bags or sealable container for dirty nappies*
- *Baby food, dish, and spoon*
- *Bib for feeding*
- *Snack, such as fruit*
- *Diluted fruit juice*
- *Sun hat or woollen hat*
- *Cardigan or sweater*
  - *Comforter*
    - *Favourite book*
      - *Favourite toy*

Handling a pushchair
Make sure that you can kick it shut, open it up one-handed, and operate the brakes.

SHOPPING
WITH YOUR
YOUNG BABY

When travelling with your baby, always plan all your movements and stops in detail, so that you can use your time efficiently.

- *Try to fit in a shopping trip between feeds or, if you think that it is going to be a longer trip than the usual interval between meals, take a snack with you*

- *Always bring basic changing equipment in case your child needs a clean nappy. Many stores these days have special dedicated areas for mothers and babies*

- *If you are travelling by car adjust your baby's seat to a reclining position so she can sleep*

Harness

Reins

Anchor Straps

Harness and reins
Keep your child safe on busy streets with a harness and reins. The harness can also be used in a high chair with anchor straps.

SHOPPING TRIPS

Taking a baby shopping brings its own problems. Your baby can easily become bored, hungry, fretful, and difficult to manage, so it's worth planning ahead quite carefully to minimize stress. Taking a car will make a world of difference: you can feed and change your baby in it, you can stack your shopping in the boot and not have to carry it, and you won't have to worry about catching buses and trains. If you don't own a car yourself, it might be worth asking a friend who does to join your shopping expedition, or asking a relative if you can borrow their car. Try to shop fairly early in the day, because the streets and shops are less busy, and there are fewer distractions for your baby. Always try to give your baby a good meal before you leave; that way you may have two or three hours to complete your purchases without her getting hungry.

Bring whatever equipment you would bring on any other trip. Toys may seem something of a burden but they will more than pay their way, because you can attach them to the backpack, pushchair, or supermarket trolley for your child to play with without her being able to throw them on to the floor. Bring some kind of small snack, too, because shopping seems to make children either hungry or fretful, and a snack will deal with both.

CARRYING YOUR BABY

You need to have your hands free for shopping, and so how you carry your baby is worth some thought and attention. Once your baby is able to sit up with good head and back control, you can put her into your shopping trolley. Many supermarkets now have trolleys with integral baby seats and harnesses, but with the older, tip-up seats you need to strap your baby in with reins. A backpack is ideal for carrying your baby on shopping trips; her interest will always be engaged, she will feel very secure with such close physical contact, and she should be well behaved and cry very little. Best of all, your hands will be left free. Try to undertake a shopping trip accompanied by your partner and have him carry the baby on his back, leaving you free to make the purchases. Reins are a very good idea for an older child, because your child will feel a sense of freedom and independence, but she will never be able to get very far away from you; a wrist link that is securely attached to her reins will prevent you becoming separated from her.

KEEPING YOUR CHILD UNDER CONTROL

Because babies are always grasping and reaching for interesting objects, walk down the centre of the aisle so that your baby is not tempted to dislodge tins and packets. One way to control your child is to keep her interested, and you can do this keeping up a running commentary, with observations or questions that engage your child. Your young child will love being involved in shopping decisions, and she will feel very important and needed if you act on her preferences. With items where brand is not important to you ask your child to select products by pointing to the one she would like you to buy. As my children got older and could toddle around the shopping trolley, I used to ask them to put all their choices into the shopping trolley themselves, so that they were constantly engaged looking for their favourite things, feeling a great sense of pride in finally finding them, and a sense of achievement in filling up the trolley. At the checkout don't feel that you have to pay for everything; without your child's seeing, you can take out those things you don't want.

One of the ways I used to distract and entertain my children on a shopping trip was to ask them if they were thirsty or hungry immediately on entering the supermarket, and buy them a drink or a healthy snack. That way they could munch or sip their way around the supermarket and feel quite happy and occupied the whole time. If, however, you have a wayward child who keeps on getting into mischief, the only way to handle the situation is to keep your child on reins or a wrist strap to prevent her from wandering off and bothering other shoppers or getting lost.

LEARNING

You can use your shopping trips as opportunities to teach your child all sorts of things – about colours, for example: "This tin is red; that packet is blue; that jar has a yellow wrapper". Your child will recognise the corn-flake packet that she sees at breakfast every morning and will soon understand what the words mean, so that from quite an early age, say, 18 months, you can say to her, "Can you see the corn flakes? Now I wonder where the jam is?" Early reading can be encouraged by teaching your child to associate the contents of a packet or tin with things that she actually eats at home. For example, if she drinks cocoa regularly, you only have to take the tin of the brand she sees every day from the shelf and ask "What does this word say?" for her to respond with "cocoa", because she has learnt from experience that cocoa is what comes out of that tin. All my children began to read food packets before they read anything else.

Trips to the supermarket will also teach your child about the act of shopping itself, and the choosing and decision-making that is involved. You can introduce her to the value of money, and to a certain degree you can teach her about manners and sociability, because she will very quickly learn the justice of allowing other people to get to the shelves when she has a great interest in doing so herself.

SHOPPING WITH YOUR TODDLER

Once your child can walk, losing her in a crowd can be a worry, so take precautions against this.

• *Use reins or a wrist strap in busy places so she can't wander*

• *Dress your toddler in something brightly coloured so that you can spot her from a distance*

• *Have some sort of family code for your children to come back to you. I used to carry a small whistle around my neck*

• *All shopping trips can be lessons even if you only teach your child about healthy eating (fresh vegetables are better than tinned)*

• *From as early an age as possible make your child learn her name, address, and telephone number, so she can repeat it if she gets lost*

• *Teach her never to walk off with any stranger*

• *Make sure your child recognises her surroundings when she's near to home by pointing out landmarks on every journey: "There's the pillarbox on the corner, and there's the blue gate, and our house is the next one along."*

Wrist straps
An adjustable strap links you and your child together at the wrists to prevent her wandering.

CAR JOURNEYS

Children can be very active on car journeys. They're learning and taking great pride in newly acquired physical skills, like jumping, skipping, hopping, climbing, and running, and it's very difficult for them to be confined in a small space. All this is intensified in hot weather because your child will become tired, touchy, and tearful more easily than when the temperature is equable. Never leave a child alone in a car in hot weather, because the temperature inside the car can rise much higher than the temperature outside, causing him to become quickly overheated and even dehydrated. You should always screen your child from bright sunlight by putting a purpose-made blind over the window through which the sun is shining. You might also think about attaching a canopy to your baby's seat, which serves the same purpose.

In the cramped circumstances of a long journey your child can't be expected to behave well, and it's your job to make sure that he's cool, fed, given a sufficient number of drinks, has enough to occupy and distract him, is taken to the lavatory without a fuss, and that accidents are accepted philosophically.

SAFETY

Whatever else, your baby must be transported safely in a car. A young baby should go in a rear-facing car seat, which can be used in the front or the back of the car, or in a carrycot with proper restraints in the back seat. If you must travel with your baby held on your knee, always sit in the back. Never sit in the front with an unrestrained baby, because if the car stops suddenly your baby will be flung out of your arms and will certainly be injured. An older baby should sit in a front-facing car seat. After any accident, you should replace your seat belts, your child's car seat, and the anchorage kit, as they will have been badly strained and may be damaged. For the same reason, you should never buy second-hand car seats, harnesses, or anchorage kits.

Misbehaviour like shouting or kicking should not be tolerated; it is extremely distracting for you while you are driving and could even be dangerous. If your child does behave badly, pull straight over to the side of the road, stop the car, and sort out the difficulty. Tell your child that you are going no further until he starts to behave himself properly.

LONGER JOURNEYS

Most children will become restless if they have to travel for longer than an hour and a half. Your child has no idea of time, so he'll be constantly asking you when you are going to arrive, or whether you are nearly there. Restlessness can be alleviated by stopping the car every hour for about five minutes and allowing your child to run around, explore, and generally get rid of excess energy. Warn him in advance about the stops so that he can get himself ready by putting on a coat and hat if it's cold outside.

BABY ON BOARD

Keep the following important items of equipment in the car more or less permanently ready for trips with your baby:

• *A car seat correctly fitted and with safety harness (see p.312)*

• *A blind to block out bright sun*

• *A bag with basic changing and feeding equipment; restock it often*

• *Baby travelling toys*

• *A rug*

• *A couple of favourite tapes*

• *Tissues*

JOURNEY CHECKLIST

As with any kind of outing with your child, the essential thing is to plan and prepare well in advance. The following tips will all help to make things go more smoothly for you:

• *Try to start travelling early in the morning, or at night when the roads are empty*

• *Carry a bag of spare clothes for each of each child in the car, be philosophical about accidents, and change your child readily into dry clothes*

• *For safety, tape cutlery to the inside of food containers*

• *Always take some soft clothing like an anorak or sweater that your child can use as a pillow*

• *Always have a supply of bags into which cartons, bottles, and wrappers can be placed after use*

• *Take a box of baby wipes to clean dirty hands and faces*

Feeding A car journey is when breastfeeding comes into its own because you have no preparations to make whatsoever. You cannot feed when the car is in motion, however, because your baby would be very unsafe. If, however, you are bottlefeeding, use disposable bottles and feeds, or make up a batch of feeds, cool them in the refrigerator, and then carry them in some form of cool-bag. Alternatively, mix the formula when you need it, in a sterilized bottle with some boiled water from a thermos flask. Never try to keep made-up feeds warm because you are only letting germs multiply. Once your baby is weaned you'll have to carry food, a feeding dish, a plastic spoon, a bib, a cup with a spout, a supply of drinks, and something your baby can nibble on, such as pieces of dry toast or rusks. You can feed your baby directly from the jar but remember that whatever he does not finish out of a feeding jar must be thrown away afterwards, because it is contaminated with saliva, and germs will grow in it very quickly.

Changing Even if you normally use fabric nappies, forget the expense and take disposable nappies with you on a journey: they're just so convenient, quick, and easy for both you and the baby. You can always change your baby on the back seat of the car or in the boot if he lies on a rug or a towel. There is no need to do any more than top and tail your baby while travelling, but be meticulous about cleaning the nappy area, and always have a supply of nappy cream to prevent nappy rash. Wipes are an essential, as is a sealable container for dirty nappies.

The older child Your child will get bored and hungry, so always have some nutritious snacks like raisins, sugarless cornflakes, or pieces of cheese in plastic bags, and take more drinks than you ever think you'll need – your child's capacity for liquid is greatly increased when he's travelling. Seedless grapes make a very useful snack, because they quench your child's thirst as well as satisfying his hunger. You'll need toys to distract your child while travelling (books may be a bad idea, though, if he suffers from motion sickness), and these can be arranged in different ways for safety and convenience. Buy or make a special cover for the front headrest of your car with pockets in the back which can carry drinks, snacks, and toys, or tie toys to coat-hooks or handles so that they don't get lost under seats. Magnetized games are particularly useful in cars because the bits cannot get lost, and you can stick Velcro on certain toys so that they will adhere to the car seat and stay in one place while your child is playing with them. I always found it best if I allowed my child to choose some of the toys that he wanted to take, and to be responsible for putting them into his own case or bag. Cassettes with music or children's stories may give you at least half an hour of peace, so always have one at the ready. "I spy" games are always a favourite, particularly if you join in, and will keep your children occupied for quite a long time if you make the object interesting. Keep a special treat tucked away in the glove compartment with which to relieve tension or tears.

MOTION SICKNESS

If you have suffered motion sickness, or there's any history of migraine, eczema, or allergies in the family, then your child is quite likely to suffer from motion sickness too. There are some things that you can do to help minimize motion sickness.

- *Don't give your child a rich or greasy meal before a journey*

- *You can give your child a motion-sickness drug, available from doctors; always give it at least half an hour before you leave*

- *Stay calm. If you're anxious your children will become anxious too. Car sickness is brought on by anxiety and excitement and is much more likely to happen on the outward journey, so be patient when you leave home*

- *Snacks that can be sucked are a good idea, because they do not create a mess, so take along a supply of glucose sweets*

- *Keeping your child occupied or distracted will help prevent car sickness, but don't let him read, as this may bring it on*

- *If you notice your child becoming pale or quiet ask him if he wants to stop. Get him to close his eyes until you reach a safe place to stop, then get him out of the car, and be very sympathetic if he actually is sick. Give him a short time to recover before you continue with your journey*

- *A supply of baby wipes will help you clean up your child (and the car if necessary), should he be sick*

- *Give your child a drink after he's been sick to get rid of the taste of vomit from his mouth*

145

PLANNING A HOLIDAY

Never think your baby is too young to travel. Children nearly always surprise us, and rise to the occasion in ways we never think possible. Travelling with young babies is a hobby in my family; I am told that when I was only six weeks old, my mother and father took me camping, living under canvas for two weeks by the sea! When my third son was only ten weeks old we took him to Italy, and while we were finding our lost luggage in Rome, he was by far the best behaved of all of us. He even philosophically accepted my efforts to find the right formula for him, which took three days.

BEFORE YOU GO

A golden rule if you are going abroad on holiday is to make sure that your hotel has facilities for children, and really likes children. Things to look for in a hotel include such child facilities as a crèche, a place where you can take your child for early supper, a children's menu, high chairs and cots, a playroom, and an outdoor play area with trained attendants. It is worth going to some trouble to ensure these things are available because if your children are not happy, you will not enjoy the holiday yourself. If you are going to the seaside make sure that the beaches are safe.

Vaccination Well ahead of time – six months at least – you must take advice on what vaccinations or immunizations are needed, because regulations are constantly changing all over the world. The reason for starting early is that some vaccinations need quite a long lead time, and for others, as with hepatitis, you may have to wait four to six weeks between injections, or you may not be able to follow one vaccination immediately with another. You can get information from your doctor, or from major outlets of your travel agent. Some travel agents have doctors on the premises who can give you the vaccinations and vaccination certificates, plus any medication you might need, such as water sterilizing tablets.

Food Another golden rule for children is to introduce them to any exotic food at home so that you can determine their likes and dislikes well in advance. If your children like experimenting with food, there is no reason at all why you should not let them eat the local food, as long as it is well cooked and clean.

AIR TRAVEL

Most airlines make special facilities available to children as long as they're given warning. Try to book a flight that won't be crowded, and if you have a baby, ask for bulk-head seats, which have special folding tables for a Moses basket or cradle. If these are not available, ask for any seat that might have more leg room. Travel cots may be available in-flight. Ask the airline staff if they will heat up baby bottles for you. On some flights children's meals might be available, if not, you'll need to take your own. Most travel agents

Use the following checklist to make sure you've got everything you need for your child.

- *Passport and inoculation documents*
- *Your baby bag*
- *Travel cot*
- *Pushchair or sling*
- *A bouncing chair if used*
- *Changing equipment or potty*
- *Feeding equipment*
- *A vacuum flask for cool drinks*
- *Toys and games*
- *Comforters*
- *Sun hat*
- *Non-crease, drip-dry clothes*
- *Plenty of clothes to protect your child from heatstroke or sunburn*

Sun protection
Dress your child in a sun hat and T-shirt and apply sunscreen regularly when she's outside playing in the sun.

will make all these enquiries on your behalf. Given that children can be unpredictable it is essential that you make very careful plans, and if possible do not travel alone. Here are some things to think about before you travel:

- Aim to reach the airport early enough to avoid long check-in queues, and give yourself plenty of time to get there.

- Put all travel documents in a special bag, inside a loose, light-weight shoulder bag. If you can, fit in your baby bag too, with spare nappies, spare clothing, and some snacks.

- Make sure that everything you take on board has an indestructible label, including your baby bag.

- Take a few of your baby's favourite toys with you or see whether any of the games suggested for use in the car (see p.145) would work on a plane to entertain your child.

- Carry your baby in a sling so that your hands are free.

- Change your baby's nappy just before getting on the plane.

- Take a folded pushchair on the plane with you; the crew will take it from you as you enter, and return it as you leave.

- Babies and children feel some pain during take-off and landing, so keep aside a little treat or your baby's comforter so she can suck on it to equalize the pressure in her ears.

SAFE SUNBATHING

Children can get heatstroke (see p.340) in a very short time and this is a dangerous condition. Most often it occurs when the nape of the neck is exposed to hot sun, which interferes with the temperature-regulating centre in the brain.

If your baby is under six months, never expose her skin to direct, strong sunlight for any length of time. The guidelines (below right) are for children over six months. Though the times in the sun seem short, please adhere to them and make your children wear T-shirts and sun hats the rest of the time. They should wear a sunscreen (see right) all the time that they are outdoors – even if they are swimming or if the weather is cloudy, as they could still burn.

If there have been no untoward effects after the first six days, you can extend the exposure up to several hours provided your child is perfectly happy and her skin does not become inflamed

You can prevent sunburn by plastering your child with sunscreen of a SP factor of 15 or above on all parts of the exposed skin, topping it up as necessary.

A baby has to be kept as cool as possible, and this means a minimum of light cotton clothing, but something that covers almost all of her body, unless she is kept constantly under a sunshade and never exposed to direct sunlight. If you can, always ensure the pram is placed where there is a light breeze to cool your baby's skin. Children sweat a lot more than adults do in a hot climate, so always have water with you and give your child as much as she wants.

SUNSCREENS

There are many sunscreens available. Use one that protects against both UVA and UVB rays, with a sun protection (SP) factor of at least 15.

For a baby, you should use the strongest sunscreen that you can find – SP factors go up to 30.

What the SP factor means is that you can stay in the sunshine that number of times longer without getting burned than you could have without the cream; if your child would normally burn after 10 minutes, then with a sunscreen of SP factor 10 she should be able to stay in the sun for 100 minutes without getting burned.

Many sunscreens say that they are waterproof, but if your child is running in and out of the sea or swimming pool, reapply sunscreen every half an hour or so.

Under other conditions reapply sunscreen to your child's skin every two hours or so.

EXPOSURE TIMES

Allow your child to be exposed to hot sun for a very short time at first, and increase the time gradually.

Day 1	5 minutes
Day 2	10 minutes
Day 3	15–20 minutes
Day 4	20–30 minutes
Day 5	45 minutes
Day 6	60 minutes

CHAPTER THREE

PLAY AND DEVELOPMENT

When your baby is born he becomes immersed in a confusing world of sights and sounds, none of which makes any sense to him. The process of identifying and memorizing the things around him begins immediately. As a parent, you can help him to make sense of his surroundings.

The starting point in your baby's social development is your physical presence. As soon as your baby is born he will become familiar with your smell and voice, and what you look like, and he will come to associate you with comfort and love. You can encourage his instinctive desire to communicate with talking, touching, eye contact, and play.

During the first year of life your baby's brain doubles in weight, not because he acquires any more brain cells, but because more and more connections are being made between existing brain cells. "Learning to think" is a complex process of building up associations that results from observing and interacting with the world.

Your child will not only mature socially and mentally, he will also become skilled physically. He will learn to sit, then crawl, and later to walk and run, and he will develop fine manipulative skills. All of these things will open up new areas of experience for him.

ALL ABOUT DEVELOPMENT

Gender is an important factor affecting development. Boys and girls have different strengths and will develop differently, be it physically, intellectually or socially. In general, girls:

• *Do better than boys at language-based skills like talking, reading, and writing*

• *Tend to be more sociable than boys and are more interested in people than things*

• *Usually walk earlier than boys*

• *Grow faster and are more predictable and regular in their growth patterns than boys*

• *Are better than boys at jumping, hopping, and balance in the preschool years*

• *Are easier to get on with than boys*

• *Cope better with stress than boys*

Jumping
Contrary to expectations, young girls are better than boys at hopping and jumping.

Development is continuous, although at times your child's progress may seem very slow. The speed and ease of acquiring skills, however, is entirely individual so don't worry if your child is slower to develop in some areas than other children of the same age.

Although you can influence the pace of your child's development by giving her the right stimulation at the right time, the stages of development occur in a strictly unchangeable sequence.

PHYSICAL DEVELOPMENT

There are a few general principles which apply to physical development in all babies. The stages or "milestones" always follow the same order, as each one depends on the previous stages. To give an obvious example, your child cannot walk until she can stand.

Often a previously learned skill may appear to be forgotten while your baby is concentrating on learning a new one, but will reappear when the new one is successfully learnt. Sometimes a generalized activity makes way for a specific one: at six months your baby may make rather random leg movements which resemble walking, but they are quite different from the ones she will make when she actually starts to walk at about one year.

One important physical milestone will be when your baby's teeth start to come through. Although this might not seem like a developmental step, teeth are essential to your baby's learning to chew solid food and to speak properly.

LOCOMOTION

It may come as something of a surprise that all locomotion – that is, walking and running – begins with the acquisition of head control. Your child cannot sit up, stand up, or crawl without being able to control the position of her head. Development of any kind proceeds from head to toe.

At first your baby's movements seem random, jerky, and quite unspecific; a newborn infant may move her arms, legs, head, hands, and feet when all she wants to do is smile. Gradually over the next three years her movements are refined, becoming increasingly specific to match the task in hand.

Crawling, though clever, is an inefficient and clumsy way to get around, but your child has to learn balance and co-ordination, and acquire self-confidence, before launching herself into space.

Manipulation The primitive grasp reflex in newborns (see p.20) must fade before your baby can grasp an object purposefully. At first she uses her mouth as the main organ for touch; the fingertips take over only as she learns how to use her hands. She will

150

refine her ability to grasp things, at first grasping them in her palm and eventually learning to use her finger and thumb. She will learn how to release as well as grasp an object.

Hearing and vision Your child's hearing is essential to her development of speech, and there are various clues you can look for very early on which indicate normal hearing: does she turn towards the direction of a sound, or respond to your voice by turning or smiling, for instance?

Your baby's vision improves rapidly during the first few weeks of her life and although she will not be able to see things at a distance, she'll be able to focus on your face at birth, provided it is only 20–25 centimetres (8–10 inches) from hers.

INTELLECTUAL DEVELOPMENT

Your baby's brain doubles in weight in the first year due not to the growth in the number of brain cells but to the connections between them. These connections only begin to form when your baby has to *think* about something. Contact with new sights, sounds, smells, tastes, and touches make your baby think, and that's why stimulation is essential from birth.

In order for your baby to understand what is going on around her, she must use her senses, her intellect, and her body to form mental connections so that she understands cause and effect. In order to pick up a favourite toy, for example, she must be able to see it, remember that she likes it, reach for it, and then pick it up.

Your baby's mental skills will advance with stimulation and teaching, so your involvement is crucial all the time, particularly when the brain goes through growth spurts in the first and third years. You are your child's first and most important teacher.

SOCIABILITY

You have a responsibility to give your child the will and ability to form loving, open relationships with others as she grows up. Babies are born into the world able to both give and receive love from the outset, so we must both answer their demands for affection and respond to their need for it.

Babies become social by imitating us and will respond to a human voice from birth, so you should talk to your baby from the day that she's born. Your child's personality and social skills can affect her achievement of developmental milestones. An independent and determined child will try new movements earlier than a more timid child, and a sociable child will seek social contact and communication with others and develop speech earlier than other children.

Your child's personality has three main components: sociability (the extent to which she seeks out and enjoys contact with others), activity (her prowess at, and enjoyment of, movement and energy), and emotion (her tendency to mood swings). If any of these traits is pronounced in your child you should try to be accommodating, at the same time encouraging the development of the other two qualities.

DEVELOPMENT IN BOYS

The pace of development is affected by many things and gender is one of them; boys and girls develop according to different "timetables". In general, boys:

- *Begin to talk at a later stage than girls and are more prone to language disorders*

- *Tend to be less sociable than girls and more interested in objects than in people*

- *Usually walk later than girls*

- *Are more likely than girls to grow in sudden spurts*

- *Refine jumping, running, and throwing after the preschool years*

- *Are more aggressive, competitive, and rebellious than girls*

- *Are more vulnerable to stress than girls and are more likely to have behavioural problems*

Active play
Building toys encourage the development of your child's manipulative abilities.

CHOOSING TOYS

Your child will grow and learn very rapidly in the first three years, so your choice of toys should reflect his changing needs.

• *Simple toys are more versatile so they have a longer life and are better for imaginative play*

• *A baby will need toys that stimulate all five senses. Introduce your baby to different colours, textures, shapes, and noises*

• *Older babies enjoy games that involve building, particularly "put-in, take-out" toys, so bricks of different sizes are ideal*

• *As your child's manipulative skills develop, he will be able to manage interlocking blocks and more advanced shape-sorters*

• *Preschool children enjoy drawing, painting, and imaginative play, and simple games like snap or picture dominoes, which improve concentration*

Painting
Give your child painting and drawing materials to allow him to develop his creativity.

PROMOTING DEVELOPMENT

The first six weeks of life are a critical learning period for your baby in which you should be actively engaged. Your role as teacher starts at your baby's birth and continues for many years; it's your job to make his world an interesting and exciting place in which he can grow and learn.

I firmly believe that the most important teacher in a baby's life is the person who most consistently looks after his health and well-being – in other words, you. From a very early age, your baby will recognise you, first by smell and sound, and enjoy a unique bond with you which means that you are best equipped to teach him about his world, for even as adults we learn best from people with whom we feel comfortable or have rapport. Your partner likewise has an important role to play. He should form a close and loving relationship with your baby as early as possible so that he becomes equally involved in teaching. Look for every opportunity to share in your baby's progress; much of his early development will be dependent on a secure and caring environment so make sure you give him lots of attention.

PROVIDING THE RIGHT ENVIRONMENT

Your baby demands and deserves a rich, stimulating environment in order to experience fully as many sensations as possible while he is still dependent on his senses for learning. To ensure this, surround your baby in the first six months with a wide variety of sounds, smells, sights, and textures. In the early months your baby cannot interact with his surroundings the way he will when he learns to move and speak. His intellectual and emotional development, therefore, will only be improved through the different experiences you introduce to him.

When your child begins to play and walk, pay attention to the way he uses his toys. Make his playthings appealing by arranging them imaginatively and, rather than buying your child new toys all the time, encourage him to interact with existing toys in different ways – for example, by showing him how to use a cardboard box as a car or a boat. Children don't always need shop-bought toys to encourage them to play. Often your child will get stimulation from improvised toys: a tent made out of sheets, for instance, a balancing board, a little hill made out of turf, or a tunnel made from blankets and chairs, all provide the backdrop for imaginative play.

In practical terms, the area in which your child plays should be safe, with potential hazards removed so that he cannot hurt himself, or break or damage anything. Sandpits in the garden are ideal (but must be covered to prevent fouling by animals), or a corner of a room can be set aside specifically as a play area.

WORKING WITH YOUR CHILD

In order to allow your child to achieve his full potential, you should set aside time to work with him, matching your efforts to your child's stages of development. Responsible parents find the role of teacher comes effortlessly and naturally. Your child is always eager to learn new things, so make the experience fun and mutually rewarding. Take any opportunity that presents itself – intimate moments of play or storytelling, for example, to teach colours, textures, opposites, and so on.

Teaching your child is not a formal process where specific rules and targets must be met. All teaching should be playful and be done with games. Feed your child's increasing curiosity and need for new experiences. Introduce new concepts, answer his queries but, most importantly, praise him at every stage so that the learning process becomes unconscious and enjoyable, and one he wants to repeat over and over with you.

When you work with your child, be sure to stop the moment he shows any sign of boredom and take care not to put him under any pressure. If he decides early on that learning is fun, he'll feel this way throughout his life and will thrive on knowledge.

THE IMPORTANCE OF PLAY

Your child's development will centre around play and this is the most natural way for him to learn. It is only in the last twenty years that the full value of development through play has been recognized, since playing was previously regarded as an empty activity, used to fill the time when children could not be usefully employed. We now recognise that play is an essential means of acquiring the majority of adult skills, particularly social ones. Your child will first learn to form relationships and to share with children of his own age through play, and toys will have a significant educational role in all your child's developmental milestones.

Choose toys for their educational value. Reading, writing, and counting proficiency requires certain basic skills that your child will acquire through building and construction toys, playing with puzzles and jigsaws, and matching colours, shapes, and textures. The best toys are the ones which children return to again and again because they are limitless in their appeal – usually ones that encourage inventiveness. For this reason a household item like a whisk or sieve may give more lasting pleasure than many an expensive and elaborate toy. By sharing and encouraging your child in his play you will strengthen the bond between you as he comes to see you as a giver of knowledge and fun.

Places to play It's nice to set aside a special activity space for your child – a sand tray, for example, or an area for messy play like painting or water games – but your child can play anywhere, as long as you take the proper safety measures (see pp.306–13). The kitchen is an ideal place, provided you are there to keep an eye on your child. You could set up a dolls' corner where the dolls can be put to bed each evening and got up in the morning for breakfast.

TELEVISION

The average western child clocks up an average of eight hours' television viewing a day. One hour a day is more than enough for your young child.

More than this may prevent him from acquiring communication, imaginative and co-ordination skills which could be more thoroughly developed through games and storytelling. You should monitor the amount of television your child watches and be wary of using it as a convenient baby-sitting tool when you don't feel like amusing him. Used carefully, however, television can be a useful aid to acquiring new concepts, like telling the time.

Research shows that your child could continue to live in the fantasy world of television long after he's stopped watching, causing nightmares if he's watched anything frightening or violent.

Swedish researchers have shown that bringing your child back into the real world – with a story, tooth-brushing, or laying out tomorrow's clothes – can banish this unpleasant effect of television.

YOUNG BABY LOCOMOTION

HEAD CONTROL

The most important physical change in your baby's first weeks will be the development of neck strength and head control.

A newborn's head is proportionately very large and heavy for his body, which means that before your baby can begin to control the rest of his body, he must first gain control of his head.

Once your baby can raise his head from the mattress he will begin to increase his strength which will encourage him to further locomotive skills. Holding your baby in the air in a face-down position will encourage him to raise his head, something that he will try for himself when lying on his stomach.

As he becomes stronger, your baby's head control is steadier, and his spine will gradually take more of the weight of his torso. This is the first stage in his learning to sit, crawl, and walk.

The first few months of your baby's development is a very exciting time for you as a parent as you watch him first see the world, then move to become involved in it. As his co-ordination and muscle strength increase your baby's body control will quickly improve. The gradual refinement of his movements and his growing curiosity about his surroundings are excellent stimulation for all aspects of his development. Every child develops at his own pace, however, and the ages given below for the various stages of co-ordination and control are only approximations.

Newborn
Your baby will flex his limbs towards his body, which will remain curled up for several weeks as he gradually straightens out of the fetal position. His head will be very floppy at first, but you will notice that he turns it to his preferred side when lying down. Always support his head and neck when lifting him.

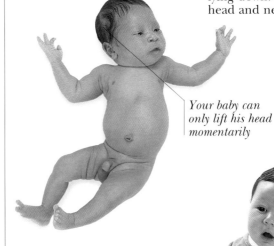

Your baby can only lift his head momentarily

If you hold your baby, he can keep his head up for a while

His neck muscles are getting stronger

1 month
Your baby will be able to lift his head slightly for a few seconds and will have lost his very newborn appearance. If you raise your baby from the mattress he may be able to keep his head up in line with his body for a second or two. His knees and hips will become stronger and will begin to straighten even more.

2 months
Your baby can hold his head up for longer now. In a prone position he'll hold his head in line with his body and will quickly develop to raising his face from the mattress to an angle of 45°.

3 months
Your baby can now lie quite flat and take the weight of his shoulders and head on outstretched arms. There is little head lag when he is held in a sitting or standing position.

Your baby can hold his head up when lying prone

Your baby loves to be held in a sitting position

4 months
Your baby now concentrates on learning to sit up unsupported. Her head control continues to increase and she turns to the left and right when her attention is caught. She can support her chest and head weight on her forearms when lying prone, raise both legs off the mattress, and rock from side to side. She learns to roll over.

YOUR BABY'S POSTURE

Although your baby's posture will mature as his muscles strengthen naturally, you may both enjoy gentle bending and stretching exercises.

Changing-time is a good opportunity to do this; your baby will come to associate the pleasure of being clean and dry with movement. Take your baby's feet gently by the ankles and bend and straighten his legs a few times. Take it slowly, and stop if your baby doesn't seem comfortable.

Your baby's head control continues to increase as he develops an interest in his surroundings

Your baby's head control and neck strength will increase with practice

5 months
Your baby has full head control even when propped in a sitting position. He may be able to take the full weight of his head, shoulders, and chest on outstretched hands. His rocking movements become stronger.

6 months
As your baby's limbs become stronger he can take a lot of his weight on his arms. He'll sit with his hands forward for support, and hold his hands out to you when he wants to be lifted.

He may even sit unsupported for a few seconds. If you bounce your baby up and down with his feet on your lap, he can take some of his own weight with his leg muscles.

SHUFFLING

Before he can crawl your baby may work out his own highly individual way of moving around using the co-ordination he has mastered.

Some babies shuffle along on their bottoms, others use crab-like, sideways movements, and others devise their own unique methods. It is not important what personal manoeuvre your baby works out: he has managed a great achievement in moving independently and this is all that matters. You should never discourage your baby from his first attempts at being mobile. They are his tools for learning to control his body and it is important that he is allowed to discover the limits of this control. Give his curiosity and spirit of adventure free rein.

ENCOURAGING MOVEMENT

Although your baby may appear to make crawling movements in his first weeks (see p.21), he'll stop this as his body straightens out from the fetal position. Before he can really begin to crawl, he must uncurl his body, control his head, lift his chest clear of the floor, and develop strength in his arms and legs.

Your encouragement and praise will make this an exciting and pleasurable time for both of you. As your baby gains head control, for instance, you can encourage him to lift his head by holding a brightly coloured toy above him. As his back and shoulder muscles gain strength, help him by occasionally pulling him into a sitting position when he is lying on his back. Once he can sit up, you can play games that make him swivel in this position; call "peek-a-boo" from his side so he has to turn to look at you. By about five months, when your baby has full head control, rocking and swinging games will give him practice in keeping his head stable.

PROPPING

From as early as six weeks you should include your baby in daily life by propping him in an upright position with pillows. As he can focus better by now, this will allow him to see what is going on and engage his interest in his surroundings. Once this stimulation begins, your baby will find the desire for involvement irresistible.

PREPARING TO CRAWL

Your baby has to be strong enough to hold his head and chest off the floor before he can crawl. By the time he's about six months old he'll be able to push his chest clear of the floor and hold this position with his knees under him, but he will be around eight months before he can pull himself forward along the floor.

It is impossible to pinpoint exactly the age at which your baby will crawl, if at all. If he's engrossed by watching what is going on around him he may hate lying on his stomach, and so leave crawling to a later stage. Some babies leave out the crawling stage altogether, but go on to learn to walk perfectly.

You can encourage your baby to crawl in a number of ways, the best being to use yourself as an enticement. Praise any efforts your baby makes in order to divert him from feeling tired or frustrated by unsuccessful attempts. Your help and support will be far more useful to him than attempts to "teach" him to crawl by moving his arms and legs in a crawling movement.

A bouncing chair
The chair's springy responses to your baby's movements encourage him to move about. Always place the chair on the floor, never on a table.

PREPARING TO STAND

Before your baby can stand he must have strength and balance. Although he is unlikely to have strong leg muscles or control over them before he is 10 or 11 months old, one of the most enjoyable games for a young baby is to be bounced up and down on your knee. Hold your baby facing you with his feet touching your knees and raise and lower him, making sure that his neck is supported. Your baby will really enjoy the sensation of taking his own weight, and it will strengthen his leg muscles in preparation for walking. From about six months he'll try to bend and straighten his legs in a jumping movement whenever he is held in a standing position. These movements are your baby's earliest attempts at walking.

EXERCISES

You can encourage your baby's physical development from a very early age by playing simple exercise games which he should enjoy. You should dress him comfortably, but in a warm room with no draughts his nappy will be all he needs.

STRENGTHENING ACTIVITIES

Flier
Lie on your back with your knees drawn up and balance your baby on his stomach, on your shins (knees). Stretch his arms out to the side – this should make him raise his head – and then bring his arms back to the original position and begin again.

Arm stretch
Lie your baby on his back and let him grasp your thumbs. Stretch one of his arms above his head. As you then lower the extended arm, raise his other arm above his head.

> Your baby will be happier if he can see you and follow your movements

SAFETY

From the moment your baby becomes mobile it is vital that your home is "childproof" (see pp.306–11) to prevent accidents.

- *Never leave your baby unattended. Even before he is mobile your baby will need to be with you for reassurance and safety*

- *Once your baby learns to roll, never leave him lying anywhere except on the floor in an area clear of sharp or hard objects*

- *Even when he has mastered control over his head, continue to put pillows around your baby's bottom and lower spine*

- *Keep all poisonous substances out of your baby's reach*

- *Securely guard all fires, cupboards, banisters, and stairways*

Crossovers
Holding your baby's hands, stretch his arms to the side then back across his chest. Repeat.

NAME *Catherine Dallas*

AGE *31 years*

OBSTETRIC HISTORY *First baby, normal delivery, no complications*

From about four months Catherine thought that Henry was a bit slow: he still didn't have control of his head, which tended to loll, and he hadn't made any attempts to sit up. If she tried to support him in a sitting position he rolled to one side or the other. When she was dressing Henry, Catherine noticed that his arms and legs flopped back to his body after she'd fitted them into a sleeve or legging.

FLOPPY INFANT SYNDROME

As Henry was her first baby, Catherine was unsure as to whether or not Henry was late in developing but wisely decided to seek her doctor's opinion. When questioned by the doctor, Catherine could remember some other signs that all was not normal with Henry; when he was first born she had noticed that his eyes flicked back and forth quite quickly but hadn't known that this wasn't usual in newborn babies. Henry had seemed rather weak with his sucking, and had a tendency to drool which indicated difficulty in swallowing – but she was told many newborns have the same trouble.

After carefully examining Henry and asking Catherine some questions the doctor said he felt that Henry should see a paediatric neurologist for a full assessment. He used the phrase "floppy infant syndrome", saying it had many causes and could take a bit of sorting out over the next few months.

Catherine was convulsed by fear and anxiety after hearing the doctor's opinion, and she desperately needed answers to her many questions. What is floppy infant syndrome? What causes it? Is it inherited? Would future babies be affected? What was the outlook for Henry? Would he ever be normal? How could she help him?

POSSIBLE CAUSES

I suggested to Catherine that we should take one step at a time: tests could answer all her questions. The list of possible causes of floppy infant syndrome is huge because the name simply describes the condition of a baby, not what's causing it. The "floppiness" can be caused by any one of hundreds of rare diseases, none of which can be diagnosed without extensive high-tech investigations. However, family history and careful clinical examination can narrow the list to one of three main categories.

Genetic This may be obvious if other family members have suffered, but may only come to light with gene testing, performed with a DNA probe which can pick up gene abnormalities.

Muscular Diseases such as muscular dystrophy may be tracked down with EMG (electromyography) and blood tests for muscle enzymes that ordinarily are confined to the muscles; their presence in blood indicates muscle breakdown. A muscle biopsy may also be carried out, so that a tiny piece of muscle can be studied under a microscope for abnormalities.

Brain The cerebellum, that part of the brain responsible for maintaining muscle tone, is situated at the back of the head and may not develop normally while your baby is in the uterus. CT (computed tomography) scanners and MRI (magnetic resonance imaging) are used to give pictures of the brain that can be examined in minute detail. Very rarely the brain can be damaged at birth but usually only in a prolonged, difficult labour.

DIAGNOSTIC CLUES

Henry's Apgar score (see p.24) had been lowish at birth for muscle tone, an early clue to what happened later. Another clue was the nystagmus (flicking eye movements) that Catherine had noticed in Henry at birth. Nystagmus often originates from damage to or incorrect development of the cerebellum, so already we had an indication that this should probably be the first area to examine.

All the signs Catherine had noted but dismissed – weak sucking, drooling, poor swallowing, nystagmus, and low muscle tone – are early symptoms of floppy infant syndrome, although it's not until they're all added together that their significance becomes obvious. I tried to reassure Catherine that she need not feel guilty about missing those early signs, since it would not have made any difference to Henry's future or his possible treatment.

LEARNING TO COPE

Before any tests were started, and with the cooperation of their doctor, I encouraged Catherine and Mike to see a psychiatric counsellor rather than try to cope alone. It's an enormous help to chat constructively to an expert who can talk through and sympathize with conflicting emotions, and help couples to cope and plan. This turned out to be very comforting for Catherine and Mike and they continued to see their counsellor for many months.

HENRY'S DIAGNOSIS

When the tests were carried out, there was good news among the bad: the genetic tests were clear, meaning that Henry's disabilities were spontaneous and future babies would most likely be perfectly normal. As far as doctors could tell, his intelligence was not impaired and the muscle biopsy showed no dystrophy. It looked as if the lesion was in the brain and MRI scans confirmed this with pictures showing a slightly small, underdeveloped cerebellum.

At 16 months Henry was behind in terms of development, but this was thought to be due to his weak muscles rather than mental retardation. He was a wonderfully sociable little boy, however, and very loving; he brought Catherine and Mike much pleasure. He was slow to speak, but made sounds so they knew he had the desire to communicate through conversation – a good sign. He had much better control over his body and was getting slowly stronger, though he would probably not walk till perhaps four or five years, and could have difficulty remaining steady. His vision and hearing are normal.

NAME *Henry Dallas*

AGE *18 months*

MEDICAL HISTORY *Normal delivery. Nystagmus (flickering eye movements) at birth and Apgar score low for muscle tone (hypotonia). Subsequent motor development slow.*

Catherine has discovered from her doctor, health visitor, and specialist that there is all kinds of help available for Henry (see Useful Addresses, p.344). She knows she must be prepared for the fact that one day Henry might have to live in a special care centre. In the meantime, she is taking Henry to physiotherapy sessions to strengthen his muscles and improve his physical co-ordination. The physiotherapist is very happy with his progress, and pleased, too, to see what a good teacher Catherine is becoming. Catherine is feeling more confident in her own strength and resourcefulness now that she realizes there is a great deal that she can do for Henry.

OLDER BABY

LOCOMOTION

STAGES OF STANDING

As your baby learns to sit unsupported for longer periods of time, her sense of balance and her desire to walk will increase.

• *From about six or seven months your baby will begin to take her full weight on her knees and hips, but she'll need to be balanced by you. She'll test her leg strength with a sort of dancing movement; a hop from one foot to another, and as she becomes more confident she'll practise bending and stretching her legs*

• *By nine months your baby's ability to balance will be greatly improved. She may be able to take all her own weight on her legs but she'll still need to hold on to something. Any stable piece of furniture will support her but she should never be left alone in this position; she'll find it difficult to sit from a standing position and a fall may seriously affect her confidence and pleasure in standing*

• *By about ten months your baby will be able to lift one foot while she stands, provided she's supported. She'll be able to pull herself into a standing position but will still have trouble lowering herself*

During the first few months of life your baby achieved head control and learned to co-ordinate and refine her movements in easily recognisable stages as her muscles became stronger and her balance improved. Now she is ready to start moving around, and the next year will be an exciting one for both of you as she learns to crawl and then to walk.

Its important to remember that all babies develop at their own speed and the ages given here are the general times by which most babies have achieved these skills. A few babies walk by six months; others show no interest in walking at all, but walk perfectly later on, so do not be too concerned if your baby's development doesn't exactly match these stages. Some babies miss out the crawling stage altogether, and go straight from shuffling (see p.156) to walking. Others crawl bear-like on their hands and feet rather than their hands and knees. Both of these are normal.

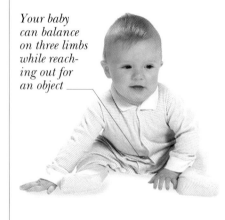

Your baby can balance on three limbs while reaching out for an object

8 months
Your baby will stretch for things that are held beyond his reach. He'll sit unsupported, briefly at first, but gradually for longer periods of time. He'll master leaning, both forwards and to the sides, and will test his own balance by rocking back and forth in a sitting position or twisting round, though he'll probably fall over.

10 months
Your baby may sit unaided for up to ten minutes. He's probably mastered creeping. He can pull himself to his feet, but you'll still have to hold him in a standing position and help him sit down again.

Your baby's arms can now take some of his weight

1 year

Your baby can creep or crawl. When held in a standing position he'll try stepping. He may try "cruising" – walking sideways while holding on to something.

Your baby will be able to turn and pick up an object behind him while sitting

14 months

After cruising your baby will perfect standing alone, and may even take his first independent step. Soon he'll be taking a few steps together in order to move between one stable support and another. He'll still need support to sit from standing.

BALANCE

Between seven months and one year your baby will develop righting reflexes which control her basic body movements.

These help her move from prone to standing positions and vice versa, to get to her hands and knees, and to sit up. They control the position and movement of her head and are responsible for the development of balance

- *By eight months your baby will lean forwards and backwards in order to test her balance*

- *At nine months your baby can lean forwards and to the side without losing her balance. She can roll over and will try to crawl*

- *From ten months she can twist her upper body while sitting. This strengthens her lateral trunk muscles and improves her ability to balance while moving*

16 months

Your baby's steps are high and unsteady, but her style will soon become more refined. She'll stand up and sit down without help, and can creep upstairs. You must be vigilant about safety; now that she's mobile she'll want to investigate everything she sees around her.

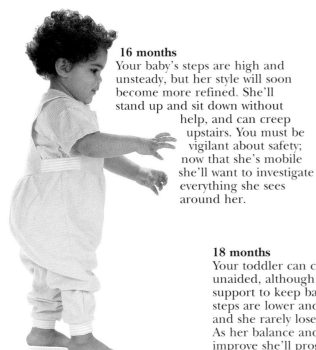

18 months

Your toddler can climb stairs unaided, although she needs support to keep balanced. Her steps are lower and more steady and she rarely loses her balance. As her balance and co-ordination improve she'll progress to walking backwards and running.

ENCOURAGING SKILLS

Your baby's first attempts at walking will be unsteady and he'll hang on to objects for support, but in a couple of months he'll be independently mobile.

• *Your baby will "cruise" before he walks – that is, haul himself up on any large item, and then sidle around it. Make sure that any unsteady or lightweight furniture is secured or removed from his path*

• *Next he'll start to move one hand over the other as he cruises rather than sliding them together and then moving both hands and feet at the same time. This is an important stage as your baby develops the confidence and balance to take all his weight, briefly, on one foot*

• *His next goal is to negotiate gaps between two supports. He'll hold on to both at once, and only let go of one support when he's holding firmly on to the other*

• *He'll soon progress to crossing wider gaps. Still holding on to a support with one hand, he'll move into the centre of the gap and, once he's got his balance, release one support and take a step towards the next one, grabbing for it with both hands*

• *Finally, your baby will begin to "toddle", staggering a couple of paces to reach the second support. He'll launch himself into the open and take several unsupported steps with confidence. He may soon lose his balance, sitting down with a thud, but he'll usually set off for his goal and waddle bow-leggedly towards it with his arms held high and wide*

The transition your child makes from an uncoordinated baby to an independent toddler is a major turning point in his development and you can help by encouraging him to stand and gently urging him on during his early attempts at walking.

He needs lots of room to move in and a soft covering under his feet so that he can fully enjoy his new-found freedom. Give him plenty of praise at every stage but try not to push him to go faster than he feels he can – walking involves tricky techniques of balance and co-ordination and so is one of the most difficult skills your child will ever learn.

HELPING YOUR CHILD STAND

Let your baby take more and more of his own standing weight from the time he can control his head. His leg muscles, hips, and knees will gradually strengthen and he'll relish taking his own weight on them. When you hold his hands he'll bounce about and play standing and bouncing games. Hold him on your lap, on cushions, on a bed, or in the bath and encourage these active games.

From around nine months your baby will take nearly his entire weight on his legs, but will still need support to do so because his muscle strength is more advanced than his balance. You can encourage him by taking him to stable pieces of furniture and getting him to grip his hands on so that he is nicely balanced. Stay close while he holds on. He'll need to develop his balance in order to stand securely, so when he is sitting, urge him to lean forward and sideways by placing toys just out of reach in front and by his sides; this will strengthen his trunk muscles. He will find it difficult to sit down from a standing position, but you can make it a little easier by gently manipulating his hips and knees. At the age of ten months your baby is far more mobile on his hands and knees. The muscles of his trunk are getting stronger all the time as he twists and turns while sitting or crawling. Offer your fingers to encourage him to pull himself up to sit and stand. He'll be delighted at his achievement so always praise him well.

Learning to stand
Teach your baby the sensation of supporting his own weight by holding his hands and playing gentle leg-bending games.

HELPING YOUR CHILD WALK

Your baby will learn to walk on his own, but it's fun to help him practise if you have the time. Put your baby on his hands and knees and sit a short distance away. This will impel him to move toward you. He'll come more eagerly if you hold out your arms, call his name, or offer a brightly coloured toy. To prompt your baby to twist, place a toy behind his back and support him as he turns around. When your baby reaches ten months he'll be able to stand up if supported by furniture. While he is standing and firmly supported, bend one of his knees and lift his foot; this will help him learn to step and bear his weight momentarily on one foot.

From 11 months, help your baby to practise walking forwards by holding his hands and guiding him. You can make cruising easier by positioning stable pieces of furniture close together around the room, but remove any items that could tip over easily when he pulls on them.

Improve your baby's stepping skills by calling to him while he is cruising around the room. Give him the courage to launch himself by moving the pieces of furniture slightly further apart. Sit a little way from him and, while he is holding on to the furniture, hold out your arms and call him to you – but always be close enough to catch him if he stumbles.

From 13 months your baby can stand alone and may take his first independent step. A stable standing toy, like a push-along trolley, is ideal encouragement for him to practise walking alone. At 15 months your baby can kneel, lower his body without support, and stand up unaided. A chair with arms will allow your baby to sit down without falling and will provide good bending practice for his hips and knees.

Practise more leg movements with your baby, using a large soft ball which he can try to kick to you. This is also good for acquiring balance. Show him how to squat, and help him master hip and knee bends – which are all the more enjoyable if you do them together to music. Games that use backwards or sideways steps will greatly increase your baby's walking and balancing skills. "Ring-A-Rosy", a game in which you hold your baby's hands while walking, sitting, and standing is a lot of fun and allows him to imitate you, making his achievement even greater.

There's no right age for your baby to start to walk but he is most likely to take his first unsupported steps between the ages of 9 and 15 months.

Toys for walking
Your toddler's mobility and independence will be enhanced by sturdy, wheeled, walking toys.

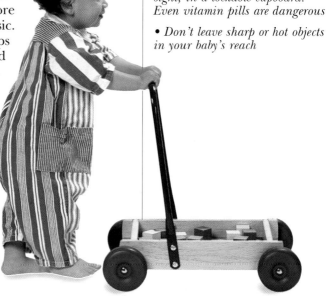

SAFETY

As your baby's independence grows, safety in his environment becomes increasingly important.

• *Keep close at hand when your baby is taking his first unsteady steps and take particular care when he walks and creeps upstairs. Make sure the floor is not slippery and don't give him shoes until he is walking outdoors*

• *Give your baby plenty of clear space for his walking attempts. Trailing flexes or small pieces of furniture might cause him to trip*

• *Special protective edges are available for sharp-cornered furniture or door handles*

• *Glass-topped items should be removed or fitted with safety film*

• *Fit safety gates to the top and bottom of your stairs. Gates at the top of the stairs should open onto the landing and should not have horizontal bars that your baby could climb*

• *Keep all poisonous substances well out of reach, and out of sight, in a lockable cupboard. Even vitamin pills are dangerous*

• *Don't leave sharp or hot objects in your baby's reach*

TODDLER LOCOMOTION

LOCOMOTION IN GIRLS

Girls seem to be on a faster timetable than boys all the way through their growth; they tend to grow more regularly and predictably than boys.

In the preschool years girls are better at jumping, hopping, and rhythmic movement and balance, so they will enjoy games that involve these. Hopscotch, skipping, and dancing games will all give your little girl a chance to develop these skills.

Between the ages of 18 months and three years your child will quickly progress in getting around. She will be very active on her feet, perfecting her walking and balancing skills, and you can encourage this development by involving her in your daily activities. She will begin to enjoy ball games, toys on wheels and games that involve hopping, jumping, or climbing. Spend time with your child encouraging her in her new skills, and building up her confidence: it will be vital in her continuing physical development.

21 months
Your child can now bend to pick up objects without toppling over. Walking becomes steadier, and he can walk with his arms by his sides instead of held out high. He can run quite well, but will have difficulty turning corners and may topple over if he stops suddenly. He may be able to kick a ball, but rather awkwardly as he can't balance well on one leg.

2 years
Your child is more fluent at ball games, both catching and kicking, and can walk backwards as well as forwards. He can go up and down stairs without holding on, putting both his feet on each step. He can now veer and swerve while running and can stop running without falling over.

2 ½ years
Your child can now jump with both feet off the ground at the same time, walk on tiptoe, and is steady on her feet – with your guidance she can carry a breakable object or hold a baby brother or sister on her knee. She can now run quite well and can glance over her shoulder without losing balance.

HOW TO HELP

Your child's toddler years are a time of great activity for both of you. She will be interested in everything she sees and is developing the skills that will allow her to take part in a number of activities for the first time. This provides a great opportunity for you to involve her in many daily tasks which will be both fun for her and important to her development.

Give your child plenty of chances to practise her walking skills by going up and down stairs with her or leaving the pushchair behind on short trips. Hold her hand if she needs support or when you go out shopping. Alternatively, reins are even safer and will give your child more freedom, making them particularly suitable for use in the park or other playing areas. Don't put too many demands on her walking abilities at this stage – she won't be able to walk further than a few hundred metres. She is bound to have some lapses in her learning so don't worry if she experiences setbacks in her walking like a stumble or fall – she will soon regain her confidence.

Agility in walking and running may also be developed by playing games which involve jumping and walking on tiptoe. Encourage your child to dance to music with you. She'll need plenty of practice at balancing, and this can be developed with ball games and other suitable toys. Start with a large, soft ball. Let her try walking along the top of a low wall, holding her hand all the time in case she gets a bit wobbly. Your child is probably too young for a bicycle, but a toy with wheels that she can sit on and propel with her feet will develop her love of motion and strengthen her muscles. Indoors, give your child soft toys like a mattress or foam rubber on which to jump and somersault. An outdoor swing will help develop strength and co-ordination skills but make sure these larger outdoor toys are safe (see p.310).

The more you involve your child in daily activities such as cleaning and washing, and climbing the stairs, the more teaching and practice your child will receive. Take sensible precautions against falls and other household dangers, but don't worry unduly; toddlers are amazingly resilient and will be oblivious to most of the bruises they inevitably receive in these active and inquisitive years.

Wheeled toys
A pushbike can be used indoors as well as out, and will improve your child's co-ordination and muscle strength.

LOCOMOTION IN BOYS

In the preschool years there is little difference between boys and girls in terms of strength and speed.

Young boys achieve jumping, hopping, rhythmic movement, and balancing skills less quickly than girls, so they tend to reach certain milestones later, such as picking up a toy from the floor without sitting down first. You should therefore give your little boy plenty of help with achieving these skills by allowing him freedom of movement. Games that involve kicking a ball, or dancing and jumping games, will all increase his skills.

PRESCHOOL LOCOMOTION

ENCOURAGING GIRLS

Girls are often considered to be less outgoing and adventurous than boys but it is important that they are encouraged to be curious and active, and to let off steam with physical activity.

• *Don't be over concerned about your little girl hurting herself or getting her clothes dirty; this attitude can inhibit your child from discovering her physical potential*

• *Girls are more naturally sociable, so encourage them to play team or co-operative games, such as hopscotch or skipping*

• *Include more energetic movements with your child, in games such as "Simon says"*

• *Girls tend to be more gifted at imaginative roleplay games, so try to encourage your little girl to include more physical creativity, with constructional and spatial skills, into her fantasy games*

• *Never hamper your daughter's adventurousness and curiosity; encourage her to climb and swing as you would a son*

Dance will improve poise and balance

Dance
Many little girls love the idea of being a dancer, and lessons can be an enjoyable social occasion as well as honing physical skills.

During these two preschool years your child is really developing his physical skills and taking a pride in acquiring each new ability. At three years your child has become much more nimble, walking upstairs with confidence. He can jump off the bottom step and stand on one foot for a second. He can swing his arms when he walks and ride a tricycle. At four your child is very active and well co-ordinated. He races about hopping, jumping, and climbing, and can walk down stairs rapidly, with one foot per step. He can even carry a drink without spilling it. By five, your child's co-ordination is finely developed. He can walk a straight line, go down stairs on alternating feet, skip a rope with alternating feet, climb confidently, and enjoy fast-moving toys and games.

ENCOURAGING SKILLS

You can encourage your three-year-old's jumping skills by playing hopscotch, or holding hands and hopping on one foot. This will work off excess energy. You can practise arm-swinging with him by marching to music. Letting him ride a tricycle will strengthen his calf muscles and encourage flexibility in his feet, while garden equipment such as a swing, see-saw, or slide will boost his physical confidence.

At four, your child should have access to outside apparatus, such as a climbing frame in the garden, to provide scope to exercise his muscles. You can also help him to master skipping and to try a wide range of other physical games.

Five-year-olds can skip rope and will enjoy toys such as stilts, a skateboard, or other challenging equipment.

Wheeled toys
A three-year-old will have enough co-ordination to manage pedalling.

Sturdy pedals are easy to manoeuvre

ADVENTUROUS PLAY

If your child is encouraged to be adventurous he will be willing to push himself to the limit and develop his full potential. A child of three or four has a very clear sense of self and his abilities and is discovering the limits of what is safe and feasible. If you are over-protective and don't allow your child to test his abilities, master a new skill, and move on, you will hold him back and he will lack co-ordination and confidence as a result. You must separate his fears from yours; his fears will make him circumspect and sensible, while your fears will cripple both his curiosity and spirit.

By the time your child is three years old he can walk and run confidently. He has boundless energy, and is ready to tackle more demanding activities so give him plenty of scope: running, climbing, and pedalling will improve his skills and help him burn off surplus energy. If you can afford it, set up a climbing frame, rope ladder, or swing in your garden where you can supervise him from the house. Depending on your child's skill and confidence, he may be ready to tackle roller skating, riding a bicycle with stabilizing wheels. Introducing your child to sports and other activities now could lay the foundations for a lifetime of enjoyment, so give him the opportunity to try lots of different things: swimming, dancing, football, or horse-riding. At the very least, try to make sure he has somewhere he can run, climb, or just kick a ball about.

You can always help your child to tackle new and difficult tasks at first, holding his hand and guiding him through them so that you are secure in your own mind that he is competent and therefore safe. Extend adventurousness and curiosity in your child across the board, not just in physical development but with toys, music, painting, books, and games.

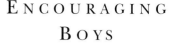

ENCOURAGING BOYS

Boys are assumed and encouraged to be adventurous in their play but it is a mistake to assume that all boys are outgoing and active. Some have an obvious preference for boisterous games while others prefer quiet contemplative activities.

• *Games on large soft cushions and foam-filled furniture are excellent fun and good for promoting balance and co-ordination*

• *Boys are usually considered to be better at "spatial relationships" – knowing, for example, how one object best fits onto another. Encourage this skill by introducing construction toys as soon as he can fit them together*

• *Provide plenty of opportunities for your little boy to be creative; items such as toilet roll tubes, old egg boxes, and yogurt cartons can be turned into anything his imagination can conjure up*

Balance and co-ordination
Encourage your child's adventurous spirit by providing equipment such as roller skates.

Adjustable roller-skates are comfortable and allow for growth

Inflatable arm-bands give your child confidence

Swimming
Your child's muscular fitness and strength, particularly in the arms, will be developed by swimming.

YOUNG BABY

MANIPULATION

YOUR BABY'S HANDS

At first your baby has little interest in his hands, but as he becomes more aware of his body they'll begin to fascinate him more and more.

When he waves his arms around, his hand will accidentally touch his face and he'll put it in his mouth to suck. At two to three months he finds the movements of his fingers fascinating and will watch them for ages. By about four months he'll grab hold of objects to "test" them in his mouth. At six months he refines his manual skills and feels with his fingers as much as his mouth.

Your baby was born with the reflex to grasp anything that is placed in his palm – such as your finger – and not let go; his grip is so strong he can support his own weight (though you should never actually let him do so). When he is not holding something his hands will be tightly closed in a fist, although they'll probably open and close when he cries, and he will open them instinctively when he is startled (see p.20). The early reflex grasp must be lost if he is to learn to select an object, and reach out and pick it up with thumb and forefinger – the basic skill of manual dexterity. Most babies will develop a mature "pincer" grip by one year of age.

Newborn
From birth your baby has the ability to grasp an object and hold on. This grasping reflex is so strong it allows him to support his own weight.

2 months
Your baby is becoming more aware of his hands and his reflex grasping action has almost gone. His hands are much more open now, too.

5 months
Your baby is eager to grab things with his whole hand. He will hold his feet, or a soft toy, and transfer them to his mouth to suck.

Your baby will love to suck his toes

6 months
Your baby holds his bottle or cup, and he'll be able to hold an object that is given to him between two hands.

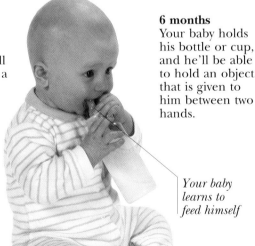

Your baby learns to feed himself

ENCOURAGING SKILLS

Even the most simple activities can add to your baby's feelings of confidence and achievement. He needs to feel that his hard work is noticed and appreciated by you, and that you are as pleased as he is about his cleverness and growing independence.

0–6 weeks Your baby must ignore his instinctive grasp reflex before he can manipulate objects. Test this reflex by letting him grasp your fingers and seeing how far you can pull him off the mattress. Encourage him to open his fingers by gently unfolding them one at a time as you play games like "this little piggy".

6 weeks Your baby's hands are opening and he is becoming aware of them. Help him to take an interest in his hands by tickling his palms and fingertips with materials of different textures: soft, furry, smooth, or ridged – corduroy for example. A gentle hand massage or rubbing of his palms will encourage him to open his hands.

2 months Your baby's hands are more open now, so continue to provide plenty of tactile stimulation by giving him objects of different textures to hold. Lay each object across his palm, following the horizontal creases, so he can wrap his hand around it.

3 months Your baby uses a wide open hand to grasp and reaches for things inaccurately. Encourage a mature grasp by giving him things to hold. Place a rattle in his hand and shake it a few times – he will be fascinated both by its feel and the sound. Put a mobile above his cot to give him something to look at, and string toys across his pram to swipe at (make sure they are safe; see p.310).

4 months As your baby starts to get his hand and arm movements under control, he'll reach out for things with increasing accuracy. Encourage him by presenting interesting objects while he is sitting propped up or lying down. He will still tend to overshoot when he reaches for something so you'll need to compensate to ensure he does get the object.

5 months Your baby will be grabbing everything within reach and he will particularly love crumpling paper, so give him tissue paper to play with. He will love you to play with his feet where he can see them so play "this little piggy" with his toes. Play giving and taking-away games to encourage him to open his fingers and let go. He will reach for a bottle to try and feed himself.

6 months His finger movements are becoming more precise all the time. You can let him hold his own bottle in two hands and give him a variety of finger foods (see p.61) for easy grasping and self-feeding. You can teach him how to feed himself with a spoon and how to pass an object from one hand to the other. As soon as this is mastered he will joyfully start to practise his letting-go skill and throw everything on the floor.

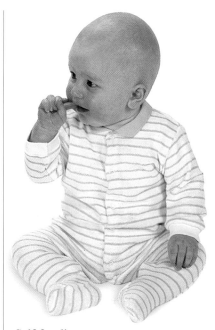

Self-feeding
At six months your baby's hand and eye co-ordination is good enough to pick up finger foods and start feeding himself, though he is not yet very accurate at getting the food into his mouth.

OLDER BABY MANIPULATION

Right- or left-handedness develops in the first few months as one or other side of your baby's brain becomes dominant: if the right side dominates she will be left-handed, and vice-versa.

Even as a newborn, your baby may have shown a tendency to turn her head more to the right than the left. Now she may start to favour one hand. Never try to dissuade her from being left-handed – you could cause psychological side effects and reading and writing problems.

By six months your baby will have learned to grasp objects voluntarily, and now she will gradually refine her handling skills as she learns to use them to eat, dress, wash, and pick things up. You'll find this time both rewarding and frustrating – your baby is learning to do more things for herself, but she won't be very adept at first so you'll have to be patient while she learns.

By 12 months your baby will have the mature adult grasp which is a fine movement achieved by bringing the thumb and index finger together (opposition). She can give something to you by releasing her grip, and she will be able to roll a ball to you.

Your baby uses his whole hand to grip

9 months
Your baby can pick up small things by bringing his thumb and index finger together. He points with his index finger when reaching for something. He's eager to feed himself.

Your baby can grip objects between his thumb and fingers

12 months
Your baby still enjoys throwing things as he practises "ungrasping". He can build a tower of two blocks, and draw lines with a pencil. His co-ordination is improving so he spills less food.

18 months
Now your toddler can turn two or three pages of a book at a time, and build a tower of three blocks. She can feed herself completely with a spoon and drink from a cup without spilling anything. She'll put on some clothes, is fascinated by zip fasteners, and enjoys finger painting and scribbling.

HOW YOU CAN HELP

Your baby's new skills can be encouraged as before in a variety of games that you can play together. Now that she's older, however, she'll be able to pursue some activities by herself; she'll also be able to apply herself to everyday tasks.

Everyday activities The business of getting food into her mouth will give your child a powerful motive to improve her hand-eye co-ordination. As soon as she is able – from about six months – let her hold her own bottle or cup while she drinks from it, and give her finger foods to encourage fine finger movements. Before long she'll be able to feed herself with a spoon, a skill you can encourage by preparing semi-solid foods that will stick to the spoon.

Dressing is another everyday activity that your baby will try increasingly to do for herself. She may be able to pull some of her clothes on and off, but won't be able to manage fastenings yet, though she will want to try.

Building blocks Once your baby is able to grasp a block, you can teach her to place one on top of another. At six or seven months she will have mastered this but you can continue to stack blocks – three or four high or side by side – for her to see and copy. As her grasp develops (see right), she practises the novel skill of letting go and dropping things, and will start to throw blocks. By one year old, she'll be able to build a tower of two blocks by herself, and by 15 months she'll probably manage a tower of three.

Games There are all sorts of simple games your baby can play to develop her skills. She'll love making noise with a wooden spoon and some pots and pans. Once she learns to let objects go, she will enjoy throwing them out of her pushchair or high chair. You can make this into a game by showing her how to put objects into a container and take them out again.

Drawing Your baby won't be able to manage a pencil or crayon until she's about a year old, but once she starts, she will love to scribble. Give her lots of scrap paper – wallpaper offcuts are good – and pin her pictures up where she can see them.

Building blocks
Help your child to develop her grasp so she can let go as well as hold on, by introducing her to toy blocks.

171

TODDLER MANIPULATION

In terms of general development the toddler stage marks a quite dramatic change from babyhood to childhood and from 18 months onwards you'll really notice this transformation, especially in manipulative skills. Over the next 18 months your baby will be getting more independent as he learns to dress himself and to manage increasingly fine movements. His creative skills also come to the fore at this stage as his building-block houses get more complicated and his drawings more recognisable.

Milestones
Your child may just be able to do up a zip fastener. He'll try an "unscrewing" movement with jar tops and door knobs by the age of two. He'll use crayons more deliberately and may be able to build a tower of four blocks.

Your child has a refined grip to clasp and twist objects

Your child can grip and pull fine materials

Thick yarn or shoelaces will be easy for your child to manage

Getting dressed
At two-and-a-half, putting on and taking off clothes will become easier and your child will be keen to do these things for himself.

Fine movements
Your child will be able to thread large beads or spools on a string by two-and-a-half years old.

Household items like cotton reels can be threaded on to string

172

ENCOURAGING SKILLS

All sorts of everyday tasks are now becoming possible for your child to manage by himself, so give him every opportunity to do things unaided. More complicated toys, especially construction or craft toys, will help him practise and develop his skills.

Dressing By the age of two, your child will be able to cope with a number of dressing skills, though putting on his socks, shoes, and gloves will still be tricky, so let him choose his own clothes and practise getting dressed. Clothes with press studs and fairly large buttons, provided the holes are not too tight, will also encourage him to develop new finger skills. Continue to encourage his dressing ability and he will soon be able to put on and take off underpants, trousers and T-shirts. Once he can cope with all his buttons, including the smaller ones, he will be able to dress and undress himself completely.

Construction toys
Interlocking building blocks are always popular toys and are ideal for developing hand movements.

Improving dexterity As soon as your child can turn a door knob with two hands and open a loose-fitting screw-top jar, give him toys that need to be fitted together. Washing and drying his hands will also be a favourite pastime so encourage him in this. Ensure that your two-year-old has plenty of colourful picture books to hand as he can now turn the pages of a book one at a time by himself. Your child can now build a tower of four blocks and with encouragement he'll make more complicated structures. Building blocks that need pressing and fitting together will help develop the small movements of his hands. Intricate tasks such as threading large beads on a piece of string or fitting together jigsaw puzzles made out of large pieces will boost his manipulation skills.

Arts and crafts Children enjoy drawing at this age, so give your child plenty of drawing materials, including a range of different crayons, and start him off by showing the effect of all the different colours. He will also enjoy using paints, especially if you allow him to be messy and paint with his hands. You can also help him to relate his drawings to the world around him by naming the colours of the crayons and then pointing out the same colours in everyday objects. He will soon be producing images of people and familiar objects and by two-and-a-half years his pictures will become more recognisable.

ENCOURAGING INDEPENDENCE

With so many new skills to learn at this stage, it is important not to expect your child to develop at a rate that is too fast for him.

All children progress at their own pace; which is decided by the speed that their developing brain and nerves allow. Your child will want to please you, and may try to do things that are more complicated than his development will allow. Failure is demoralizing because he feels he's let you down. A better approach is to give him all the help and encouragement he needs, showing him how pleased you are with every task he manages, without setting him goals that are beyond his abilities.

Choosing clothes
Encourage your child's interest in dressing himself by letting him choose the clothes he is to wear.

173

PRESCHOOL

MANIPULATION

DRAWING

Your child's improving manual dexterity is clearly demonstrated by her ability to copy a circle.

2¹/₂ years
Her earliest attempts at a circle may end up as a continuous round shape, like a spiral.

3 years
Her attempts become more controlled but the circle may not quite join up or the lines may overshoot.

3¹/₂ years
Your child should be able to draw a closed figure, either a true circle or an oval shape.

Your three-year-old is maturing rapidly and by now can probably dress and undress herself completely, as long as the fastenings are all easy to reach. She can draw and colour quite accurately and her drawings are becoming more recognisable. By the age of four she will have mastered the complicated action of using scissors. Building blocks are becoming too simple for her, so she is ready to move on to more sophisticated construction sets. She is already doing very simple tasks around the house and from four years old she will get much better at jobs such as setting the table, washing her face and hands, making her bed, and putting her clothes tidily away.

Crafts
Your four- or five-year-old's ability to use scissors represents a huge step forward in manual dexterity and brain–muscle co-ordination. Give him simple models to make. Any scissors he uses should be blunt-ended.

Drawing
From three years on your child becomes more skilful at drawing as she begins to master skills like copying two straight lines drawn at right angles. By four years she begins to include more detail on her figures. You can make simple puzzles for her – draw an incomplete person and ask her to complete it.

TEETH

In the past it was thought that the primary teeth (milk teeth) were not very important because the adult teeth would be following on behind in due course. Now we know that they are vital because they guide in the adult teeth so that they grow in the correct position. In addition, if the primary teeth are lost through decay this can spread to the bone beneath, causing erosion of the support needed by the adult teeth.

Cutting time There is no standard time for your baby to cut her first tooth. Some babies are born with one tooth, while others still have none at 12 months of age. (If a baby is born with a tooth this is sometimes removed if it is crooked or badly positioned, for instance, or if it is loose and there is a risk of its falling out and causing the baby to choke.) As a general rule, though, teething starts at around six months to cope with solid food and a changing diet, after which many teeth appear up to the end of her first year. If you are on the lookout you will probably notice your baby's first tooth as it starts to push its way through the gum and form a small, pale bump. Your baby will be teething for most of the second year and you should be prepared for the molars, which come through last, to be a bit upsetting.

Signs of teething You can tell when your baby is cutting a tooth because she will be irritable. The gum will be red and swollen, and you may be able to feel the tooth through the gum. Your baby's cheeks may be red, and she will probably dribble. Giving your baby something to chew on can help. Symptoms such as a high temperature, vomiting, or diarrhoea are never caused by teething, so you should not dismiss them – inform your doctor.

USING THE TEETH

A raw carrot or a rusk will give your baby something firm to chew on when she is teething. This principle continues to hold good once she has all her teeth.

Chewy foods, and particularly fresh fruit and raw vegetables, will encourage the development of strong jaw muscles. They also strengthen the teeth and have a cleansing effect as the fibres within them are shredded during the chewing process. Your baby's diet should contain plenty of calcium and vitamin D (from dairy foods, and fatty fish such as herring) to ensure the healthy formation of the permanent teeth that are already growing in the jawbones.

How the teeth come in
The numbers indicate the order in which the teeth arrive. The first to erupt are usually the lower front two teeth, then the upper two front teeth. Upper side teeth come next, followed by the lower side teeth. After this, the first upper molars erupt and then come the first lower molars. The upper canines come in next, one each side, followed by the lower canines. The second molars erupt first in the lower jaw, and then they appear in the upper jaw.

V I S I O N

H E L P I N G   Y O U R   B A B Y

The development of normal vision requires two properly functioning eyes and plenty of visual stimulation. Try the following ideas to stimulate your baby's eyesight:

• *From the day he's born, put a photo of a face – yours or one cut from a magazine – at the side of the cot for your baby to look at*

• *A simple mobile over the cot, or brightly coloured objects on elastic will give your baby something interesting to look at*

• *Your baby is never too young to go sightseeing. If he is in a pushchair he'll be able to look all around himself*

Recognising faces

Give your baby an unbreakable mirror so that he can look at his own reflection.

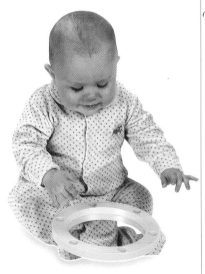

A newborn baby is not blind just because he cannot change focus. He can see everything at his fixed focus of 20–25 centimetres (8–10 inches) as plainly as you or I. It used to be thought that a newborn baby's visual world need not be very stimulating because he could not see. We now know that, right from birth, your baby needs lots of visual stimulation in order to develop his eyesight fully. However a newborn baby's vision is more limited than an older child's, so you will have to fit his visual world into a range that he can perceive. The colour-sensitive cells in a newborn's eyes are not fully developed so he will only see the world in muted shades.

Your newborn Although your baby's eyesight is limited, his eyes are very sensitive to the human face and anything that moves. At first he won't be able to focus on anything further than 25 centimetres (10 inches) away, but if you bring your face to within 20 centimetres (8 inches) of his he will see you and you will notice that his eyes move in recognition and his expression changes.

Increasing recognition If you talk excitedly to your newborn, move your eyes, and open and close your mouth, your baby will respond from within a few minutes of birth by opening his mouth and sticking out his tongue. A baby of only a few hours old can bring his eyes to bear on an object and follow it if it moves. At two weeks a baby will automatically raise a hand to protect himself from something that is moving quickly towards him. At three weeks his whole body may react with excited jerking movements when your face comes into focus. Your baby can "pull" focus by eight weeks and he should recognise your face and respond to it with smiles and waving arms. He is also more conscious of other objects but, because your baby can only focus on nearby objects, the world appears rather flat and distant details are lost to him.

Depth of vision By three to four months your baby can take in details and is able to build up a three-dimensional picture of the world – a necessary step before he becomes mobile, as he probably won't start crawling until his vision allows him to understand depth as well as height and width. He can tell the difference between pictures with two and three items, and can recognise patterns. This eye for detail improves until, by five to six months, he can discriminate between different facial expressions, such as sadness, fear, and joy, and will respond to them with his own expression. He will show excitement when he sees his feed being prepared.

A sense of permanence From six months he can identify objects and can adjust his position to see those that most interest him. From now on the biggest development in your baby's visual skill is the way his brain interprets the information his eyes see.

TESTING VISION

The first test of vision, which you can carry out at birth, is to note your baby's reaction to your face when it is held 25 centimetres (8–10 inches) from his. If he sees your face, his facial expression should change; his eyes will dart to your face and he may open and shut his mouth. There are many clues that will warn parents if a child has a sight defect. If you're in any doubt about your baby's vision, or if your child's eyes water a lot and bright lights cause him discomfort, consult your doctor. The following eye conditions may show up even in a very young baby. Although you should not try to diagnose them yourself, here are some things you might observe; if you do, consult your doctor.

Lazy eye If your child suffers from weak eye muscles he may turn his head so that the eye with better sight can more easily follow the action around him. Check that both eyelids are level when your baby is concentrating on a moving object. If he obviously favours one eye over the other, consult your doctor.

Squint (strabismus) If you notice that only one of your baby's eyes is focused on the object of interest and the other is pointing too far in or too far out, he may be suffering from strabismus. He may tilt his head or hold it in an unusual position to get his vision in line. Find an interesting object, such as a toy and, keeping your child's head still (you may need another adult to help you), move the toy to spell the letter H in the air. Check that both eyes follow the toy in unison. (See also **Squint**, p.287.)

Colour blindness The most common form is the inability to distinguish between red and green (mostly, but not exclusively, found in boys). Use colourful sweets, such as jelly beans, and ask your child to pick out certain colours. If he hasn't learned his colours yet, ask him to pick out the same colours as you.

Peripheral vision To test whether your child has a normal field of vision extending wide to either side, choose a favourite toy and, with your child staring directly ahead, slowly move it from the outside to in front of his face until he sees it. His field of vision should extend to about 45° on either side.

Visual accuracy Test the accuracy of your child's vision with the following games. Stand about 6 metres (20 feet) away and hold up some fingers. Ask him how many fingers you are holding up, or get him to hold up the same number as you. If he fails, you should consult your doctor.

THE VISUALLY IMPAIRED BABY

If your child's vision is poor, you need to be sensitive to his needs. Ensure he receives professional attention and regular check-ups.

- *Long-sighted children receive six-monthly check-ups to see if their prescription for spectacles needs changing. A child who is long-sighted or has astigmatism may only need to wear glasses for two or three years before his eye-sight develops normally*

- *The earlier children start wearing glasses, the more likely they are to accept them. At first a child may take them off and play with them, but he'll soon show a preference for seeing the world clearly*

- *A visually impaired child needs stimulation by touch, noise, and smell, so choose toys that have interesting textures and make different noises. Puzzles are particularly important; those with large, colourful pieces are best*

Brightly coloured toys
Your child will need visual stimulation if he has impaired vision, so toys with a variety of shapes and colours are important.

HEARING

By explaining sounds and playing appropriate games with your baby, you can help him to listen in a discerning way to the confusion of sounds that he hears.

- *Be theatrical about explaining sounds. For example, put your finger to your lips and say "Sssh, let's be quiet as mice" to explain the idea of quietness*

- *Describe sounds and music with appropriate adjectives such as "loud" or "soft"*

- *Teach the concept of high and low notes with songs*

- *Teach rhythm with rhymes and clapping songs – this will also help your child's speech*

- *Name every new sound, such as the cat purring, and imitate it*

Your baby needs to be able to hear the full range of sounds that are essential for speech if he is to be able to talk correctly. Only when your child proves, first that he can hear, later that he can imitate sound, and eventually that he can use different sounds correctly to form speech, can you be sure that he can discriminate between different sounds across the full normal range of hearing.

There are various clues to your child's hearing ability that you should be aware of, and several simple tests you can carry out to judge his progress. Carefully observe his reactions to different sounds and make a note of what you see. If anything about the way your baby responds to sounds concerns you, tell your doctor or health visitor who will be able to conduct a more thorough test on your baby's hearing.

Your newborn baby reacts to noises without really understanding them. If he is startled by a sudden loud noise, such as a hand clap or a door slamming, he may throw out his arms and legs in a "startle" reflex action, as though to save himself from falling. A little later, sudden sounds will make him blink or open his eyes wide in surprise. By four weeks he will begin to notice sudden prolonged noises, like the sound of your vacuum cleaner.

By the time he is four months old your baby should be able to discriminate between certain sounds. For example, when he hears your voice he will quieten or smile, and will turn his head and eyes towards your sound, even if he cannot see where you are.

After six months your baby should turn at once to investigate quiet noises made on each side of him, or at the sound of your voice from across the room. A nine-month-old baby should be babbling to hear his own voice, and will listen attentively to familiar sounds and search for quiet sounds made out of sight.

EARLY TESTS

The first testing your child undergoes to measure his reaction to sound may well be in the maternity unit shortly after birth. This testing will use soft sounds (clapping, singing, ringing) to measure your baby's response to noise. Responses may vary from a slight movement of the head to a change in breathing rate. More formal tests are conducted during routine developmental assessments at about six weeks, and between six and ten months.

The problem with early testing is that, until about seven months, babies react inconsistently to noise, and require careful monitoring with sophisticated machinery to achieve reliable results.

Parents with profoundly deaf children usually become aware of the problem fairly quickly. It is often more difficult to identify those with partial hearing loss, because their symptoms can be mistaken for inattentiveness, slow learning, or shyness. If you are worried about your child's hearing, you should have him examined by your doctor as soon as possible so that he can receive proper help.

TESTING HEARING

There are simple tests you can do to check your baby's hearing from about six months of age. For the best results the tests need to be carried out in a quiet room with no distractions.

You will need a high-pitched rattle, some hard tissue paper, and a china cup, a spoon, and a bell. Sit the baby on your lap, no less than 4 feet from any wall, and ask another adult to take up a position to the side of your baby, level with his ear and outside his immediate range of vision.

The tester should stand 45 centimetres (18 inches) away for a six-month-old, and 1 metre (3 feet) away for a nine-month-old and make sounds at the level of the baby's ear in the following order:

• Produce low-pitched and high-pitched sounds with your voice.

• Shake the rattle.

• Tap the spoon against the cup.

• Crumple the tissue paper.

• Ring the handbell.

If you get no response to any of the sounds, wait two seconds before repeating it. Wait a further two seconds and if there is still no response after three tries, go on to the next sound.

Children of nine months and upwards should turn at once when they hear the sound and will often smile. Younger babies may be slower to react. A clear response to three of these sounds means your baby has enough hearing to speak. If the response is less, repeat the test within three months before seeing your doctor.

18 months to 2 years For an older baby or toddler you should judge his response to spoken instructions. Sit him opposite you at a low table, with another familiar adult (such as his father) close by. Ask him to hand certain objects to daddy, such as a ball, cup and spoon, doll, toy car, or building block, and see how he responds. Ask him again from different distances up to 3 metres (10 feet). For children up to three years you could try the same test while partly covering your mouth with a piece of card to muffle the sound.

It is important that you don't carry out these hearing tests too often, because even quite a young child will come to know what to expect and will turn to the tester whether or not he can hear the sound.

OLDER BABY

THE HEARING-IMPAIRED CHILD

Children must be able to hear in order to speak, and must speak to learn, read, and write, so it is essential to pick up any hearing impairment early and seek professional help as soon as possible.

Children with incurable hearing loss can function quite well with a hearing aid, and many doctors now fit them during infancy rather than at four or five years. In profoundly deaf children, however, comprehension of sound and language is significantly impaired.

There are many ways to approach communication for profoundly deaf children, and they are often used in combination. Among them are: cochlear implants, one of several signing languages, lip-reading, and oral language.

Simple hearing test
A six-month-old baby with normal hearing will turn his head if you ring a small bell near him, just outside his field of vision.

MENTAL DEVELOPMENT

Your baby is born with a finite number of brain cells, yet his brain doubles in weight between birth and 12 months. The increase in weight is due to the growth of connections between the different cells used in thinking. When your baby sees a piece of bread, points to it, reaches for it, picks it up, puts it in his mouth, chews it, tastes it, and swallows it, he's built up eight brain connections and slotted it all into his memory.

PREDICTING INTELLIGENCE

Although it's difficult to say what "normal" intelligence is, many experts in the field of development can define the sequence and rate of mental development in the average child and use this to predict intelligence. Remember that the average child doesn't exist: an average is theoretical, so you should never apply it to your own child, nor should you compare him with other children of his age.

There are major variations in the rate of development from child to child, and there is no correct age when any milestones should be reached. Most children have growth spurts and pauses. Some show a temporary developmental pause and then go on to develop normally; others appear advanced in infancy but turn out to be average in later years. Then there is the well-known "slow starter", the child who is slightly behind in infancy, yet later does very well. A very few children show a progressive slowing in the rate of development. There are children in whom it is so difficult to predict the course of development that the outlook can only be guessed at cautiously and after repeated examinations. The conclusion is that you should not try to predict your baby's intelligence unless there is a very good reason to do so.

The great majority of babies turn out to be perfectly normal children. Sadly, a very small number lag seriously behind in all fields of development and, unless the lag is due to a serious physical handicap, can grow up to be educationally under par. Throughout the first three years the mentally impaired child shows below-average concentration and interest in his surroundings. He is late in aspects of development such as head control, sitting up, and grasping his toes, and in outgrowing his primitive birth reflexes, which may persist long after the usual age.

While there are clear indicators that a child is mentally slow, it is more difficult to spot the child with above-average abilities. A particularly intelligent baby may reach developmental milestones earlier than average, but the real indicators of his superior intelligence are more subtle: he'll display a greater variety of behaviour, a greater interest in his surroundings, and more interaction with his environment than the average baby.

THE PARENT'S ROLE

Very few children are retarded, and equally few are especially gifted, so the chances are that your child falls within the normal range of intelligence. Your task as a parent is to accept his abilities and to help him develop his strengths by careful teaching. Remember, too, that there are many fields of ability: we tend to think of intelligence rather narrowly as verbal and arithmetic skills, but your child may have creative and artistic abilities which are just as valuable and just as much in need of nurturing. Never push your child: accept him for who he is, give him every opportunity to develop his talents; show him and let him know that you love and respect him just as he is.

INTELLIGENCE TESTING

Modern systems of intelligence testing were developed in 1905 by two Frenchmen. Originally they were intended to predict whether children were likely to do well at school, and concentrated on judgement, comprehension, and reasoning. Modern testing views intelligence as the ability to process information, and so the tests are devised to see how well a child is acquiring thinking skills and applying them to everyday life. They are limited to skills that are important at school, and don't take account of creativity or artistic talent. It is wrong to use IQ scores to predict how successful a child will be in later life, since thinking skills develop over time.

CREATIVITY

All children have some creative ability, and developing this in the preschool years is just as important as teaching letters and numbers. There are a whole range of skills and mental processes that you can encourage in your child to stimulate his creative abilities: point out the things happening around him, show him patterns, colours, flowers, animals, smells, act out empathy for other people, talk about feelings, invent stories, and imagine "What would happen if…?" Dressing up, painting and drawing, or making toys are all practical activities which can help your child develop his creativity and imagination.

Making costumes
Encourage your child to make his own dressing-up toys with a variety of coloured card, crayons, scissors, and sticky tape.

THE MALE BRAIN

Even while your baby is in the womb his brain is programmed for maleness. Differences in brain structure and function between boys and girls affect the way they develop as they grow up.

• *A boy's brain weight and volume are greater than a girl's by about 10–15 per cent*

• *When the right side of the brain is ready to send connections to the left, the appropriate cells don't yet exist in boys. As a result the fibres go back into the right side. This enriches connections within the right lobe and could explain why boys have greater spatial awareness than girls*

• *Boys show less fear on separation than girls because they have slower message transmission than girls until the brain matures. From as young as nine or ten months they bring the fear under control by activity such as playing with a toy or crawling to investigate an object so as to distract themselves. This mode of behaviour continues into adulthood*

MENTAL DEVELOPMENT

YOUR BABY'S SMILE

The first time your baby smiles at you is an exciting milestone in your relationship; it's also an important sign that she is developing mentally.

When your baby begins to smile, she is demonstrating that she can recognise you and that she wants to engage with you in an exchange – she's already being sociable. She will start to respond to your talking to her with smiles, because she has learned that this pleases you and makes you talk to her more – her first attempts at "conversation" (see p.198).

Smiling is an important indicator of a baby's maturity and desire for interaction with other people, and experts consider that a baby who smiles early in a sociable way may be showing the first signs of superior intelligence.

A coloured rattle will catch your baby's attention

Stimulating your baby
Encourage your child to focus on objects by rattling and shaking toys in her line of vision.

Your baby's world is a confused blur of sights and sounds at first, and in the early weeks she is fully occupied with sorting out the things that have significance: your face and voice will be among the first things she recognises. She will show her recognition with responses such as smiling, jerking her legs and arms, or cooing and gurgling. She demonstrates her good memory and her hearing by quietening if you play a recording of the human heartbeat – something that has comforted her for nine months.

Newborn Within half an hour of birth your baby will flicker her eyes when spoken to. After one week she knows your voice and after two she will show that she recognises you. If spoken to from 20–25 centimetres (8–10 inches) where she can see your face, she will open and close her mouth in response.

Recognising mother
Your baby will recognise your voice and face and show signs of this at a very early age.

1 month She will respond to the tone of your voice, becoming calm if you speak soothingly and distressed in response to rough tones. She gets very excited and her whole body jerks when she attempts to "speak". She follows a moving object with her eyes.

2 months She smiles readily in response to your face and voice. She looks around in response to sounds, and stares at objects with intense interest.

3 months Your baby is becoming more aware of her body, and will look at her hands and move them. She responds to conversation by smiling, gurgling, and moving her body

4 months Your baby is curious about all sights, sounds, and people. She likes to sit propped against cushions so she can look around her. She now recognises familiar objects and remembers routines; she'll get excited at the sight of a breast or bottle. She plays with her feet when lying on her back.

5 months Your baby now spends longer examining things, showing that her concentration is developing. She turns to unseen sounds, and moves her arms and legs to attract your attention.

6 months Your baby makes sounds to attract your attention, and puts out her arms to be picked up. She "speaks" and smiles to her reflection in a mirror. She may start to show shyness with strangers.

HOW YOU CAN HELP

From the earliest days you should talk and sing to your baby. Her movements and sounds are her earliest attempts at speaking, so answer them to encourage her; make sure she can see your face clearly and make eye contact with her at all times, smile a lot, and exaggerate your mouth movements.

Feed her curiosity Everything is new and interesting to your baby, so show her objects and give her a chance to hold them. By the time she is two months old, she will like to sit propped up so that she can look around her; put lots of small, soft toys within her reach where she can see and touch them. Talk to her constantly.

Encourage awareness of herself Your baby's discovery of her own body is a gradual process. When she is about eight weeks old, you can start showing her her hands, and play simple physical games. By six months she will smile at herself in the mirror.

PERCEPTION

Your baby experiences things through her senses just as you do, but she has to learn to single out what is important and what is not. Help her to connect the information given by her different senses: show her a rattle, allow her to touch it, then shake it and draw her attention to the sound. Touch is one of the main ways that your baby explores her environment, so introduce her to lots of different textures.

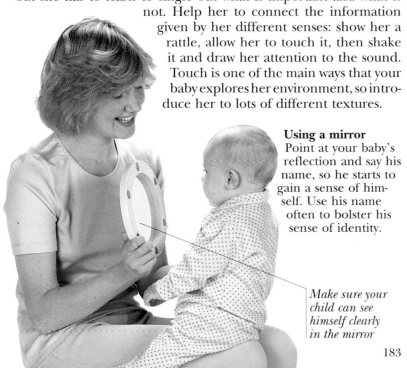

Using a mirror
Point at your baby's reflection and say his name, so he starts to gain a sense of himself. Use his name often to bolster his sense of identity.

Make sure your child can see himself clearly in the mirror

From an early stage, your baby can make basic distinctions between big and small. She will also show interest in new sights and sounds, as the following test, which can be carried out from four months, demonstrates.

• *Show your baby a card with a small circle above a large circle drawn on it*

• *Next show her a card with a small triangle above a large triangle. She is already starting to see the relationship between the small and large shapes*

• *Now show her a card with a small diamond above a large one. Because this fits the pattern set by the first two, she will probably show no interest in it*

• *If you show her a card with a large triangle above a small one she will probably show renewed interest because the pattern of small above large has changed*

Test cards
Your baby will be able to make quite sophisticated distinctions involving pattern and shape.

L EARNING THROUGH P LAY

Babies and children learn through play, and play is a very serious business! Everything is a learning experience for your baby, and anything new is fun, so learning and playing are indistinguishable. If you are aware of the skills he's developing in his first six months, you can choose games and toys that will interest him and are best suited to encourage his abilities. At this age, toys that stimulate his senses will be most interesting to him.

Simple games Because your baby is fascinated by your face, "peek-a-boo" is one of the most successful games you can play with him. Hide your face in your hands or with a scarf or towel, then peek out at him saying "peek-a-boo" as you do it. Babies develop a sense of humour quite early, and this is a game that they find endlessly amusing. When he's old enough to sit up without support, roll a large, soft ball gently towards him; he will eventually try to push it back to you with his hands. Then you've got a real game going and he's acquiring early ball sense.

Rhymes and songs Your baby will love listening to rhymes even when he's very young, because he likes to be talked to, and rhythmic sounds are easier for him to listen to than normal speech. He will love to be sung to, as well, whether it's a soothing lullaby or a more lively tune sung while you bounce him on your knee. Rhyming, rhythmic songs and games encourage early speech.

Physical activities Even a very young baby can benefit from play such as bouncing, swinging, and rocking. They will make him aware of his own body and improve his locomotive skills such as crawling and walking as well as balance and co-ordination.

Feed his senses Your baby explores the world through his senses, and he will find anything new interesting (see **Testing perception**, p.183). Allow him to spend as much time as possible propped up in a sitting position so that he can see what is going on around him, and leave small toys within his reach so he can handle them – toys that make noises or are made of differently textured materials are best. Catch his interest first by showing him the toys up close, and demonstrating how the sound can be made – even something as simple as a beaker filled with fairly large beans will serve as a toy. When he's older and able to grasp objects, you can give him stacking beakers or rings – ones with large pieces are suitable while his grasp is still quite primitive. The kitchen is a good source of interesting toys for your child; wooden spoons, spatulas, small pans and lids, colanders and sieves, funnels, a set of measuring spoons, plastic cups, ice cube trays, or egg cartons. Let your baby create his own use for them.

Look and learn
Colour, shape and noise are all interesting to your baby, so choose toys that give a variety of these things.

184

A rattle is an ideal toy as your baby gradually learns to grasp objects during the first six months

By about four months your baby explores the world through his mouth, so provide toys that are safe to chew

Toys that do different things are a good buy; this camera incorporates a mirror, makes clicking noises, and can be chewed

Your baby will love toys that make a noise, so hang an easily operated musical box over his cot or pram

CHOOSING TOYS

Many parents find it difficult to choose toys for a new baby – relatives even more so. A young baby won't be able to interact with his toys much at first, so they should be soft, simple, sturdy, and attractive to look at and touch.

Soft toys Your baby will like soft toys that he can squeeze and that are nice to touch. Make sure they are washable and colourfast, because he will keep putting them in his mouth.

Mobiles For a newborn, a mobile hung 25 centimetres (10 inches) above a cot or pram provides visual stimulation, but make sure it's out of his reach. Change the parts around every few days to hold his interest.

Noisy toys Rattles, soft toys that squeak, and musical toys are all suitable for a young baby. By six months, he loves to play with a music box that he can operate perhaps by pressing a button or pulling a string.

Books Your baby is never too young to be read to. From three to four months choose books with large, brightly coloured pictures; point to common objects and name them while he's sitting on your knee. Faces always attract him, so show him pictures in magazines and point out the parts of your face, then his face, and then the same parts in the pictures.

SAFETY

Safety is the most important consideration when choosing toys. With a young baby bear in mind that he is likely to put everything in his mouth.

• *Toys such as rattles should be lightweight in case your baby hits himself with them*

• *Avoid toys with small holes that could trap your baby's fingers*

• *Long strings could be swallowed or wrapped around your baby's neck*

• *Soft toys should be made of flame-retardant material, and should also be colourfast; otherwise your baby could suck the dye off and become ill*

• *Small parts that could choke your baby, such as eyes on soft toys, should be firmly attached*

MENTAL DEVELOPMENT

LEARNING SPURTS

Your baby's mental development goes in spurts, rather than moving at a constant rate.

During a learning spurt your child will latch on to new ideas and skills very quickly, and put them into practice immediately.

During these rapid learning phases, skills that he's already acquired may seem to slip a bit because your baby's concentration is totally taken up with learning something new. Once a new skill has been mastered he'll regain any lost skills.

If your baby clearly enjoys certain activities then repeat them. Don't hesitate, however, to introduce your baby to new ideas, because he can absorb information very quickly and develop new skills at an astonishing speed. Aim to entertain him over as wide and interesting a range as possible. Your baby will latch on to what he wants and ignore the rest.

A learning spurt is usually followed by a period when development appears to slow down as your baby consolidates newly learned skills and prepares for the next spurt. This is a good time to help him to practise skills he has just acquired until they are absorbed into his repertoire.

Your baby is developing new mental abilities at an amazing rate, most of it through play, and you can help by giving him lots of interesting new experiences. Try to suppress any anxieties about what your child should be learning at this stage. Be guided by him and respond to his needs. He will develop much faster if you let him learn what he wants to, rather than what you think is best.

7 months   Your baby is beginning to know the meaning of words and understands "no". He shows signs of determination by going for toys that are out of reach. Your baby takes a keen interest in games, and concentrates deeply on his toys. He will look around for a toy he has dropped, demonstrating a developing memory.

8 months   Your baby's memory really takes a leap forward at eight months when he recognises familiar games and rhymes, and will turn his head when he hears his name. He can anticipate movement and will hold out his hands to be washed, but turn his face away from a flannel.

9 months   Your baby is becoming familiar with routines, such as waving bye-bye and putting out his foot so you can put on his sock. He also knows "pat-a-cake" all the way through. Your baby knows what a doll or teddy is and will pat it, and he'll look round corners for a toy, and for Daddy, if you say "Where's Daddy?". This is a very important perceptual step: he's learned that things are still there even if he can't see them.

10 months   Your baby may point out things in a book by the time he is ten months but he won't concentrate for long. He will be constantly dropping toys out of his pram and wanting them picked up because he's learned the "letting go" skill. He may say one word with meaning. He is also starting to understand the concepts of "here" and "there", "in" and "out", and "up" and "down".

11 months   Your baby's sense of humour really shows by now. He loves jokes and will repeat anything that makes you laugh. His interest in books is developing and he likes to have items pointed out, then he points them out if you ask him. He will repeat his name and shake his head for "no".

1 year   Once your baby is a year old he'll kiss, and say two or three words with meaning. He'll pick up a toy and hand it to you, and may point to an object that he recognises in a picture spontaneously. He starts to understand simple questions.

STYLES OF PERCEPTION

From about six months old a child is developing his own "style of perception" – that is, the time and care he takes to look at a situation before making a decision. Broadly speaking, most people fall into one of two styles: reflective or impulsive. A reflective baby will look at something with fixed concentration, and remain very still, whereas an impulsive baby will become excited, and look away after only a short period of examination.

When your baby is 18 months old, you can tell which style most closely describes him by trying a simple test: show your baby a card on which there is a picture, and below, variations of this picture. Ask him to select the picture that exactly matches the picture at the top. A reflective child will look at all the options carefully before making a choice, and is usually right. An impulsive child is more likely to look at all the pictures quickly and then make a snap decision, which is often the wrong one.

Reflective children often do slightly better at school, especially in learning to read. An impulsive child may therefore need more help with schooling. Reflectiveness, however, is not always best. There are occasions when your child has to think fast, such as when playing games, and an impulsive child may be better able to make a good decision in the short time available.

HELPING YOUR CHILD'S MENTAL DEVELOPMENT

To stretch your child's memory, play hide-and-seek with a toy. Place a toy in front of your baby and let him reach for it several times, then put a piece of paper in front to hide it. Your baby will move the paper to find the toy. Give him simple tasks such as putting things in and taking them out of containers

Choose soft baby books with large colourful illustrations, and set aside a quiet time each day to read. Children especially enjoy tales about mother and baby animals, and such stories will help them learn about the sounds animals make. You could also read different kinds of well illustrated books and magazines to your baby. Try naming several items on a page, and then take your baby's hand and point to them. Name the items again.

At one year old your baby will begin to understand cause and effect if you describe your actions while, for example, putting his coat on him and taking it off, or dressing and undressing a doll. Describe what is happening when he plays. For instance, if he knocks over his bricks, say "All fall down". Play lots of water games with him; give him pots, jars, and jugs that he can use to pour, empty, and fill. Put his toys just out of reach and retrieve them when he asks. Encourage independence with self-feeding.

An older child, of around 15 months, can be given simple tasks, such as tidying up and putting things away in the right place or fetching something for you, to stimulate his sense of achievement and to encourage his feelings of pride. Help him to string words together to make simple sentences of three or four words. Introduce the concept of possession, particularly with his own things: "That's Michael's ball, your ball."

MEMORY

Now that your baby is older, his developing memory becomes more apparent. There are many things you can do to help.

• *Repeat a short rhyme to your child over and over again, until he learns how to say it himself*

• *Sing a brief song to your baby, accentuating the rhythm with handclaps, head nods, and gestures of your body*

• *Reading aloud to your baby is by far the best way to develop memory. If a story is repeated several times he will anticipate events and say them before you get there. If you hesitate dramatically in mid-sentence, he will supply the missing word, such as duck, tree, baby, or kitten*

• *Reciting sequences of numbers will stimulate his memory, as will parroting the alphabet, especially if you give it a definite rhythm or rhyming pattern*

HOME-MADE TOYS

A baby under one year doesn't need shop-bought toys. Use colourful, noisy, household items to stimulate and fascinate her.

• *Anything that rolls: cotton reels or the cardboard tube inside kitchen rolls and toilet rolls*

• *Interesting textures: pieces of felt, a string of beads, thick strands of wool, or bean bags*

• *Interesting shapes: plastic ice cube trays, whisks, egg cartons, colanders and sieves, or plastic bottles of all shapes and sizes*

• *Anything that's noisy: wooden spoons and spatulas, small saucepans and lids, cake tins, or plastic cups*

• *Anything that rattles: plastic jars with seeds, beads, or paper clips inside (but make sure the lid's on tight)*

Noisy
A baby will love playing with pots, pans, and saucepan lids. The more noise she can make the more fun she'll have.

LEARNING THROUGH PLAY

Your baby learns through play, and to develop fully she needs all her senses in use: sight, hearing, smell, touch, and taste. To provide the necessary stimulation, her toys and games should be full of variety so that they will appeal to all these senses. While you should obviously play with your baby as much as possible, it is also important that she learns to play on her own so that her sense of exploration and imagination is given full rein.

At seven months your baby's mouth is still an important sense organ and she'll want interesting objects that she can investigate safely. Her toys should be bright, colourful and have an interesting shape to stimulate her perception of form and space as well as her sense of colour. Primary colours are best at this age. Always name the colour of an object she plays with.

Stimulate your child's hearing with toys that make ringing or rattling sounds when she shakes them. Musical boxes provide endless fascination for young children, particularly ones with a string your baby can pull. As your baby's manipulative abilities improve, she'll become absorbed by touch as well as sound. She will love toys that make a noise when she squeezes them. Activity centres, which have a series of knobs and buttons that your baby can push or turn to make noises, can be attached to a cot or a bath. As well as stimulating both her hearing and sense of touch, they will help her understand the link between cause and effect. Rubber balls of all sizes are always a favourite.

Any fairly small objects that are interesting to touch with holes or handles into which your baby can poke her fingers or wrap them around are ideal. Look for objects that are brightly coloured and, if possible, make a noise, like rings with bells on them. She'll love a large, specially designed baby mirror placed in her cot for her to stare into. Never put one of your own mirrors in the cot as it could easily break.

When she is ten months to one year old, your baby will pick up small objects like pencils, crayons, and, eventually, paint brushes. She'll be more mobile now and will enjoy being able to push or pull toys like trains, cars, or trolleys.

From one year to 18 months, having achieved some measure of dexterity, your baby will enjoy toys that challenge her manipulative abilities, such as puzzles. Nesting and stacking toys that can be built up or fitted together will encourage dexterity and spatial visualization. Now that she speaks and understands some words and ideas, she'll love stories and books. Those with brightly coloured illustrations and different textures are best.

Toys that your baby can push or pull around build limbs and muscles

Books should have large, simple illustrations, and be made of a chewable material

Building with blocks gives your baby a sense of achievement

Musical or noisy toys will attract her attention

Colouring materials will satisfy your baby's need for scribbling

PLAYING TOGETHER

Your baby will enjoy playing games with you. To ensure she makes the most of new toys, show her how they can be used and encourage her to be imaginative with them.

- *Roll a ball to her and encourage her to roll it back to you; her hand–eye co-ordination will develop*

- *Show her how to build a more complicated structure with blocks, such as a bridge; she will improve her delicate manipulative skills*

- *Fill a container with water or sand and show her how to fill up measuring cups and containers; she'll experience the movement of different substances*

Water play
All babies enjoy splashing in water or floating a boat in a bowl. Provide unbreakable containers to pour and fill.

TOYS AND GAMES

As your baby grows, her developing skills and mental abilities will be reflected in toys that capture her imagination. Free-standing rattles that she can swipe at while feeding, for example, will keep her amused at first. Large soft blocks are ideal for a six-month-old baby because they can be used for building and throwing, but an older baby will prefer hard blocks of wood or plastic, stable enough for more complicated structures. Puzzles and games that challenge your baby, such as simple jigsaws, are important for her development. They should have knobs to make the pieces easier to pick up, or a very few large pieces that are simple to put together.

189

MENTAL DEVELOPMENT

IMAGINATION

Most children over the age of 15 months or so begin to develop a vivid imagination, and there are substantial individual differences. In general, the greater the intelligence the greater the imagination.

Between 15 and 18 months imagination begins to appear in doll play. At three years your child will have imaginary play-mates behind the sofa and she will tell tall stories and play highly imaginative games with friends. Her imagination may lead to the development of fears: of the dark, of noises, or of animals, for example.

At the toddler stage, your child starts to become an independent, person. Her speech will progress during this phase and she'll be able to ask for what she wants, and do some of the things you want her to do – if she so chooses. She'll have an insatiable curiosity about her world and everything in it, will be able to cope with increasingly complex ideas, and will be eager to put all she learns to good use.

MILESTONES

18 months Your baby will be able to ask for food, drinks, and toys. She probably tells you when she wants to go to the potty, but can't wait and so has frequent accidents. She will carry out several simple requests and begin to understand more complex ones, such as "Please get your hairbrush from the bathroom". She may also grab your arm or use other gestures to get your attention. Her vocabulary may consist of about 30 words.

2 years Your child's vocabulary of names and objects will increase rapidly. She will describe and identify familiar items. She will obey complicated orders, and find a toy that she played with before. She will talk non-stop and ask occasional questions.

Shortly after this she will know who she is and say her own name. She'll try to build houses and castles with blocks, and repeat new words when encouraged. She'll begin to pit her will against yours and may become rather negative – saying "no" fairly often and not always fitting in with your wishes. She may know the difference between one and several, but she has little idea of the magnitude of numbers and so anything more than one may be "lots".

2 1/2–3 years Your child will start to add detail to broad concepts, as in "A horse has a long tail", and be able to draw horizontal and vertical lines. She'll be able to say one or two nursery rhymes and find them in her book, and she'll know some colours. She will also ask "why?" and say "won't" and "can't". She may make an attempt at copying a circle that you have drawn for her (see p.174), but probably won't be able to complete it. Your child will now enjoy helping with household tasks. She will begin to grasp the concept of numbers and may be able to count to three. A boy will have noticed that his sex organs stick out from his body, in contrast to those of little girls he has seen.

Chores
Your toddler enjoys helping you with some simple household tasks, such as sweeping.

Your child can understand prepositions, such as "in", "on", "under", "behind", and "after". At around three years old, she'll be able to form more complex sentences and her vocabulary may consist of 200–300 words. This, together with her ever-increasing curiosity, will lead her to ask incessant questions. She can distinguish between "now" and "then" and will refer to the past. She knows her own gender. She'll become more sociable and like to play with others.

REASONING

As a toddler, your child may have satisfied her curiosity, absorbing a great deal of new information in the process, but rarely related it to anything else in her life. What happens in the third year, however, is that your child starts to think about her experiences and to learn from them. Information is sifted, matched up to other experiences to see if they fit together, or if they differ greatly, and it is then put into similar or different pigeonholes. Your child is learning to reason.

Your child starts to plan ahead, and becomes much more creative and imaginative. Gradually all the information that she has absorbed so far becomes available to apply to a given situation. This new ability to think, imagine, and create changes your child's perception of the world considerably.

Many familiar things in the house or garden no longer contain the same interest. She needs wider horizons; she needs to explore, to push the frontiers of her experience and knowledge further and further back. Your child becomes very interested in how things work. She is greedy for information and is constantly asking "why?".

A huge step is realizing that time is not just in the present: there is today, yesterday, and tomorrow. Planning for the future is one of the most critical aspects of our intellect and it is during this third year that you will hear your child say for the first time, "I will eat that later" or "We can go tomorrow".

FORMING CONCEPTS

This is an important step forward for her. One way in which it will be obvious is when, between the ages of 18 months and two years, she starts sorting objects as a form of play: she might sort her building blocks out from her other toys, for example, or the different animals in a toy farmyard. You'll notice, too, that she's begun to understand how things are grouped: she knows, for instance, that her toy ball and an apple are similar in shape and that they roll; that sparrows and crows are alike because they have feathers and fly; that animals that bark and have four legs are dogs.

Some time before her third birthday, your toddler will begin to give these concepts names – round, bird, dog. She will use the names in all cases where they are appropriate – whether the dog in question, for instance, is a family pet, a dog she sees on television or in a book, or a toy dog. By the time she is three years old she will describe things in a way that shows she also understands their differences: "our dog, "toy dog".

COLOURS

To help your child grasp the notion of colour, always mention that of something that you are using or wanting.

• *Household items: "I'm looking for the green packet'; "Where's that red tin gone?"; "Oh, I've found the jar with the blue label"*

• *Your child's clothes: "That's a pretty pink dress"; "What a nice red jumper"*

• *Flowers, animals, and especially birds: "Can you see the robin's red breast?"*

• *Show your child how colours are made: "Look, if we mix a little bit of red with this white we will get pink; yellow mixed with blue will make green"*

• *Teach your child the colours of the rainbow and get her to pick them out if you see a real rainbow*

Concept of roundness
A toddler can begin to deal with sophisticated ideas. She will understand that roundness, for example, is a property of different objects.

LEARNING THROUGH PLAY

Play helps learning in many ways. It improves manual dexterity – building a tower of blocks or doing a jigsaw puzzle teaches a child how to make her hands work for her as tools. Playing with other children teaches her it's important to get on with others; she will discover friendship and learn to be kind and show consideration for other people.

Social play helps to make a child's language more sophisticated because the more imaginative the play, the more complex the ideas that have to be put into words. Play aids physical development; the freedom to swing, climb, skip, run, and jump helps to perfect muscular co-ordination and physical skills. Play also improves hearing and vision considerably.

TYPES OF PLAY

Girls and boys love dolls; dolls are children's pretend families, helping them to create a make-believe world into which they can escape. While playing with dolls, your child is understanding human emotions. She will mother the doll, give it instructions, then dress it, put it to bed, and kiss it goodnight. In this way your child is re-enacting the things that happen to her, and learning to relate them to other people. Even action dolls for boys can bring out protective feelings. A child can also use dolls to get rid of aggressive instincts that might otherwise be directed against other children.

An important concept for a child to grasp is that of classification – whether things are the same or different. Toys of farmyard animals can help form this idea; with a variety of sheep, horses, and chickens your child will be able to sort out the animals that look the same. You can help by showing her the differences and naming the animals as you put them into groups.

Children love playing with water, especially in the bath. Give your child empty plastic bottles and containers so she can create a variety of water effects. All children love blowing bubbles; put some washing-up liquid in a beaker and shape a pipe-cleaner with a circle at one end. Paddling pools, such as the small blow-up kind, are ideal in the summer and needn't be expensive. Another summer game is to lay a tarpaulin on the ground and spray a hose over it; your child will enjoy sliding around on the slippery surface.

Painting encourages your child's creative urges. She'll love finger painting and can produce a range of interesting prints and patterns with combs, pegs, sponges, cotton reels, or cardboard tubes. Try cutting star shapes and other patterns out of pieces of potato so she can create unusual designs. Plastic egg boxes or baking trays will make good palettes for the aspiring painter. Give your child thick brushes so that she sees bold results immediately. Provide pastry brushes, cotton wool balls, corks, straws, and pipe cleaners for variety.

Costumes
Children love dressing up, so stock a box with old shoes, shirts, skirts, dresses, hats, and scarves, and include some cheap jewellery.

TOYS AND GAMES

Up to two years of age, your child will spend longer on toys that she can use independently, particularly those that imitate the adult world. Dolls, toy houses, and cars, for example, will enable her to act out the scenes she sees in real life. As she gets older, she will acquire new skills and enjoy anything that tests them – building and knocking down, or constructing and taking apart. Household items such as plastic containers and cardboard tubes will stimulate her creativity and imagination. Drawing, painting, making shapes with clay or plasticine, and fitting together puzzles encourage creativity. Long before she's able to write or draw formally, your child will love scribbling and using colours, so give her crayons and lots of paper. A box of coloured chalks and a blackboard and easel, set up at her height, will be useful because she'll be able to draw, then rub out her work and start again.

Children love being part of the domestic routine. A small child can be given a little bowl with some flour to mix each time you bake; she can help also with carrying, and use a small dustpan and brush to help with the cleaning.

A toy telephone will enable your child to imitate adults and feed the need for conversation and other word play

Your toddler is able to make increasingly complex use of building toys

Your child's picture books should now introduce simple vocabulary

Fuel your child's artistic talents with painting sets or play dough

OUTDOOR SAFETY

Once a child is old enough to have large toys to play with in the garden, a whole new set of hazards can arise.

It is impossible to provide a totally safe environment for your child, but if you take precautions the risk of serious accidents can be greatly reduced. For example, make sure that outdoor equipment is carefully installed and regularly checked for faults

- *Young children should always be properly supervised, and never left alone to play outdoors, especially in paddling pools*

- *Play equipment such as slides and swings should be checked regularly for strength, stability, and signs of corrosion. They should be installed on a soft, flat surface, such as grass or sand – never concrete*

- *Check all play equipment to ensure that there is no risk of scissoring, shearing, or pinching injuries and that surfaces are free from snags and splinters*

- *Instruct your children carefully on what they can and can't do on play equipment*

- *Ensure that tents, playhouses, and tunnels are made of flame-retardant material*

- *Make sure that sandpits are covered when not in use to stop animals fouling them*

- *Fence off ponds*

- *Always empty a paddling pool after use*

193

PRESCHOOL

MENTAL DEVELOPMENT

GIFTEDNESS

It is tempting to think your child is gifted if he is further ahead than others in one or two areas.

Truly gifted children, however, are advanced in most aspects of achievement and in the acquisition of skills. They will enjoy all kinds of brain exercises and may even find some of them very easy. A gifted child invariably learns quickly and is able to use that learning in a broad and flexible way. If this applies to your child it will be important to provide him with plenty of stimulation, new games, new ideas for play, and plenty of creative opportunities. Otherwise he is liable to become bored and frustrated if he is not being stretched by his play (see p.252).

Puzzles
You can aid your preschool child's mental development with some simple teasers.

The development of your child as an independent and reasoning individual really blossoms during the preschool years. His use of language will be much more fluent and he'll start to relate speech to the written word. His steadily improving grasp of shapes and understanding of sequences will mean he can solve more complex puzzles, such as re-arranging pictures into the correct order, or copying a design. He'll also be much more imaginative in his play so that he will be able to keep himself amused for longer periods, without expecting you to join in.

A three-year-old child will want to help with simple household tasks, such as sweeping up or laying the table. His make-believe play will be more vivid, as he invents people and objects and puts them into more complex situations, which is why girls enjoy Wendy houses and boys make camps. He'll enjoy playing on the floor, alone or with siblings, for much longer periods. And he is beginning to understand that some enjoyable things must be put off to the future, such as a visit to a favourite relative, or being able to buy an ice-cream.

He is more independent and more self-centred at the age of four. He may be cheeky, and more argumentative about getting his own way. He will have mastered the concepts of past, present and future though he may not understand how near or far off his birthday is.

By the age of five he will be more sensible and controlled, and will be able to play games that have more complicated rules. He'll be able to appreciate clock time and it will help him relate to a daily routine. His sense of humour will also be more developed now and he will be able to tell simple jokes and act out comical situations – anything for a laugh.

Ask your child which part is missing from this picture

Ask your child to put the pictures in the correct order

Make patterns with specially painted blocks for your child to copy

Make a jigsaw by cutting up a postcard or an old photograph

PERCEPTION

Perceptual style – the way in which a child takes in a situation – depends on whether he is able to shut out what's going on in the background or takes a lot of notice of it. The former is called field independency and the latter is field dependency.

Measurements of field independence or dependence show a strong difference between girls and boys. Boys are usually more field independent, and are therefore able to pick out a shape from a complicated background more easily than girls. This could be because boys are usually far better at spatial visualization at a much earlier age than girls.

It can be quite helpful to know if your child is field independent in his interests and personality. If he is he will generally be able to focus on objects or tasks, while field-dependent children tend to focus more on people. This may account for the fact that baby girls, being more field dependent, are much more sociable from the outset than boys.

TESTING PERCEPTION

You can assess your child's field dependence or independence by seeing whether or not he is able to pick out a geometric shape from a complicated drawing. Show your child a simple shape, such as a circle, square or triangle, and then ask him to find a figure exactly like that in a more complex drawing.

In order to find the figure your child has to ignore the background detail (the field) and pay attention only to shapes. Generally speaking, children become increasingly field independent as they get older. After a while you will be able to introduce more complicated shapes – such as a hidden animal – in more and more complex backgrounds.

If your child is more field dependent, he'll rely more on outside clues, and so on your prompting and your encouragement. In contrast, however, your field-independent child, because of his greater ability to extract parts from wholes, will tend to be better at some cognitive tasks, such as those that require good spatial sense – playing chess, for example.

Jigsaws
Wooden jigsaw puzzles are easier to handle and don't bend like cardboard ones.

LEARNING DISABILITIES

Children learn at different rates so apparent problems, such as a delay in learning to read, may simply be a normal variation in timing, rather than a sign of any disability. But there may be other signs that might indicate a learning disability of which you should be aware.

• *Learning disabilities rarely occur alone. They are usually part of a broader picture including perhaps poor co-ordination, poor memory, and the inability to draw and to fit differently shaped blocks into matching holes in a board*

• *Common features that accompany learning difficulties include a short attention span, aimless over-activity, poor concentration, impulsiveness, aggressiveness, and clumsiness. Such a child's eyesight and hearing should be tested in order to pick up any possible weaknesses*

• *Dyslexia is a learning disability which should be spotted early on. Commonly called word-blindness, this condition is part of a wider spectrum of learning problems including difficulty in spelling and writing. Early signs include delayed language development, apparent hearing problems, and clumsiness, but a proper diagnosis can only be made by a professional child psychologist (see p.253)*

LEARNING THROUGH PLAY

Play will continue to make a positive contribution to your preschool child's development. Once she has practised her creative interests at play, she can apply them to the real world. Sometimes your child will be absorbed in a make-believe world of her own and won't need your involvement: at other times you can add to her enjoyment by suggesting new games, or new ways to play with her toys.

Your child's insatiable curiosity needs more stimulation than your home can offer, so go to the local park regularly and plan outings to the countryside, or to a wildlife park.

Make-believe play Your child will create a little world of her own as part of her imitation of adults. An instant tent or playhouse can be made from a couple of chairs, or a small table draped with a blanket. Children love playing with cardboard boxes, so long as they are big enough to climb into. Small ones become boats and cars; piles of them turn into castles and houses. Boxes laid on their sides are tunnels, and laid end to end become trains.

• Let your child know in advance what to expect, say by reading a book with her, so she'll get the most out of the experience

Dressing up is a favourite game at this age: a few simple props can transform your child into a doctor or fire-fighter and, in her fantasy world, she is the adult, and a teddy bear or doll serves as child. It often surprised me who my sons thought were family.

• Talk about items of interest, and take crayons and paper, or a colouring book, and encourage her to draw what she sees

Messy play Any play involving water, sand, mud, or dough will stretch your child's intellect. Your child may build a wall in the sandpit which then becomes a castle, or she may simply enjoy playing with a bucket full of water and floating objects, which will keep popping up to the surface no matter how often she pushes them down. To make your supervision easier, set aside a time when messy play is allowed and a place where the mess can be contained, and encourage your child to look forward to it.

• The seaside is full of new sights, sounds, and smells – don't forget a bucket and spade. Sand castles are a perennial favourite

• Provide a cheap camera to make a record of the trip and put her photos in an album

Domestic play By now your child has mastered the co-ordination needed to help around the house. It's play rather than work because she's so keen to copy you. She helps in the kitchen by tearing salad leaves or arranging bread on a plate, and will enjoy laying the table, so improving manipulative and counting skills as well as independence and self-worth.

Musical play Any child with normal hearing can hear and enjoy musical sounds. She probably won't be able to play melodies, but she may be able to hum them and will enjoy banging out a rhythm. Rattles, wooden clappers, trumpets, and drums are all very good for this purpose, as are old pans or baking tins and wooden spoons. A xylophone will enable her to identify musical sounds and experiment with high and low notes. It's best not to buy a xylophone

Make-believe play
Your little girl will readily adopt a mother's role towards her doll and may create a whole imaginary world around this relationship.

or other instrument until she's shown interest over the long term and then it's worth investing in a good quality one from a music shop, which will be better for your child's developing ear.

SHARING TOYS

Your child wants to be sociable so she has to learn the difficult skill of sharing. It's easiest if she learns to share with you first, so set her a good example: "Here's some of Mummy's ice cream"; "You can have half of my apple". Then introduce the concept of "One for you, one for me". Only then say "May I have your pencil?"; "May I play with your dolly?"

A chalk board with coloured chalks is a good way of introducing your child to numbers and letters

A sturdy tape machine will enable your child to listen to her favourite songs and stories

Soft balls are safe for indoor play

Introduce your child to more complicated building sets

SIMPLE GAMES

Your child at four or five is old enough to understand simple board games. She will enjoy uncomplicated games involving a spinning wheel, dice, or moving pieces, as well as card games which rely on pictures, such as "Old Maid" and "Snap".

• *Many games will help her improve her counting skills and also her developing ability to concentrate. Games with rules that have to be followed can serve as an introduction to the concept that the real world is full of accepted standards*

• *She will have to learn to take her turn and to wait patiently while others take theirs. This will help her to realize that other people have rights and needs that sometimes take priority over hers*

• *The winning and losing element of games will teach her to understand and cope with disappointment and to try harder next time, as well as enjoy the success of winning. Don't concentrate too much on winning; it could make her unduly agressive and competitive in later life*

A musical toy, such as a xylophone, will allow your child to experiment with sounds

SPEECH AND LANGUAGE

FIRST SOUNDS

Your baby first starts to communicate with you at birth, but without sounds.

Within half an hour of birth your baby moves her eyes at your voice and when you're 25 centimetres (10 inches) away from her face she will smile and mouth in imitation and recognition of hearing speech. She is born to talk!

Crying becomes the major way of saying she's discontented; burbles of contentment don't appear for another six weeks.

Social smiling at six weeks marks her desire to converse and a few weeks later she'll start to make vowel sounds, such as "eh", "ah", "uh", "oh". By the time she's three or four months old, she'll be making a variety of sounds: vocalizations, laughing, squealing, and blowing between her lips. Around five to six months her first consonants appear – "m", "p", and "b" – and so she may say "ma" or "pa" very early on, though she will attach no meaning to these sounds.

Babies need and want to communicate from the very earliest days, and even before they begin to vocalize they will listen to and try to imitate sounds. The basics of languages are built into babies' brains. A deaf infant starts to babble at the same age as a child with normal hearing, so we know that auditory stimulation is not necessary for language development. Some theorists even say we have a "language acquisition device" somewhere in the brain that makes language inevitable.

Before your baby is six weeks old, she will have learned that if she smiles or makes sounds, you will respond. What is remarkable is that even at this early stage she realizes that she can call the shots: she smiles, you are pleased and so talk to her more, and she can keep a two-way "conversation" going. By smiling and talking to your baby and showing your pleasure when she responds, you are giving her her very first lesson in communication.

Newborn Your baby will respond to human voices from the moment of birth, and she will try to imitate gestures and expressions. She will sense when you are talking to her and will respond with sounds and by moving her entire body.

4–6 weeks She can already recognise your voice. She'll respond to your smiles and speech by gurgling, and wait for you to reply. Keep your face close to hers when you talk to her so that she can see you, and reward her sounds with more smiles and talking.

4 months Your baby now has a range of sounds, including squeals and blowing between her lips. She communicates with you through laughter, so laugh and giggle a lot when you talk to her.

6 months There are many signs that your baby is beginning to understand what you say. She babbles and strings sounds together. Singing to her, repeating rhymes, and speaking rhythmically will all help her to understand language and encourage early speaking.

Talking to your baby
Your earliest conversations with your baby will involve smiles rather than sounds.

BEGINNING TO TALK

For your baby to talk, she must first understand what you say, and her understanding will increase rapidly towards the end of the first year. From six months onward, she will understand when you say "no" firmly, and at nine months can follow simple orders such as waving bye-bye. You can help her by making meanings clear with theatrical emphasis and gestures: read to her, show her pictures and repeat the names of the things she can see, and give her a clear, slow running commentary about everyday actions.

Children who are sung to, have nursery rhymes repeated to them, are spoken to in a rhythmical way, and are involved in singing and rhyming and clapping games, speak earlier and better than children who don't, so you should do all these things from your child's earliest days. As soon as your child says her first word, or what you think might be a word, repeat it to her. Tell her she's a clever girl and show her how pleased you are with her.

7 months By now you will be able to discern clear syllables in your baby's sounds, such as "ba" or "ka". She will probably use a special sound to attract your attention, such as a cough or a squeal, and will have started to play games with her tongue and lips.

8–9 months Your baby's range of sounds is increasing, and she has added the consonants "t", "d", and "w" to her repertoire. She will start to imitate real speech sounds, and may use one word with meaning. She pays close attention to adult conversations.

11 months By now your baby is almost certainly using one word with meaning, and can understand a few simple words, such as bath, drink, and dinner. Praise her for every new word, and repeat it; she will say it over and over when she sees your approval. You are your child's first model of good speech, so speak clearly and slowly to her.

15 months Your baby is breaking gradually into jargon – that is, strings of sounds with the odd recognisable word and with the phrasing and inflections of real speech. This is a sign that she is just about to start talking. She may start to use some favourite phrase of yours, such as "oh dear", in appropriate situations.

18 months Your baby may be able to use about ten words with meaning. Her understanding is increasing all the time, and she can point out many objects in her picture books or in the world around her if you ask her to.

Teaching words
As your child begins to learn her first words, play a game of handing her objects and repeating their names.

OLDER BABY

FIRST WORDS

Acquiring speech is a complex process, and there are a few typical ways in which children simplify pronunciation.

Your child may acquire words a little at a time, so that "dog" starts out as "d", then "do", then finally "dog". Some difficulty with consonants is normal until four or five years of age.

Double consonants are especially difficult; your child might say "pay" for "play". She'll simplify words that contain sounds made in different parts of the mouth, so that "ball" becomes "baw". You can help her by stressing the last letter of words.

Make every effort to encourage and understand your child's attempts at communication.

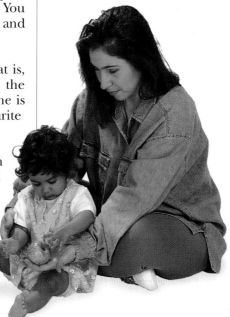

SPEECH AND LANGUAGE

Right from the moment of birth, girls are more responsive to the human voice than boys, and they have better verbal skills throughout childhood.

Girls talk sooner than boys, and begin to string words into sentences earlier. They have better articulation, pronunciation, and grammar, and are better at verbal reasoning. They also learn to read earlier than boys.

The structure of the female brain is believed to be the reason for girls' superior verbal skills (see p.180): the speech centres are more tightly organized in the female brain than in the male brain, and have more and better connections with other functions of the brain.

Your baby is learning new words all the time now and he's also starting to put them together. His pronunciation will be indistinct, but this is no cause for worry; if he is using words with meaning and putting them together, then his language is developing. Mild speech defects, such as lisping, are very common in children, and usually disappear without any treatment. There is great variation in the speed at which children acquire speech, so don't feel the need to compare your child with others of his age, and don't worry if his development doesn't match the timetable outlined below: I give these dates merely as average guidelines, and no child corresponds exactly to the average.

18 months – 2 years Your baby's speech will become more complex during this time. He will probably have a vocabulary of about thirty words, including possessives ("mine"), and negatives, ("won't"), instead of simply "no". He is starting to combine words to make simple statements, such as "ball gone", or questions: "Where Daddy?" He understands that conversation is a two-way thing and will wait his turn to speak, and he uses language to give information, to ask for things, to tell how he feels, or to relate to other people.

Remember that he can understand a lot more words than he can use, so you can continue to help him by teaching him new words. Use adjectives whenever you can, and combine them with nouns: "good boy", "hot water", "big dog". Introduce adverbs too: "Run quickly", "Pat the dog gently". When you use prepositions – "on", "under", "behind" – always show him what you mean.

2–3 years Your toddler probably has a vocabulary of 200–300 words by now, and he can talk at some length. He is interested in learning new words. His attention span is longer, and he will listen to you when you explain things or give reasons. He will still mispronounce words, and may lisp, but his fluency and confidence are improving all the time. He can connect two ideas in a single sentence, "I get teddy and play in garden", and can use pronouns such as "I", "me", and "you" correctly.

You can help your child to increase his vocabulary by using unfamiliar words in your speech in such a way that he can guess at their meaning, and repeat them frequently so that he can learn how they are used. Read to him often, and explain new words as they arise. He will like to hear the same stories read over and over, and will be able to understand increasingly complicated narratives.

Your child's use of language is becoming more social now, and he will talk more to other children than to adults, so contact with children is the best way to help him develop his abilities.

TALKING TO YOUR CHILD

It is important that you continue to talk to your toddler, and go on introducing new words and making your meaning clear with gestures and facial expression. It is just as important, however, that you allow him to respond so he learns that conversation works two ways. If he initiates a conversation by showing you something or asking you a question, always give him your attention. If you are impatient, or just respond with "That's nice" without even looking at him, he'll become discouraged and give up trying to talk to you.

Talk about everything you are doing in detail. When you are dressing him, give a running commentary: "Now we'll do up your buttons … one, two, three." Describe objects you are using: "Let's put the apples in the glass bowl"; "Would you like a yellow sweet or a red sweet?"

While you shouldn't correct your child when he makes mistakes, there is no reason why you should talk to him in his own baby language. If he makes a mistake in grammar or pronunciation – "Granny goed" – just repeat his words giving the correct form: "Yes, Granny went home".

LANGUAGE AND UNDERSTANDING

You will be able to observe the way your toddler gradually gains concepts in his use of language. He will often use the same word to describe similar things, so that apples, oranges, and peaches are all "apple", because they are all round and fruit; and horses, cows, and sheep are all "horse" because they are all large animals with four legs. This doesn't necessarily mean that he can't tell the difference; only that he doesn't have words to describe all of them, so he uses the nearest one.

By the same token, the questions your child asks you may be very simple because he can't fully express what it is he wants to know. So when he says "What's that", he may be asking "What is it? What is it called? What does it do? How does it work?" all at once. Give him as much information as you think he can understand: "This is washing powder. It's just like soap, and I put it in the washing machine to make our clothes clean." Always try to answer the question he is really asking.

LANGUAGE IN BOYS

Boys are almost always slower than girls at developing language skills, and this discrepancy lasts right through childhood.

Boys are later in talking than girls, are slower to put words together in sentences, and take longer to learn to read. Speech disorders such as stuttering are far more common in boys than in girls, and boys outnumber girls in remedial reading classes by four to one.

Although this difference in linguistic ability levels out somewhat during the teenage years, you can help your son's language skills in the preschool years by reading aloud to him and playing lots of word games.

Socializing
During the third year, your child's verbal skills will be improved by talking to other children.

PRESCHOOL

SPEECH AND LANGUAGE

GIRLS' TALK

Studies of the way children use language show marked differences in the way girls and boys speak to each other, which can be seen even in the preschool years.

The reason for these differences has to do with the way the sexes behave in groups. Girls want to be part of the group, so their talk is aimed at promoting unity and reaching compromises. Girls:

• *Use language as a way of forming close, intimate friendships*

• *Make suggestions when playing in groups – "Let's play house"*

• *Give reasons for their suggestions: "Let's play in the garden because there's more room."*

As your child's world becomes wider, her language will have to keep pace with new experiences and ideas. Her perception of the world is becoming more complex, and so is her vocabulary; for example, she will start to realize that mauve is different from purple, and look for the words to express this difference.

3 years Your child will enjoy learning new words, so she listens to adult conversations carefully, and her attention span is increasing. She can understand words that describe how she feels, such as "cold", "tired", and "hungry". She is also beginning to understand words such as "on", "under", and "behind", though this will take longer. She should be able to give her first and last name. Because her mind is racing ahead of her ability to form words at this stage, she may start to stutter, but this is likely to be temporary. If she hasn't overcome her stutter by about four-and-a-half, or earlier if it is severe, it might be worth consulting a speech therapist.

4 years Children of this age talk a great deal: they boast, exaggerate, tell tall tales, and have conversations with imaginary friends. Your child will ask lots of questions, as much out of a desire to keep you talking as out of any real curiosity, because she loves conversation. She will enjoy inventing silly words, and may indulge in mildly obscene verbal play, especially to do with the lavatory and the potty. She will probably start to use slang, and she may call you names and threaten you.

5 years Your five-year-old will ask innumerable questions, and now she really is seeking new information. She loves to be read to. She is aware that there is a "right" way to say things and will often ask you what it is. She can understand opposites, and it's very easy to make a game out of this, where you give a word such as "soft", "up", "cold" and she has to give the opposite. She will also be able to define words if you ask her, and this is a very good way of getting her to use her skills of classification as well as verbal skills. In fact all word games are excellent mental exercise, because clear speaking goes hand in hand with clear thinking.

Girls at play
Close friendships form the basis of a girl's social world, and this will be reflected in her choice of language.

BOOKS AND READING

Encouraging an interest in books is probably the best single thing you can do for your child, so read to her often; her attention span is increasing now and she will be able to listen to stories with sustained interest. Words are crucial to the way our brains work; they are our main means of communicating, and they form the basis for everything your child will learn in school. Books will provide your child with new words and new ideas, and will explain to her how the world works.

Reading to your child
Even after your child has begun to read for herself, reading to her will be a very valuable time of sharing and learning.

Let your child know that you regard reading as a pleasure. Have plenty of books in the house and make it clear to your child that they are all available for her to look at. Store her own books on low shelves where she can easily browse through them.

Choose books for your child that are visually appealing; first reading books should be short, with only a few pages, and should have large illustrations, large print, and a simple vocabulary. Be willing to read your child's favourite books over and over again; eventually she will memorize the words, and when she is ready to start reading herself, the familiar words will be easier to recognise.

TEACHING LETTERS AND NUMBERS

Take every opportunity to help your child become familiar with letters or numbers. Show your child how her own name is spelt, and let her try to copy it. As you read to her, pick out a simple word like "cat" and point it out every time it recurs. Then show your child what it looks like, and ask her if she can find it on a certain page. When you are doing routine tasks, count out loud; doing up the buttons on your child's cardigan, for instance, or laying the table. When you are out shopping, you could ask your child to fetch things for you: three packets of soup, or two oranges.

Boys' talk

The way little boys talk to each other when at play is markedly different from the way little girls interact with one another, and this reflects attitudes that will continue all through adult life.

In any kind of group situation, boys usually want to stand out from the crowd, so the things they say are intended to enhance their status in the eyes of their playmates. Boys:

• *Tell jokes and stories far more than girls, as this allows them to be the centre of attention; they will often interrupt a story being told by another boy*

• *Give orders and try to grab favourable positions for themselves: "OK, we're going to play doctors. I'll be the doctor, you be the patient"*

• *Back up their suggestions by insisting, by appealing to the rules, or even by threats: "You have to be the patient because it's your turn. I won't play with you if you don't"*

Aids to learning
Give your child numbers and letters to play with. Magnetic ones can be attached to the refrigerator door.

203

GIRLS'
BEHAVIOUR

Girls tend to develop social skills and enjoy the company of other people far earlier than boys do. While not all children conform to a stereotype, in general, girls:

* *Are more sociable than boys, and form closer friendships from an earlier age*

* *Are more compliant with adult requests than boys tend to be in early childhood*

* *Show fewer competitive traits and are less socially aggressive and dominant than boys*

* *Cope far more easily with physical, emotional, and intellectual stress than boys*

SOCIAL BEHAVIOUR

Many features of your child's personality will have a vital bearing on her development as well as her future prospects in life. Helpful traits include the ability to get on well with people, to concentrate, to profit from mistakes, willingness to work hard, good powers of observation, thoroughness, creativity, an enquiring mind, and determination. Less helpful traits are slowness of thought, a child's difficulty in expressing herself, overactivity, and diminished concentration, which may occur even in a highly intelligent child.

Your newborn baby needs to interact socially, especially with you, her parents. She learns to be sociable by imitating you, first with facial expressions, then with gestures and movements, and finally with complete patterns of behaviour. In this way the relationship between parent and child forms the blueprint for all subsequent relationships, so it is your responsibility to be more aware of your behaviour and responses than ever before. From the moment you begin to talk to your baby she begins to develop into a social being because she longs to converse with you.

Like all other development, social development has its own well-defined stages. Everyone has heard of the "Terrible Twos" when your child enters a stage of refusing to obey, and of doing what she is told not to do. This is her way of asserting her independence and, although at times you'll believe that it will go on forever, it's simply a stage in her learning to interact with other people.

PREDICTING PERSONALITY

It would be marvellous if we could predict the future personality of a child when she was still an infant. Certainly we can do so with intelligence. Personality and character, however, derive partly from heredity and partly from environment so there always remains the possibility that, as the result of a bad environment or the lack of secure, loving relationships, a child may not have the opportunities to grow up as a loving and lovable adult.

In view of the profound effect of environment and family on character, predictions during infancy are doomed to failure. However, observant parents with several children can detect differences in their personalities from the outset. Perhaps it's a good thing that personality prediction is so difficult. From the point of view of adoption it would be a pity if such predictions were possible. Adoptive parents have a right to want to know the intelligence of the child whom they are thinking of adopting. They must not expect to know what her personality will be like. All parents take huge risks when having children, not even knowing if they will be mentally normal. If they're not willing to take that risk they should not consider having children.

INDIVIDUALITY

Your baby's individuality will gradually become more and more apparent as she grows and learns. You should treasure your baby's individuality and nurture her growth and strength.

The gradual insight you gain into your baby's personality is like watching a thrilling film in slow motion. All her preferences, the things that make her laugh and cry, the foods she likes, her favourite toys, come together to create her unique personality.

Baby types There's much evidence now that within a week or so of birth infants show a primitive form of all the traits they will show as they grow up and probably later in life. Undeniably environment has a profound effect on character formation but much of the child's basic character is inherited from her parents, so it's fair to say that each baby will show basic personality traits that don't change much with age.

The traits that are easily recognisable by any parent are the amount of energy your child has, how well she can control her body (as opposed to being floppy), self-reliance, social responsiveness, family attachment, communicativeness, adaptability to various situations, exploitation of the environment, sense of humour, emotional expressiveness, reaction to success, reaction to restriction, readiness of smiling, and readiness of crying. Between six weeks and three months your baby will probably fall into one of three personality types:

She may be quite "good" or "easy"; eating and sleeping and merging comfortably with her surroundings when awake, and seldom getting over-enthusiastic in her responses.

She may be what is sometimes referred to as a high-keyed "sparkler", becoming as demanding in her bids for entertainment and companionship as she first was for food and comfort; the zest for living keeps her growing in self-play.

She may be an "in betweener", having up-days and hours and down-days and hours and asking only that you respond in kind to her moods of the moment.

While personality differences may be apparent very early on, it's in the first few months that each new baby starts to become more distinctly herself. Here are some traits you may notice as she grows:

- Easy-going, placid, daydreaming.

- Cross and irritable, a leader.

- Sociable, a follower.

- Serious, determined.

- Independent, often perverse.

- Imaginative, sometimes difficult.

BOYS' BEHAVIOUR

Boys tend to be slower to develop social skills than girls. While not all boys will show these traits to a marked degree, in general, boys:

- *Tend to be slower to develop social skills than girls*

- *Are far more socially aggressive than girls*

- *Have more friendships than girls, but they tend to be superficial and short-lived*

- *Are more emotionally vulnerable than girls*

- *Tend to have more behavioural problems, particularly when around authority figures*

Social skills
Young children play alongside each other rather than together, but will enjoy the company.

YOUNG BABY

SOCIAL BEHAVIOUR

BONDING

The relationship between you and your baby begins from the moment you give birth and every aspect of your being becomes a comfort and joy to your baby.

He'll respond to your smell, the sound of your voice, the touch of your skin, and the sight of your face. This bond is so complete, your baby will be able to single you out from others in an astoundingly short time. The same will occur with your partner if he spends time alone with the baby.

Make every effort to ensure that the contact you and your partner have with your baby is pleasant, calm, and loving, even if at times this seems impossible.

An early start
By developing a close, loving relationship with your baby from birth, you are laying the foundations of a good relationship in future years.

Your baby's first six months are, surprisingly, a crucial time for his social development. It is during these early weeks that your baby comes to understand the pleasure of social interaction and the importance of communication. He grows beyond the basic requirements of warmth and feeding as he begins to enjoy the social aspects of being alive. Because you embody comfort, pleasure, and security for your baby, you are naturally the best person to teach him loving relationships, the basics of which are learned through the initial skin contact that he loves so much during the first few weeks.

Newborn From the very beginning, your baby will desire close contact with you. He'll appeal to you through head nodding, mouth and tongue movements, and jerks of his body. These are his earliest conversations; he's engaging with you and you should answer with noises, laughter, and bobbing head movements. He will soon learn that he can make you respond.

3 months Your baby's conversational gestures are far more controlled. He'll turn towards the sound of your voice and wriggle with pleasure on seeing you. He understands that a smile is a happy greeting, his earliest "hello".

4 months By now your baby is such a social being he'll cry soon after being left alone, even if he has many toys around him. He'll be happy to respond to people who acknowledge him, but will have a special response for you and the rest of the family.

5 months At this age your baby has four main methods of communication: sounds, gestures, facial expressions, and crying, and unless he is asleep, he'll make the most of all four. He can tell the difference between an angry voice and a friendly one, and will react to each differently. He now shows a certain shyness with strangers, but will smile at a familiar face.

6 months Your baby's social advances are far more physical, even aggressive, but may be offset by a growing fear of strangers, and a possessiveness over you. He'll explore much more with his hands, patting and touching your face and hands rather than just searching your face with his eyes.

RESPONDING TO YOUR BABY

Any response you make to your baby's attempts at conversation will further his understanding of communication, so you must try to be positive all the time. If a baby's gurgling is met with silence, he'll soon grow tired of such an unrewarding game and may well give up on all but the most basic communication. Always encourage a "two-way" conversation, either by imitating your baby's gestures and noises in an overt way, or by chatting to him in order to elicit a response. Be theatrical with voice and gesture. The broader your gestures the more he understands, the more fun he has, and the closer the bond becomes.

A young baby is sensitive to sudden noises, so bear in mind that, although a wide variety of noises are tranquillizing for him, harsh or very loud noises will frighten and upset him.

Encourage your baby to cope with new faces by introducing him to any visitors he has not met before. This will allow him to get used to strangers in the security of your home. The more your baby enjoys social intercourse with you, the more likely he is actively to seek it as he grows older. Songs and rhythmic games will encourage him to equate joyful times with mixing with others.

YOUR BABY AS PART OF THE FAMILY

Your baby is longing to be a member of the family group with all its routines, rules, and customs. To become interested he needs to learn how to fit in. For this reason you should include him in family activities, outings, shopping, daily chores, and visiting friends from as early as possible.

The family group will be the basis of your baby's learning about the workings of groups in general. His behaviour with family members will teach him about his expected behaviour with strangers, and will open him to the social customs of his society.

Your baby learns chiefly through imitation, so by copying your behaviour he learns his own standards of social interaction.

DIFFICULT BABIES

A demanding baby, one who cries constantly and cannot be comforted, can be very difficult to cope with. It is vital that you share the responsibility with your partner and try very hard to control your temper. There are many causes of, and solutions to, a crying baby, and constant tears is a phase that is fortunately short-lived. If your baby is difficult it's important to understand why he is crying, keeping you awake, or ignoring you on purpose. Whatever his particular problem, your calm, loving, and understanding approach will have a far more positive effect on your baby than being chastised or ignored. Your health visitor can offer advice and support.

If you have an anti-social baby, for example one who is discontented when hungry but never enjoys feeding or being held, you may feel rejected by him, or responsible for his unhappiness. Try to keep these negative thoughts at bay. No matter how much he rejects you, keep trying to engage his interest. It has to be said though that some babies are anti-social from birth and reject cuddles. Don't blame yourself once you've tried everything.

One of the family
Try to include your baby in your activities, even if they do not directly involve him.

OLDER BABY

SOCIAL BEHAVIOUR

A WILL OF HIS OWN

From six months onwards your baby will show his assertiveness in his demands and preferences. Your older baby is:

- *Very keen to show how grown up he is becoming*

- *Determined to be independent and to manage without help*

- *Demonstrating likes and dislikes with certainty and assertion, if not consistency*

- *Unable to consider consequences and gets very angry when he has to wait, often showing this with violent noises and actions*

- *Aware that he is a separate being from you and, as such, is determined to have his own way*

- *Often confused and unhappy at the conflict between his urge to be independent and his desire to love and please you*

- *More wilful than his intellectual maturity will allow*

- *Extreme in his emotions, from great happiness to outbursts of temper tantrums*

- *Seemingly infatuated with saying the word "no"*

Your baby is becoming more socially adept by now, and takes a great deal of pleasure in meeting and being with other people. His interactions with you are increasingly comprehensive as he learns to understand certain words and phrases, and uses the communication skills he has learned in order to mix with others in the world around him.

Touching, smiling, and all the contact of general company are vital to your baby's happiness at this stage, as he gradually learns to refine his conversational gestures and cries into recognisable signs of communication.

6–8 months Closeness to another baby will be a delight. He'll reach out and touch new friends and will enjoy social games like "Peek-a-boo" and "Pat-a-Cake". He will try to communicate with a series of shrieks, grunts, raspberries, and coughs, and will mimic facial expressions and conversational gestures. You should "answer" him in order to simulate these "conversations" and impress upon him that social interaction is a two-way activity.

8–12 months He will respond to his own name now, and will understand that a firm "no" means that he should stop whatever he is doing. He is affectionate and will demand closeness with you, particularly big hugs and intimate smiles. Certain social rituals are common to him now – like saying "bye-bye" – which he'll imitate with little prompting. He'll no longer calmly allow a toy to be taken away and he'll show anger if this happens.

12–15 months His sociability is constantly expanding and he enjoys being in groups, especially when he can follow conversations and join in whenever there's a lull. Despite his outgoing attitude, he will still need to be close to you for reassurance and security, and will often look to you when meeting new people – just holding hands will give him the confidence he needs. He can say a few words, ask for things, and show thanks when things are done for him in an obvious way. He likes to be helpful, and enjoys sharing tasks with you.

15–18 months By now your baby is even more helpful with daily chores, and loves the independence of dressing and undressing himself. He is very affectionate, and shows love for his family, pets, and favourite toys. He imitates adult behaviour and is fascinated by adult interaction and conversation. Despite being socially aware, he will tend to play alone and, although he will enjoy playing near another child, he will not tend to play with him.

HOW TO HELP

The concept of sharing is particularly difficult for your baby to grasp. It is unrealistic to expect your baby to give a toy to another baby if he is still playing with it. It is equally unfair to expect your baby to understand that he cannot take another baby's toy simply because he wants it. This, then, gives rise to a situation whereby you can demonstrate the basics of give and take. Your child of 18 months is generally able to comprehend reciprocity, but you must demonstrate it in a way that is reasonable to him; if he takes another baby's toy he must replace it with one of his own so that they can both play. Your baby is wholly capable of unselfishness and generosity, but any such act must be seen to be a pleasure for both parties. If your baby is willing to share his sweets with other members of the family, encourage these small acts of generosity with others and try to build on them.

You should always include your baby in social gatherings and teach him the basic pleasantries from as early as possible. Introduce him to lots of new faces so he doesn't become dependent on you and the family alone for social stimulation. It will help him to feel secure when he is away from you or his usual carer, although this shouldn't happen too frequently, or for long periods of time.

INTRODUCING DISCIPLINE

Discipline should be applied first with the tone of the voice, later with the word "no", then by distraction, and only finally with very mild punishment. Smacking, threats, and withdrawal of pleasures have no place with small children. If you are too severe or liberal your baby may become insecure. Before he is three, your child can not respond to reason, and he still cannot grasp the connection between cause and effect. He will understand perfectly well that he has done wrong, or that you are angry, but it will take him some time to remember to connect a particular action with a particular outcome. For this reason it is vital that you point out a mistake to your child immediately so that he links the action with the punishment. You should also bear in mind that your baby's memory is very short, so if you brood over your anger and act later, he will not understand and will not learn from your attempts at correction. During a baby's first year there are very few reasons for saying "No". I kept the rules for my children to a minimum, and I had only one unbreakable rule in their first year: when they were doing something that was unsafe for themselves or others, I would say "No" firmly while removing an object or stopping my child performing a dangerous activity. I did not wait for my child to stop. As I was trying to teach what was unsafe, I always offered an explanation of why I was stopping him.

Your baby will be very receptive to justice and fair play, and to their opposites. He immediately recognises inconsistency, and so gently applied and consistent discipline will help your child to develop self-control and a conscience, which in turn will help him in his decision-making in later life. It will also give him a sense of responsibility towards others.

FEAR OF STRANGERS

It is not uncommon for a normally talkative and sociable child to become withdrawn, even tearful, when introduced to strangers or taken to a strange place. This is quite normal and should never be ridiculed or made into an issue.

Don't insist that he joins in immediately with the group. A gentle introduction from you works by far the best, and your baby will soon forget his nerves and find his place within the social gathering.

Even a very shy child, if gently encouraged, will join in with new friends after an hour or so, but rushing him may make him more insecure. A favourite toy will bolster his confidence, so don't take this security away. Once he feels relaxed, he'll play happily with his new playmates.

SOCIAL BEHAVIOUR

IDENTIFYING WITH OTHERS

By the time your child reaches the age of three she will begin the process of identification, both with herself and with other people around her.

You will start to see evidence of her self-awareness as she takes steps to command and control herself, showing that she can put herself in the position of others. You may overhear your child scolding herself when she thinks she has done something which you would disapprove of. She will begin to act out the part of the adults known to her, particularly you, often adopting phrases that you use regularly.

This will all become part of the process of her exploring and getting to know the way the world works and her own part in it. Now is the time to introduce her to the idea of a wider circle of people, teaching her to respect and be polite to them. Introduce her to visitors to the house – delivery people, postman, and window cleaner – as well as your own friends, and make meeting people part of her daily routine.

From her first moments your baby looked to you as the centre of her world – the main provider of affection and care. However, as she gets older and her self awareness and life experiences develop, she'll begin to see you as a separate person and will extend her interest to other people. Although you cannot make friends for her, you can help by introducing her to a few first companions. She will soon learn to adapt her skills and develop the social habits of older boys and girls.

18 months – 2 years At this age you should encourage your child to interact with other children. Invite children to the house and give her games and play material to facilitate socializing. Be patient; although her initial reaction may be self-centred, she will modify selfish behaviour if it is played down and achievements praised.

2–2½ years As she is learning to share, encourage games that involve giving to others and respecting their wishes. She may demonstrate feelings of rivalry as a consequence and try to force her will on others. You will need to use discipline fairly while still encouraging and supporting all her efforts and achievements, since approval is more important at this stage.

2½–3 years As your child continues to socialize, she becomes more independent from you and more outgoing towards other children. She will start to be more generous and unselfish in play with others, and form stronger friendships with adults and children, showing signs of sympathy when others are in distress. Always encourage truthfulness and honesty in relationships with others.

RIGHT AND WRONG

Your child will only learn the differences between right and wrong if they are clearly pointed out. In the first year you can act out why hot or sharp things are dangerous using sounds and actions. If your child understands why you want her to do something she is much more likely to do it willingly, so try to explain and then ask her opinion. There are situations that are non-negotiable: where your child's safety is threatened, when the thoughts and feelings of others should be considered, and where your child is tempted to tamper with the truth. You should be very firm on these points, and she will gradually learn a sense of responsibility for disciplining herself as she grows up. Cheekiness can often be mistaken for impertinence, but unless your child is imposing on the feelings of others, she may be displaying nothing more than a healthy resistance to authority which can be useful, if sensibly directed.

A spoilt or over-indulged child will behave in a self-centred way and this may be the result of the over-protectiveness, favouritism, or the high expectations of her parents. The best cure is to let her go to playgroup or preschool at two-and-a-half to three in order to get her used to mixing with other children.

SHARING

Young children are naturally selfish and usually begin to think of others only when they're taught to do so. Your child has to understand that other children feel as she does before she is able to grasp the importance of thinking of other people's feelings. Do not worry if your child seems to be slow in learning to share; it's very difficult, but with your patience she will successfully acquire this skill.

MEETING OTHER CHILDREN

Just like all the other lessons she has to learn through life, your child's ability to make friends could be slow to develop, so introduce it to her gradually. Invite friends around, one at a time to begin with, to a familiar home environment where she is sure of herself. Be near at hand to give her help and support should she need it. She will then begin to build up a small circle of friends and gain confidence through her own place in it – an essential way to learn the ground rules for future friendships.

Shyness is something that affects many children. Common types of shy behaviour include disliking new experiences, social gatherings, talking to unknown people, and difficulty in making friends.

Toys for sharing
Encourage co-operation with others by getting your child to complete a puzzle such as this one with a friend.

Don't think of shyness as something wrong with your child; many well-adjusted adults are quite shy. The best way of dealing with it is not by criticism or forcing change but by preparing your child for any situation she's likely to find difficult.

Excessive shyness does not mean that your child is retarded, and you should avoid becoming over-protective and over-anxious. In most cases time and patience are all that is needed.

TANTRUMS

Toddlers between the ages of two and three often have temper tantrums as a means of giving vent to frustration when they do not get what they want.

This is quite normal because your child will not have sufficient judgment to control her strength of will or the language to express herself clearly, but as her knowledge and experience of the world broadens, so the occasions when her will is pitched directly against yours become less likely.

A tantrum may be brought on by such feelings as frustration, anger, jealousy, and dislike. Anger is brought on by not getting her own way; frustration by her not being sufficiently strong or well co-ordinated to do what she wants. It will usually involve your child throwing herself on the floor, kicking and screaming.

The best thing you can do is to stay calm, since any attention on your part will only prolong the attack. If she has one in public, take her away from too much attention, without fuss.

At home an effective technique is simply to leave the room. Explain to your child that, while you still love her, you have to leave the room because you are getting angry. Never confine her in another room because this denies her the option of coming back and saying sorry.

PRESCHOOL

SOCIAL BEHAVIOUR

GROWING UP LIKE MUM

By the age of three your little girl is aware of the fact that she is female and that she'll grow up to be a woman.

This makes her very attentive to you – her mother. Her view of gender roles will be influenced by your attitudes. If you:

• *Regard yourself as equal to your partner, your daughter will see this as normal*

• *Treat other women as close friends and confidantes, your daughter will see relationships with adult women in this way*

• *See working as integral to family life, your daughter will view a career as compatible with having a family*

Your preschooler faces many changes in how she sees herself as her independence grows and her personality matures. Sudden upheavals can cause your child to exhibit quite violent changes of mood as she tries to relate her changing identity to her family life and the guidelines she has learnt for social behaviour, both of which are relatively constant. Be patient and allow her to mature in her own time. The difficult stages are easily outweighed by the thrilling ones, and your child must experience both in order to become a socially adept member of her community.

3 years If your child has been brought up to relate to new friends she will separate from you easily from the age of three-and-a-half onwards, and at about the same time is learning to play interactive games such as tag. She is generous and generally sympathetic when someone else is distressed.

4 years During the fourth year your child has an expanding sense of self, indicated by bragging, boasting, and out-of-bounds behaviour. She begins to realize that other children are separate entities. Your four-year-old wants to be grown up. She becomes argumentative, and may be selfish, rough, or impatient, especially with younger friends or brothers and sisters. She'll express affection at bedtimes but might be jealous of you and your partner together. Four-year-old boys, in particular, have silly, boisterous humour.

5 years During the fifth year, your child may be serious, businesslike, and realistic. She gets excited in anticipation of the future. At this age your little girl is sympathetic, affectionate, and helpful. She has a strong feeling for the family, and appearance is very important to her. She is not afraid to call people names. For a little boy, mother is the centre of his universe. He takes others and himself for granted and is interested in immediate experiences.

A role model
When your little girl starts to realize that she will grow up like her mother, she will take a special interest in your activities.

SEXUALITY AND GENDER

3 years By the time she is three years old your child already has an interest in her own gender and the differentiation of herself from boys. At about the age of three-and-a-half she'll express "I like" and then slightly later "I love" and she will affirm, if questioned, that she is a girl rather than a boy. She will begin to express interest in physiological differences between the genders and in boys' and girls' postures for urinating.

She makes no distinctions between gender at play and realizes that people touch out of friendship as well as out of love. She begins to become interested in babies and wants her family to have one. She will ask questions such as "What can the baby do when it comes?", or "Where does it come from?" and most three-year-olds don't understand when they get the answer that the baby grows inside its mother. It is still vital, however, that you answer your child's questions as frankly and honestly as possible so that her trust in you is not undermined.

4 years By the age of four, children are extremely conscious of their navel and under social stress they may grasp their genitals and may need to urinate. They may play a game of "show", indulge in verbal play or name-calling, and make jokes about passing urine or stools. They have an interest in other people's bathrooms and may demand privacy for themselves but be extremely interested in the bathroom activities of others. They may begin to segregate themselves along gender lines. All your answers to your child's questions on sex should stress the aspects of loving, caring, and the responsibilities that an intimate relationship demands. Your child may also question how babies get out of their mother's tummies and may spontaneously think babies are born through the navel. This is a time when gender-stereotyped behaviour is learned more from peers than parents.

5 years At five your child will be familiar with, but not much interested in, physical differences between the genders. She'll be more modest and less self-exposing and will play less in the bathroom than earlier. She'll be aware of sex organs when she sees adults undressed and will wonder why her dad doesn't have breasts or her sister doesn't have a penis. Most children of five take the opposite sex for granted and there's little distinction between the role of gender in play. There may be frequent boy–girl pairs. Girls' interest in babies continues: they may ask for a baby of their own and they may even dramatize this in games. Your five-year-old will constantly ask, "Where do babies come from?", and will accept "Mummy's tummy" as an answer, but some fix on the idea that you buy a baby at hospital. She will make little connection between the size of a pregnant woman and the presence of a baby inside her.

GROWING UP LIKE DAD

Your little boy will have realized by the age of three that he will grow up to be a man, and he will become particularly interested in his father.

Your little boy will watch your partner and learn from him what it is to be a man. If your partner:

- *Treats women, particularly you or his daughters, in a caring and considerate way, your little boy will believe that this is the correct way to treat women*

- *Sees other men as friends, your son will also find older men approachable*

- *Enjoys and participates in family life, your child will follow this example*

- *Resolves disputes with rudeness and violence, he will too*

A sense of identity
Your little boy will gain his idea of what it is to grow up as a man by observing his father.

RELATIONSHIPS

FAVOURITISM

It is all too easy to favour one child above the other, or at least to treat him in a way that seems like favouritism.

If a child is born several years after a previous one and is much wanted, for example, he may be treated preferentially. Sometimes it happens that the mother's favourite is the boy, the father's favourite is the girl, and a third-born child is no-one's favourite.

Favouritism reveals itself in many different ways, some of them apparently inconsequential, but very important in the mind of a child. A favoured child may be:

- *Reprimanded less*
- *Allowed to do a greater variety of activities*
- *Given more treats, such as rides on father's back, or sweets*
- *Defended when he gets into trouble for being naughty*
- *Given more time and attention*

Of course, all children have different needs, and it is impossible to treat them absolutely equally, but you should beware of favouring one child, or even appearing to; children are very quick to notice such behaviour and a child who feels left out will suffer a blow to his confidence.

Children who grow up in a stable, secure environment and feel loved by their parents are likely to become well-adjusted adults. Ideally, you and your partner will have equal but complementary roles: you have authority over some situations, your partner has authority over others, so that your child cannot play one of you against the other. The way a child interacts with his parents and siblings evolves gradually between the ages of three and five.

MOTHER AND CHILD

3 years At the age of three, children generally have good relationships with their mothers. Quite often the mother is the favourite parent with whom children like to discuss and relive past events. By three and a half the mother–child relationship can sometimes become more difficult. Children can be simultaneously demanding and resistant. A child may refuse to eat, dress, or take a nap for his mother, but be quite compliant with someone else.

4 years By the age of four your child will take pride in you, quote things that you say, and boast about you to friends, though at home he'll still resist your authority.

5 years The mother–child relationship is generally more smooth: the child likes to do things that you request, enjoys playing around you, and needs to be aware of your presence without having your full attention. Children quite often express affection, such as, "I like you, Mummy", and, although they accept punishment from you, it may not have a great impact on them. Boys may talk about marrying mummy.

FATHER AND CHILD

3 years At three years the mother tends to be the favourite parent, but the father can take over in many situations. For instance, a child may cling less at bedtime and go to sleep more quickly in the presence of the father. At the age of three and a half, girls may express closeness to their fathers.

4 years Children boast about their fathers outside the home, and quote them as an authority. Some children may feel jealous of their father spending a lot of time with their mother and feel they are being deprived of maternal attention. If this is the case a child may verbally express dislike for his father.

5 years By five years of age, children are likely to accept fathers taking a caring role if mother is busy, ill, or away. Relationships with father are generally smooth, pleasant, and undisturbed and children often value special outings with their fathers. They usually accept punishment better from mothers than fathers. Fathers may have more authority and tend to be disobeyed less.

Sibling relationships
Your child will enjoy the companionship of a sibling to play with, but don't be surprised by quarrels, since these are quite natural.

SIBLINGS

At the age of four, relationships with siblings can be turbulent. A child is old enough to be a nuisance to older siblings and can be selfish, rough, and impatient with younger siblings. Quarrels and physical fights over toys and possessions are common and there will be complaints about fairness: "He's got more than me!".

A five-year-old child is usually good with younger brothers and sisters. Girls, especially, can be protective and kind towards younger members of the family, and are helpful rather than domineering. Having said this, a five-year-old is still too young to be responsible for younger siblings; and although he may be caring while an adult is present, he may resort to teasing when left alone with a sister or brother. Five-year-olds usually interact well with older siblings, sometimes adopting a baby role in domestic play.

THE ONLY CHILD

Although there are benefits to being an only child, such as having lots of love and attention, there are also disadvantages. Without the presence of other children of a comparable age, the only child can sometimes feel lonely, and reticent about mixing in groups. As long as you are aware of this, you can do things to compensate. It is important to introduce your child to other children at an early age. Encourage him to invite friends home and to visit other friends' houses, and arrange outings with other young children.

Another problem associated with only children is the tendency that some parents have to be possessive and overprotective. This can be dangerous for both parent and child. If you don't allow your child a sense of adventure and the freedom to experiment and explore, he may become timid and wary of new people and experiences. Parents, meanwhile, will have a more acute sense of loss when the child does become independent.

An only child needs the same amount of discipline as other children. Try not to be over-indulgent, and make your child realize that he cannot always expect to have your undivided attention.

REJECTION

Although unusual, some parents emotionally reject their children and this can express itself in criticisms and unfavourable comparisons with siblings.

The consequences of parental rejection can be acute. Signs of profound insecurity in a rejected child can be as follows:

- *Excessive fear or shyness*
- *Crying a lot*
- *Aggressiveness and tantrums*
- *Jealousy and attention-seeking*
- *Excessive clinging to mother, thumb-sucking, or masturbation*
- *Bedwetting or soiling*
- *Physical tics*
- *Headbanging*
- *Bullying, stealing, or lying*
- *Cruelty to animals*

MAKING FRIENDS

By the time your child reaches the age of four he is likely to be able to play with other children in an interactive, imaginative, and sustained way. The members of your child's group may change rapidly and there may not be an allegiance to a special friend at this stage, though girls are more likely than boys to pair off with a particular friend. Although children may tease and chant at peers of the opposite sex, gender is not usually a criterion for selecting friends – neither is race.

By the age of five, children tend to select a single playmate, but their play is not necessarily interactive: children often play "in parallel", in that they sit at the same table doing different things. The most frequent grouping is of two children of the same gender, but even at this age, gender is still not a major selection criterion for making new friends.

Although group play demands some co-operation from children, this is quite superficial, since children can often play with their own ends in mind, and have little concern for the group as a whole.

SOCIAL GROUPS

Although children do not fit into rigid stereotypes, there are some common features in most groups of preschool children. The "star" is the child who is popular with everyone; the "rejectee" tends to be least popular; the "neglectee" doesn't evoke strong feelings in other children and, although he does not have any enemies, he probably has no friends; and the "clique" is a small group of children who repeatedly seek out each other's company.

The problems experienced by the rejectee are obvious and are usually quickly spotted by nursery staff. Neglectees, however, may suffer a form of social isolation that is more subtle but equally damaging. The typical neglectee is quiet, reserved, and may blend easily into the background.

THE LONER

Isolation in the early years of childhood can have several long term negative effects. Studies have shown that children who have problems interacting with their peers not only suffer in the preschool years but have more emotional disturbance in later life than "sociable" children, and this can incline them to suicide in adolescence and adulthood. The loner is also more likely to play truant and be involved in vandalism and petty crime. For this reason, making efforts to help an unpopular child is always worthwhile. Encouragingly, preschoolers seem better able to develop new social skills than older children or adults.

Playing together
Children will often play next to each other even if they are not involved in the same game.

The first signs that a child is a loner may appear when he starts nursery school. Whereas other children pair off or form groups, this child remains solitary. When children are asked to find a partner, the loner will be the last one left without a partner and, when asked to stand in a line, he will find himself at the back.

If you think that your child is being neglected it is important to take steps to help his social development. Fortunately, preschool children can learn new social skills easily if helped by sympathetic staff and you.

HOW TO HELP

If your child has poor social skills there are various ways that you or your child's nursery school teacher can help. These include attaching a child to something or someone that raises their standing, or giving a child a responsibility that will boost confidence.

Opposite pairing This involves pairing a neglected or unsociable child with a child who is outgoing and sociable. By being seen as the friend of a popular child, the neglected child will gain a significantly higher level of social acceptance in a short time – in cases as little as three weeks.

Younger pairing Pairing a child with poor social skills with a younger child can be another way of conferring status. A study carried out in the 1980s showed that when unpopular children between the ages of four and five played with children younger than themselves, their level of popularity increased by at least 50 per cent. Younger playmates offer positive social experiences to neglectees and rejectees, which helps build their self-esteem and assertiveness.

Clique activities Although it might seem bad for children to form small, exclusive groups within a large group, allowing them to mix in their preferred clique motivates them to get on with their peers outside the clique. Clique-based activities give children a sense of security and confidence about all social relationships.

Small groups It is sometimes mistakenly assumed that an unsociable child will become sociable when surrounded by a big group. In fact small groupings are better at facilitating friendships because in a large group the unsociable child can remain very much in the background; in a small group he can't be ignored. A nursery school teacher can help by placing an unsociable child in a small group – say three or four children – then gradually extending the size of the group.

Star responsibility Establishing definite roles such as giving the most popular children responsible tasks to do, appears to have a settling effect on all children of nursery school age. Tasks could include giving out the straws for milk, or organizing tidying up. Unsociable children appear to benefit from this strategy as much as other children.

YOUR CHILD'S NEW WORLD

Now that your child is socializing with children of his own age, whether at nursery school or at play, he will have new concerns of which you will become aware.

• *Clothes are one of the first ways of expressing individuality and children may identify themselves with a particular peer group by the clothes they wear. By the time your child reaches nursery school age he will probably want to select his clothes each day. Encourage his sense of identity and independence by having a flexible attitude towards clothes*

• *Toys, sports equipment, any sort of collection, such as a stamp or sticker collection, books, and comics are all powerful indicators of status among children. Even earning money for doing odd jobs is a sign of prowess*

• *Academic or athletic success, or popularity also confer distinction. Some children also derive status from their parents – a high profile or professional career, affluence, or being well-travelled are all things that carry prestige*

• *If you feel that your child attaches too much value to a particular thing, or values something that is inappropriate, help him to reassess priorities and perhaps reward him for some achievement that you consider worthy*

LYING

In order for a child to tell a lie he must have reached a stage in his psychological development where he can distinguish fantasy from reality. For example, if a 15-month-old baby is chastised by her mother for daubing poster paint on a wall, and he shakes his head vigorously in denial, he is not lying – it may be that he has genuinely forgotten the action, wishes that he hadn't done it, or simply cannot recognise the difference between fantasy and reality. Only when a child reaches the age of three or four years will he be capable of lying, and most children will lie if they find a situation sufficiently threatening.

HOW SERIOUS IS LYING?

Children lie for many different reasons and some types of lying are more serious than others. For instance, a make-believe lie is a natural part of a child's fantasy life, whereas a cover-up lie is a conscious attempt to avoid punishment.

Exploratory lying This is done simply to see your response. For example, a four-year-old child will tell his mother that he did not like his dinner even though he ate it all. This is designed to see how you will react. In most cases, your response to this kind of lying is enough to discourage him from doing it again. Some children, however, recognise that it wins attention and will employ it over and over again as they grow up. For this reason it is serious and must be discouraged.

Bragging This type of lying usually takes the form of a greatly exaggerated story and is done to boost the child's self-confidence. A five-year-old will state boldly that he has received many expensive birthday presents or that he lives in a huge house in an attempt to impress his friends. Although bragging is generally harmless, you can discourage your child from this type of lying by reinforcing his genuine achievements.

For a small number of children, bragging can become a permanent habit. Children who brag frequently do so because they desperately want to impress their friends and parents and they want to be loved. The danger is that people will come to view everything your child says with scepticism. Bragging lies can become a child's hallmark and he may lose many friends as a result.

Make-believe lies These are lies that mix reality and fantasy and they serve to add excitement to everyday experiences. For instance, a four-year-old may have a vivid imaginary world consisting of fairies,

Talking it through
If you discover that your child has been lying, explain what he has done wrong patiently but firmly, rather than getting angry.

monsters, and invisible friends, all of which he can describe in colourful detail. Childhood fantasies do not really constitute lies and they should be seen as a normal phase of child development.

Cover-up lies Lies that aim to deliberately mislead are the type that parents worry about most. Children tell cover-up lies to avoid being punished and they learn this tactic at a relatively early age. In one survey mothers were asked to identify the most common reason for their four-year-olds lying to them. Nearly half of them said that it was a lie to escape a reprimand. Cover-up lies become more sophisticated and plausible as a child gets older.

Lies to avoid punishment can put parents in a difficult position. If you punish your child every time he does something wrong, he may learn to lie in response. On the other hand, if you don't reprimand your child then he's likely to carry on behaving in the same way. A balance needs to be struck between being too liberal and too punitive. I tried to encourage the truth with my children by saying that a child who told the truth would never be punished. They realized I was aware of the effort taken to be honest and promised not to lie; they rarely did.

DEALING WITH LYING

A study carried out several years ago investigated the impact of different parental responses on lying. It was found that children whose parents used moral principles to explain to their children why lying is wrong effectively reduced the frequency of lying. A parental response involving punishment increased the frequency of lying.

Children sometimes tell cover-up lies, not to escape punishment, but because they fear that their bad behaviour will stop you from loving them. Therefore any punishment for lying should be accompanied by reassurance. A child needs to be aware that punishment and parental love are not mutually exclusive. There is much research to show that parents who are honest with their children receive honesty in return. Make it easy for your child to confess to his misdeeds by speaking to him calmly rather than getting angry and making accusations.

Children often say things that are inaccurate or untrue and one important reason is that they hear their parents doing it: adults frequently tell "white lies" to avoid hurting other people's feelings unnecessarily. Your child may hear you saying something that contradicts what you normally say. If the reason for such tactful conversation is not explained to him, he can't understand why it is wrong for him to do the same.

Explaining about lying If your child continues to exaggerate the truth, it is important that you stress why telling lies is such a bad idea. If he is old enough to understand, you could try telling him the story of "The Boy Who Cried 'Wolf!'". Afterwards, talk about it and make sure that he understands that if you can't tell the difference between what is true and what is not true, you might not know when something really important has happened to him.

HELPING A CHILD WHO LIES

Because children lie for different reasons, every child must be treated individually. There are, however, a number of do's and don'ts that apply to all children.

- *Act calmly – the child may genuinely be confusing reality and fantasy*

- *Try to understand the motive for a lie. Your child is not lying because he wants to be malicious, but because he is afraid of the punishment he'll receive*

- *Explain to your child why it is wrong to lie. Use examples that he can understand*

- *Make punishments reasonable. If you over-punish your child, he will be more determined to lie in the future*

- *Make your child aware that although you are angry with him, you still love him*

- *Don't ridicule the child who persists with bragging lies. Bragging indicates low self-esteem and you should work to increase your child's self-confidence with praise and affection*

- *Don't use physical punishment on a child who lies. Research shows that constant smacking for lies only encourages children to lie more, because they are afraid of being smacked again*

WHEN THINGS GO WRONG

There are two broad categories of abnormal social development: habit disorders and behavioural disorders. The chart below sets out some of the most common and lists some of the factors that cause them. These are never sole causes, however, only characteristics of the environment created by parents. Many other factors

FACTOR	HABIT DISORDER	BEHAVIOUR DISORDER	APPROACH
Overstrictness.	Bedwetting.	Bullying, smacking other children, biting.	Relax over-authoritarian attitudes to toilet training. Don't scold. Give the child dedicated time. Show more affection and praise more.
	Faecal soiling (see also below).	Lying, blaming others, stealing, refusal to share.	More relaxed attitude to bowel control. Never "toilet train".
		Destructiveness.	Child needs outlets for aggressive behaviour. Allow boisterous play.
Overprotection.	Undereating (due to overfeeding).	Antisocial behaviour, refusal to "join in".	Be more flexible and relaxed about food.
	Negativism, "cissy".	Becomes a loner.	Encourage child to be independent. Develop her self-respect and self-worth.
Lack of affection.	Overeating to compensate.	Stealing, lying, delinquency.	Make sure child is shown affection and given praise.
Neglect or disorganized home.	Pica (see p.222).	Lying, stealing.	Give focused attention once a day.
	Faecal soiling (see also above).	Destructiveness, bullying.	Give more dedicated attention every day.
Prudishness, repressiveness about nudity, overstrictness.	Possibly obsessive masturbation.	Prurient interest in sex, very early sexual intercourse.	Be open. Don't discourage questions about facts of life. If you can, be relaxed about nudity.

may be involved. Of course by no means all children respond to these family traits with any kind of a disorder. The table is suggested only as a guide to help parents.

Habit disorders involve problems with eating, passing stools, sleeping, or speaking, and behaviour disorders involve problems with social conduct, such as stealing, truancy, or vandalism. Parents may sometimes feel that their child with a behavioural problem is being manipulative or vindictive. It should be realized, however, that preschoolers are generally too young to behave in a calculated way.

HABIT DISORDERS

Problems such as bedwetting, faecal soiling, overeating, and faddy eating are found in most normal children and, as long as they only occur occasionally, they should not be perceived as disorders. However, when a child repeatedly wets her bed or overeats to the extent that she becomes obese, help should be sought. Habit disorders usually result from family factors, emotional trauma or conflict (such as a new baby in the family, a new home, or a change of school), or delayed development. Occasionally, there is a physiological basis for bedwetting and you should eliminate this possibility first.

Bedwetting Enuresis is the commonest habit disorder and is never the child's fault. It is usually nocturnal, and the most common reason is developmental delay. Most children are dry during the day and night by the age of five. Habitual bedwetting in a six-year-old could be considered abnormal but is probably the result of stress to the child; it will improve when the stress is removed. Occasional bedwetting is very common and is often caused by excitement, fear, illness, or a sense of threat, so it can be ignored completely.

In some families there is a history of bedwetting, so a child should never be blamed for her slowness. Only about one in ten children suffering from enuresis have a physical or emotional disturbance, and these children usually suffer from enuresis during the day as well as the night. Physical causes include physiological or anatomical disturbance of bladder function, urinary infection, nocturnal epilepsy, and congenital abnormalities of the bladder.

Bedwetting is sometimes an emotional response to excessive parental pressure to be clean and dry. Insufficient or inconsistent encouragement or unrealistically high expectations before the child is developmentally ready are common reasons. Bedwetting is exacerbated by parental disapproval and teasing by siblings. Never scold or ridicule bedwetting, and always praise success.

Measures such as restricting fluid before bedtime and waking and lifting during the night are rarely successful. The pad and buzzer method of treating enuresis, in which a buzzer sounds when the bedclothes become wet, is successful in only a few cases, and it shouldn't be used on children under the age of six. The best approach to bedwetting is to treat it as lateness rather than illness and not to draw attention to it. Very young children may stop bedwetting if they are allowed to sleep in their parents' bedroom, and parents should try and overcome the basic insecurity of the child.

FAECAL SOILING

Unlike bedwetting, faecal soiling is unusual in toilet-trained children and almost always indicates stress or emotional disturbance.

Nevertheless, a physical cause should be ruled out first. There are three types of faecal soiling: soiling that has been present from babyhood; regressive soiling, in which a toilet-trained child reverts to an earlier stage of development; and aggressive soiling, which is an emotional response to overstrict parenting, or over-severe or out-of-date toilet training (see p.113).

Aggressive soiling usually occurs in children who have been "toilet-trained" too early in life, because the parents place exaggerated emphasis on being clean. If a child feels stifled and isn't allowed to play and get dirty she may express her frustration and anger through soiling.

The most effective way to deal with soiling is to reduce a child's anxiety. Overstrict parents should become more relaxed, and stressful or traumatic events need to be dealt with sympathetically.

DEPRESSION

Children become depressed when they face stress they can't cope with: moving house, changing school and leaving friends behind, separation from parents, divorce, or being the subject of abuse are all examples.

It is now believed that any evaluation of learning disabilities in a child should include routine checking for depression, since the two often go hand in hand.

A depressed child may cry more than normal, lack interest in games and friends, and be irritable when efforts are being made to rouse her from her apathy. Depression rarely occurs on its own in children; it's usually combined with phobias, obsessions, and compulsive behaviour. Sleep disturbance, anorexia, lack of concentration which in turn causes difficulties at school, and tense, restless behaviour are common features. Chronic depression affects the development of a child's personality – a depressed child who is hostile and rebellious may become anti-social and even delinquent as she grows up.

There are many ways to help a depressed child. If her environment is insecure, a period as a day-patient or in-patient in a children's unit may be useful provided it is combined with help from the whole family. Psychotherapy can help to relieve unconscious conflicts in the child, whether about growing up or over-dependence on parents. Parents too, may need help and therapy – if they are over-protective, for instance. Every effort should be made to identify and reduce the stress on the child.

Eating disorders Refusing to eat, overeating, being excessively fussy or faddy, and pica (eating things not usually considered edible), may all be classified as eating disorders if they occur frequently.

Persistent refusal to eat or picking at food is common in children of preschool age. Poor appetite may be the result of anxiety or it may indicate a problem between parent and child. Parents may be overanxious, with exaggerated ideas about nutritional needs, or food may be used as a symbol of affection. Overfeeding results in undereating. Fortunately, food refusal in young children rarely leads to undernourishment – the best treatment is to adopt a more flexible approach to food and offer a wide range of foods.

Faddy or fussy eating is common in otherwise healthy children and many children go through phases of faddiness that pass. Faddy eating, unless it is excessive, is not really a problem. It is often a child's natural way of selecting a balanced diet.

Overeating is a more serious problem than food refusal or faddiness in that it can lead to obesity. Obesity is not only bad for a child's health, it also means that she may be teased by her peers and suffer low self-esteem.

Children overeat for many different reasons; sometimes a child uses food to compensate for the fact that she feels unloved and insecure; sometimes a parent who feels inadequate will overfeed a child to make up for not giving them enough love and affection. To prevent overeating, it is essential to identify the underlying reason, whether it is insecurity on the part of the child, or conscious or unconscious overfeeding on the part of the parent. A doctor will be able to suggest a suitable reducing diet.

Pica is the consumption of substances without any nutritional value, such as soil, gravel, chalk, paint, clothing, or even faeces. It occurs most frequently among children from neglected, poor, or disorganized homes. Children with pica may show other signs of disturbed behaviour.

BEHAVIOURAL DISORDERS

Anti-social behaviour usually stems from a problem within the family or in the family's inability to adjust to society at large. A child may fail to identify herself as part of a family and to accept parental attitudes and standards of behaviour. This is most likely to happen in disorganized or disordered homes, where there are no consistent adult role-models, or where a child is constantly being moved around, scolded, punished, or being mentally, physically, or socially abused. Common symptoms of behavioural disorders are bad language, temper tantrums, disobedience, aggression, stealing, and lying. As a child grows up she may stay out late, play truant from school, and take drugs.

Psychologists, child psychiatrists, and social workers can provide a diagnosis of a behavioural disorder, and in some cases psychotherapy is recommended for the child. Since the problem often indicates an underlying problem in the family, the whole family rather than just the individual child may receive counselling, and be assigned a social worker.

OTHER PROBLEM BEHAVIOUR

Most children at some stage will indulge in behaviour which you find worrying, unacceptable, or just annoying. In the majority of cases, the reasons are quite innocent and the phase will soon pass.

Negativism Stubbornness, selfishness, and disobedience are all characteristics of negativism. To some extent, all preschoolers are negativistic. They may seem to delight in doing the opposite of what they are asked: when you want your child to go out she decides to stay in, or when you want her to eat her food she'll refuse it.

There are many reasons for resisting parental authority and parents can misinterpret them. A child may be negativistic, not because she wants to revolt against authority, but because she simply wants to continue with what she is doing. She has no conception of time, and sees no reason why she should stop playing an enjoyable game. Reasons such as a mealtime or going to bed are quite irrelevant if she is not hungry or tired.

Another explanation for negativism is that a young child cannot distinguish between two opposites. She is inexperienced, her life is charged with alternatives, and often she finds it impossible to differentiate between yes and no, give and take, or push and pull. Her interest in these double alternatives is so evenly balanced that she goes from one extreme to the other.

Flagrant negativism may be the result of insufficient parental encouragement. Even if your child is slow to perform a task or makes a mess, it's important that you encourage learning early on.

Stealing Between the ages of two and five or six, a child may be so attracted to an object – a toy, coins left on a table, or a sweet – that she takes it when she hopes no-one is looking. Sometimes she will do it in such a way that her theft will be discovered. Neither is a sign of a deep-rooted problem. Rather it is the normal result of overwhelming desire unchecked by social inhibitions. Do not punish the act, but do not ignore it. Tell your child clearly and calmly that it is unacceptable and insist that the object be returned. In all likelihood, one or a few such interchanges are all that's required to end the behaviour.

Resistance to school A child who says she doesn't want to go to school or, more commonly, complains of a stomach- or headache on school mornings may be coming down with a mild illness; she may be unhappy about something in school; or she may not wish to leave you because of shyness or something she is worried about at home. It's best not to force your child to go to school at first, unless this is a recognised and oft-repeated pattern. If an illness does not reveal itself in a day or two or if your child perks up once the threat of school is removed, you should talk to her teacher to help uncover any problems. If all is well at school and reluctance to leave home is the possible cause, try a loving but firm goodbye and a warm but restrained welcome home. If the behaviour persists, consult your doctor.

SEXUAL MISBEHAVIOUR

Adults tend to classify some aspects of normal development (such as games of "show") as prurient. They are quite normal stages of development, and it is only adult interference that leads to exaggerations of sexual play.

True sexual misbehaviour may occur in isolation or together with other forms of antisocial behaviour, such as truancy. Sexual curiosity and masturbation are common and normal features of childhood, and become abnormal only because of their frequency or the circumstances in which they occur. Unless you consider a child's sexual behaviour completely unacceptable, it is important to retain a sensible attitude to this feature of childhood. Even if you do consider behaviour questionable, consult your doctor before labelling your child's behaviour abnormal.

PRESCHOOL

EARLY EDUCATION

CHOOSING A NURSERY

When she's three or four your child will be able to go to nursery school, if you choose. Whether you feel this is the correct step will largely depend on her nature. For example, is she still shy and clinging, or naturally outgoing? Only you can know whether she is ready.

Before making a decision, visit several nursery schools in your area. Prepare a checklist of important points so you do not forget any of them. For example, are the teachers relaxed or formal? Is it a happy environment? What is the standard of facilities? How many children are there, and are they well supervised? What subjects are taught? Does the school feel safe? Are the children happy?

You should sit in on a few classes and spend a whole morning or afternoon there, and also speak to mothers whose children already attend. You will then have all the information you need to decide.

The choice as to whether or not you decide to send your child to preschool will depend largely upon the options available and whether or not they suit her needs. Find out what's available in your area and spend what time you can visiting nursery schools and talking to teachers and other parents so as to get a good idea of what is being provided.

CHOOSING PRESCHOOL EDUCATION

There is no single kind of preschool that is best for every child. Each child should be in a school that fits her particular needs. All evaluations of preschool education show mixed results. One long-term assessment showed that boys in Montessori programmes sustained gains in reading and maths throughout their school careers. Other research shows that intellectual gains are found in all but the poorest of programmes. But it's difficult to know how long these benefits last. Evaluations of Head Start, an American-based preschool organization, for example, show that apparent IQ differences between children in Head Start and those who don't attend preschool diminish over time. Whatever the benefits of preschool education, there is no substitute for a loving and caring home environment.

Playgroups often take children from as early as two-and-a-half years old. They provide the opportunity for interaction with other children of the same age and help develop early social skills, but in a less formal atmosphere than nursery school.

Preschool has some benefits. Your child can develop a greater sense of confidence and therefore more self-control, as well as learning to share, to be concerned for the needs of others, and to take turns. Your child's skill in planning ahead and co-operating with others will improve through fantasy and group play.

The opportunities for play in preschool enhance the various ways that your child thinks – that is, imaginatively, speculatively and inventively. These are characteristics often found in intellectual and creative children. Some preschools are designed to help disadvantaged children by building up their confidence. Children who attend such schools turn out to be less likely to repeat a year than their peers who did not attend preschool, less in need of special education, and less likely to show delinquent behaviour when they reach adolescence.

I think there are very few risks to your child attending preschool, certainly no more than when she ventures outside of the family; she'll just encounter them sooner. Risks may include minor health problems, or exposure to behaviour you find objectionable, such as swearing and rude stories.

SETTLING IN

You can help your child adjust to nursery school by taking her along for one or two visits well in advance of her start date. Encourage her to play with the other children, and to sit at one of the desks or play with some of the equipment. But try not to push her to socialize with other children if she doesn't seem keen at first. Some children are naturally more gregarious than others and she will adjust in her own good time. The aim is to make her visits as enjoyable as possible. If you stress all the fun things she will do, her eager anticipation for school will be stronger than her worry about leaving you. If she is having trouble adjusting, most nursery schools will let you stay with her on the first day, and for steadily decreasing periods of time on the following days. Make sure you collect her yourself for the first week when she is most insecure. Once she is confident that she's not being abandoned, you'll be free to make other arrangements for collection.

Your child's personality, maturity, place in the family, and willingness to leave home will all influence the way she settles down at preschool. In general, boys are more likely than girls of the same age to cry when their mothers first leave them at nursery school and they tend to cry when frustrated or angry with a teacher or helper. On the other hand, your child may enjoy being with other children as much as she does anything else about preschool. It's not unusual for two little boys or girls to rush eagerly towards each other when they meet at school.

Although your child is now attending nursery school, this doesn't mean that your part in her education is finished. Ask her what she has done at the nursery school and who she played with. By getting her to talk over her school experiences you will be consolidating the new words and skills she is learning. You can help her to improve her use of language by repeating what she says in the correct form, though not by directly correcting her. Your child will be constantly seeking new information and you should always try to answer her questions truthfully. If you don't know the answer it is best to suggest you both look it up in a book, or ask daddy whether he knows, rather than just try to fob her off.

HOW CHILDREN BEHAVE AT NURSERY SCHOOL

As a rule boys are more task-oriented in nursery school play and little girls talk more about being friends, recognising similarities in each other, admiring one another's clothes, discussing who's friends with who, and so on.

Dominant and aggressive behaviour in little boys is very much in evidence in a preschool setting. Intelligence and ability to get along with others are as important to popularity in preschool as a boy's size or physical prowess. Popularity fluctuates from day to day. Hitting is a common form of aggressiveness. A few girls strike out at other girls, but their hitting is usually not effective. Boys take longer to learn not to hit others and make unprovoked, if rather mild, attacks on girls. They will, for example, push little girls or gesture menacingly at them.

APPROACHES TO PRESCHOOL

No single method of preschool has proved to be significantly better for every child. Many parents send their children to preschool to give them an opportunity to play and be sociable; others simply because it allows their children physical outlets that won't damage the furniture.

Structured classes are better suited to the needs of most small children. A chaotic environment may cause some boys to react in a way that some teachers describe as hyperactive. Structures vary within preschools. Some nursery schools follow a timetable for certain activities each day along the lines advocated by Dr Montessori, and organize the school around an orderly child-sized environment with specific behavioural guidelines, such as putting things away when they are finished with.

A child who finds tasks easy and has lots of local friends may be suited to a traditional school. However, a child who has few local playmates and wants to socialize may enjoy a less structured preschool.

GIRLS AT SCHOOL

Girls, in general, have a greater aptitude for subjects involving language skills, such as reading. They're also more likely to prefer games that involve social interaction with other girls.

This innate tendency may be reinforced by parents and teachers who steer them towards certain activities that involve "playing quietly" and away from others more associated with boys. Whatever the reasons, girls at school generally follow certain patterns of behaviour. They:

• Prefer to play with other girls in games involving a strong element of co-operation. They will often shy away from boys, especially those engaged in boisterous or aggressive play

• Tend to choose activities involving books (words or pictures). On the other hand, they will be more anxious than boys about maths and other number-based activities

• Are generally well motivated and more willing to conform. However, this may mean that teachers assume they are coping well with lessons and so they may receive less attention than boys

GOING TO SCHOOL

Starting school will be a great milestone for your child, and for you too. You'll both have to make adjustments: your child will discover a new and exciting world, and you will have to adjust to his new-found independence.

IS YOUR CHILD READY?

There is a legal maximum age by which your child must have begun school – in the UK, five years – but many parents are keen to send their children earlier if places are available, to give them a "head start". It is biology and not the calendar that determines your child's readiness for school. Certain physical skills are therefore usually taken as signs that he has reached the level of mental development necessary for school success. These include being able to catch a large ball, hop on one foot, and run and stop on a signal. Your child must be capable of taking care of his bodily needs, such as going to the toilet independently, doing up his shoes, and dressing himself. He should also know his full name and be able to ask clear and concise questions. Many five-year-olds are proud of learning numbers and their ability to count. They also demonstrate their maturity by making strong efforts to keep themselves under control. You can begin to introduce all these things to your child before he starts school.

If you are unsure whether your child is ready, ask a nursery-school teacher. A teacher with ten years' experience has probably taught around five hundred children and so should be very accurate at predicting whether your child will do well at school.

SCHOOL READINESS CHECKLIST

Your child needn't have mastered every skill on the list. Use it only as a guide, and consult a teacher at your chosen school.

• *Join in the shared activities of a group*

• *Listen to a story and re-tell events in sequence*

• *Join in and readily follow instructions for games or new activities*

• *Express ideas and needs clearly to others*

• *Hop, skip, and jump*

• *Help about the house doing simple tasks*

• *Recognise basic colours and shapes*

• *Recognise similarities and differences in sound*

• *Join in songs and know some simple ones by heart*

• *Cope with buttons, shoelaces, and zip fasteners, and cut with scissors*

• *Copy simple figures, including a circle, square and triangle*

• *Attend to personal toiletry needs*

HELPING YOUR CHILD TO LIKE SCHOOL

Your child is more likely to succeed at school if he has the right frame of mind to begin with. You can achieve this by preparing your child before he starts so that he is physically and mentally ready for the demands that school will make on him. Encourage him to carry out simple tasks so that he understands the concept of responsibility. Make sure his play involves imagination and creativity, as well as opportunities for learning and developing his memory. It is important, too, that the school provides the right environment for your child's education, with motivated teachers who have a good relationship with their pupils.

Your child will undoubtedly benefit if you take an interest in his schoolwork and can continue his education at home. However, there is a real danger that you will do more harm than good if your methods are very different from those being taught at school. Teaching methods change over the years so the current system probably bears no relation to the way you were taught. To avoid this, talk to your child's teacher about the school's particular methods and find out at first hand about the subjects they are teaching and the course books that are in use. You may be able to borrow books and equipment overnight. Some schools actively encourage parents to sit in on lessons as observers, or you may even be able to help out. But don't overdo the schoolwork. Home should also be a place of comfort and refuge so you will need to strike a balance between helping your child progress with his education and overloading him with work.

YOUR CHANGING RELATIONSHIP

Your child's first days at school mark a change in his relationship with you. Up to now he has been dependent on you for everything, but now he'll have to begin to learn to become independent, responsible for all his own decisions and actions. This change doesn't happen overnight but it is important to begin the process by encouraging your child to take on more and more responsibility. By now he should already wash and dress himself and he might be expected to look after his schoolbag, books, and other equipment, and to lay his things out each night for the next day.

He'll feel very grown up, and will not want to be fussed over, but you should always be ready to give a cuddle whenever he shows he needs one. It is hard for your child to accept that he is not fully grown up, and the emotional drain of daily social interaction may occasionally be too much for him. As with most things, a cuddle from you is the best remedy and will set him up for the next day.

You may find that your child won't want such public displays of affection as he used to have, particularly not in front of his new friends. Don't feel snubbed. He is simply asserting himself as independent – grown up enough not to need a kiss from mum.

More than anything else it's important not to push too hard, even in asking what happened during his day. Clever prompting will be all you need to hear about his time at school, but prying will only make him secretive.

BOYS AT SCHOOL

Boys, generally, have a greater aptitude for activities involving spatial skills, such as building games. They're likely to prefer games that involve competition and physical activity.

As with girls, this innate tendency may be strengthened by adults. Boys may be encouraged to take up "boyish" activities that "let off steam" or involve construction, and unconsciously discouraged from contemplative pursuits, such as reading. As a result they tend to behave in certain ways at school. They:

- *Prefer playing with other boys, especially in energetic games that involve physical activity such as climbing or mock fighting*

- *Concentrate on toys that aid mathematical and spatial skills. They will also persevere with a difficult maths question until they solve it*

- *Become more disruptive if they do not get attention or are having difficulty with a subject. This may mean that the teacher will spend a disproportionate amount of time with the boys compared with girls*

CHAPTER FOUR

FAMILY LIFE

If you have never had a child you may imagine that you can incorporate a baby into your life with minimal disruption. This is rarely the case. A new baby is a 24-hour-a-day commitment and you will find that, at least for a few months, your normal lifestyle will have to be greatly modified. This will be all the more true if you have twins or even triplets.

Your relationship with your partner will also be different. There will be less time for intimacy and companionship and you may find you need to stop and take stock of your joint responsibilities. Child care is often thought of as a woman's job, but there is no biological reason why this should be so. Shared parenting will reap benefits for you and your partner, as well as your child.

You may want to involve other members of your family in helping to bring up your baby, especially if you are a single parent, or if you and your partner both go out to work. Alternatively, you may decide to employ a nanny, au pair, or childminder, or send your child to a day nursery or crèche. Whichever choice you make, planning ahead and organizing your time is of paramount importance.

MOTHER KNOWS BEST?

The argument that women are better equipped for parenthood than men is no longer valid.

Sixty years ago it was not uncommon for a women to have ten children or more, and young girls were more likely to be involved in looking after them. Nowadays most mothers have never seen a newborn until they give birth.

If a woman does have more experience of looking after a baby than her partner, it is important that she doesn't mock his efforts, since he may respond by withdrawing his help altogether. When this happens, the role of each parent becomes polarized, increasing pressure on the mother and isolating the father from the family unit.

BECOMING A FAMILY

No matter how many baby books you read, and no matter how well prepared you are, you can still be knocked sideways by the impact of a newborn baby on your life. As well as the physical requirements of looking after a baby, your normal domestic work will at least quadruple. Instead of doing a clothes wash once a week, you may find you have to do one every day. Such repetitive chores can create a heavy, tiring work-load.

After the first few weeks, when relatives and neighbours stop dropping around to offer congratulations, the novelty of being home alone with a new baby can wear off rapidly. Mothers who have given up a job or a career may find that what they miss is not their work, but their work environment. They miss social interaction with their friends and colleagues. In particular they miss the difference between work and home. With a young baby you do not have the luxury of leaving your work behind.

Many people also find that making the transition from being a couple to being a family can prove more traumatic than they imagine. The dynamics in a relationship need to adapt to a new addition. Problems can arise when a couple find it difficult to fit another person into the complex equation of human emotions that makes up a relationship.

NEW RESPONSIBILITIES

The arrival of a child means that choices become stark: beforehand, for instance, if neither partner wanted to clean the bathroom floor, it could be left until later. But a baby can never be left until later. His needs take priority and somebody has to take immediate responsibility for meeting them. Time that was previously spent on other things must now be given to the baby.

Ideally these lifestyle changes are shared equally within a partnership, but in practice women very often end up taking on the main burden. Depending on individual expectations, this can lead to deep resentment within a relationship, causing a couple to move apart after the birth of their baby.

Research in America has shown that one in every two marriages goes into decline after the birth of the first child. All of the couples in the study, no matter how well-adjusted, experienced

Shared parenting
Spend time with your partner getting to know your child and learning to be parents together.

on average a 20 per cent increase in conflict within their marriage during the first year of parenthood. Although conflict can sometimes be healthy, it is often not what new parents expect.

To reduce the stress placed on a partnership, it is vital that each partner has at least some idea of what to expect and is able to compromise. Having a baby means rearranging your life.

EQUAL PARENTING

Although the role of men in parenting has changed over the last few decades, the attitude that child care is primarily a woman's responsibility still persists. Ideally, you and your partner should discuss your respective roles before your baby is born. Women should make their partners aware that being a good father doesn't just mean helping: it means fathering the child as well.

In a recent survey, 74 per cent of fathers said that child care should be shared equally. But when asked, "Do you share child care equally with your partner?", 87 per cent replied "no". In other words, almost nine out of ten women will not receive equal help from their partners.

This isn't just damaging for women, it is also very limiting for men in two ways. First, a father's relationship with his partner may suffer if she feels resentment at a lack of help and support. Second, if a father doesn't play an active role in the early months and years of his baby's life, he may lose the chance to form a close childhood bond with his son or daughter. A detached father will have a negative effect on his child. Girls may have trouble interacting with men, and boys will be deprived of a male role model.

FATHERING

Many of us remember our fathers seeming more distant and unapproachable than our mothers, but there is no reason why a child cannot enjoy an equally close relationship with both parents. A baby's relationships do not operate on an either/or basis and you should never worry that if a baby spends an equal amount of time with his father, he might love his mother less. All young children need as much love as they can get, and both parents should do their utmost to provide it.

For a father to take on an equal role as a parent, he will have to overcome cultural pressures, and perhaps change his own attitudes too. He will also have to recognise his role as a carer rather than just a provider. Some men confuse parenthood with taking care of the bills, because that is what their own fathers did.

Today it may be economic factors that determine who is left holding the baby. If a woman earns more than her partner, or if he is unemployed, many couples can't afford to let misplaced male pride reduce their weekly income. While the rise of the house-husband has undoubtedly benefited lots of families, it is important to bear in mind that the man left at home with a small child suffers from the same problems as a woman: isolation and boredom.

Parental bonding
Your child cannot have too much love and attention, so both of you should give as much as possible.

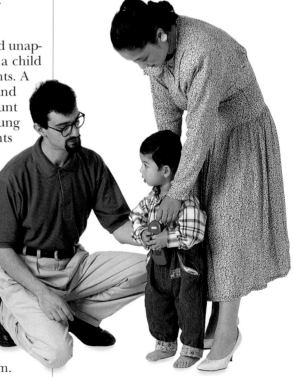

231

A FATHER'S STORY

Anna and Henry Ewington experienced a bad few months after their son Alexander was born. Anna was exhausted, depressed, and overwhelmed and Henry didn't feel very paternal.

Henry attributes this to the fact that he measured fatherhood in terms of doing things, and that Anna quickly took all responsibility for the baby.

Henry's frustration intensified Anna's difficulties. For the first three months she experienced periods of postnatal depression. Their sex life deteriorated and Henry started to feel rejected by Anna, both physically and emotionally. In just a few months they decided it was make or break.

"We decided it had to be 'make' instead of break when we found out Anna was pregnant with Leora only ten months after the birth of Alex. I realised then that I had to give Anna enormous credit for being able to cope with it all. I half expected her to cave in, but instead she became stronger, perhaps because of having to cope with Alex."

During the third month of Anna's pregnancy she had a threatened miscarriage. She was advised to stay in bed, and Henry decided to take unpaid leave from work so that he could look after her.

"For the first time since the birth Anna felt as though I was doing my bit, and I felt, for once, that I was the lynch-pin of our family unit. Despite the emotional strain, I'm glad we went through it. It has made me an equal parent with Anna, whereas before I felt like an observer."

GRANDPARENTS

With the arrival of a first child, grandparents can be supportive, or they can be the source of increased tension, especially if family relations are already strained. You will probably find that you see more of your in-laws once your baby is born, and hopefully this will contribute to a happier family life.

Sometimes, however, the intimacy and interdependency of family relations means there is a thin line between helpfulness and interference. Ideally, you and your partner will have discussed the role you want grandparents to play. Once both of you have decided how much help you do or don't want, you will find it easier to establish your authority by setting out the rules in advance.

It is understandable that many grandparents, particularly grandmothers, want to show you how they coped with a crying baby or a disobedient toddler. This advice is usually well-meant and may be welcome. If it isn't, say so. Point out that it is your baby and that discipline – or any other matter – is therefore your responsibility. If you occasionally make mistakes they will be your own.

It certainly is worth persevering to overcome problems with parents so your child will be able to reap the benefits from a secure and loving relationship with her grandparents.

A SPECIAL RELATIONSHIP

A good relationship between a grandparent and grandchild is rewarding for the whole family. Grandparents can offer a more relaxed perspective about your children, parents can rest secure in the knowledge that when grandparents are in attendance their baby will be well looked after, and a baby can learn to form an important emotional bond beyond her mother and father.

Grandparents can form special relationships with their grandchildren for several reasons. First, they see them less frequently than their parents, which alleviates the strain of day-to-day care. Second, ultimate responsibility for a child rests with her parents. This frees grandparents to enjoy the thrill of parenthood

Second time around
Your parents and your partner's parents are likely to have a relaxed attitude towards child care.

without the accompanying worries and stresses. Third, a grand-parent has already brought up at least one child, and problems are always easier to cope with the second time around. Grandparents are also likely to have more quality time to spend with their grand-children.

As children become young adults with problems of their own, grandparents can offer a broader perspective on the difficulties facing them. A grandparent is likely to be the oldest person that your child will ever know as a friend, and can give your child an insight into how things were in the past, as well as being a lot more interesting and loving than history books.

Not all families, however, can enjoy the benefits of an extended family. This is particularly true today, as financial pressures force couples to move to where they can find work. Divorce can limit grandparents' access to their grandchildren. This can be terribly upsetting for grandparents and grandchildren alike, and it helps if a child continues to see her grandparents regularly.

LOVE AND SECURITY

The most basic needs of any young child are physical care and emotional love and security. If a child feels well cared for, she will develop into a more outgoing, and relaxed person. A child who is given enough love and security at an early age is likely to become less demanding as she grows older. Conversely, a child that is emo-tionally neglected may grow up insecure, clingy, and fearful.

It is important that parents do not shy away from giving their child adequate love and security for fear of "spoiling" her. Although it is true that a child should not get into the habit of thinking she can have anything she wants, it is even more important that she doesn't get into the habit of thinking she is not loved.

Remember, your child's way of seeing things is very different from yours. Small and apparently trivial displays of affection (a hug, a pat, a kiss) will do much more to shape the personality of your young child than anything else. It is no good loving your child and trying not to show it, in the mistaken assumption that this will make her a "stronger" person. In fact the opposite is true.

Affection produces emotional and physical results. For instance, when young babies are held in their mother's arms they breathe more slowly, have a steadier respiration, cry less, and sleep more. This isn't so surprising, as cuddling takes a child back to the com-forting sensation of the uterus when she was warm and secure. Hugging is also the best way of communicating to a young child that you love and care for her. If your child sees her parents hug-ging each other she will know that, in spite of any arguments you might have, you still love each other.

Even if your child can feel that you love her through your physical affection, it is also important that she hears it. Toddlers especially need to hear that you love them. They have reached the stage where they can tell you that they love you, and they need this affection to be reciprocated. Never be shy of showing your love – it is the most important thing you will ever share.

GIVING
AFFECTION

Loving touch is crucial to our well-being and, in the case of babies has even been shown to promote physical development.

If you're not sure how to increase the amount of physical affection you show your child, consider some of the following suggestions. These combine physical attention with love and companionship – exactly what every child needs.

• Try carrying a young baby in a sling; almost all newborn babies love the sensation of being strapped close to you

• Every so often give your baby a soothing rub with baby lotion or a massage (see pp. 76–77)

• Share a bath together, or take your baby swimming at the local pool. Hold her tightly in the water so that she feels warm and secure

• As she gets older, do some exer-cise together – this doesn't have to be anything more complicated than putting a record on and dancing around the room

• Have a few rough-and-tumble games; many mothers leave this to the father or to other children, and particularly neglect to do so with girls

• Curl up in bed with your child, and every now and then have a lie-in, so that your child starts the day knowing she is well loved

NAME *Nicole Killen*

AGE *34 years*

OCCUPATION *Concession manageress in fashion store*

OBSTETRIC HISTORY *Normal pregnancy. Matthew born two days after due date*

Nicole was convinced that one day she would meet a wonderful man who loved her completely, and that they would have a caring relationship in a loving home. But it didn't happen.

"Whether it was circumstance or coincidence I don't know, but when I found out I was pregnant with Matthew, it seemed as though I was being given a chance actively to take control of my life, instead of waiting for someone else – who might never arrive – to do it for me."

THE SINGLE PARENT

When Nicole became pregnant with Matthew three years ago, she found herself in a difficult and unexpected situation. At the time she was having a non-committal affair with a work colleague.

"I found myself in a quandary because throughout my whole life I never once envisaged myself as a single mother. I had grown up thinking a child should be the product of a loving relationship. But I knew that this wasn't a relationship I wanted to remain permanent."

FIRST REACTIONS

"The thought of becoming an unmarried single mother took a lot of getting used to. Initially, my own mother, who is quite conservative, reacted very badly which made things even harder. She's come round to the idea now, but that's because Matthew is a lovable toddler whom she adores madly."

Nicole took three months' maternity leave after Matthew was born, then she was offered three further months on half pay. The first three months went quite smoothly – Matthew was quite a placid baby and by the eighth week he usually slept five hours each night. "In fact, although I was exhausted, Matthew gave me so much joy that I took an unexpected delight in having him all to myself."

UNEXPECTED PROBLEMS

After three months Nicole was torn between staying at home and going back to work, but in the end, despite financial pressures, she decided to stay at home. "I felt Matthew was just too young to leave with an unknown childminder. It was only towards the end of the fifth month that I started to experience problems.

"The worst bit was never having anyone to moan to at the end of the day. You can't moan to a six-month-old. Little problems and nagging worries soon developed into overblown crises that kept me awake for hours at night. The week before my six-month maternity leave was up, Matthew got a mild chest infection. Although it wasn't serious, I became so worried that I developed severe insomnia and was prescribed tranquillizers."

Matthew's chest infection lasted for three weeks and the doctor then diagnosed asthma. Nicole was immediately convinced that Matthew was an "ill" baby who would be sick for the rest of his life. "If there had been someone else to share the worry with, I'm sure I wouldn't have reacted so badly", she recalls.

RETURNING TO WORK

"I felt I had to put off returning to work for another month. Then when the day finally arrived I was surprised by my own anxiety – not so much because I had to leave Matthew (I left him asleep with my mother) but because halfway to work I started to wonder if I could still do my job. The job I have is quite high-pressured – part of my salary is based on commission – and things have to be up and running from 9 a.m. to 6.30 p.m. without a break. I worked four days a week, and it wasn't easy worrying all day at work, and then worrying all night at home."

At this point Nicole's mother moved in with her for five weeks so that she could have some time to adjust to being a single working mother. Having her there made Nicole realize that, although she couldn't afford it, she had to consider full-time help at least until the end of the first year. She contacted a local parents' group, who sent her advice on hiring a nanny or an au pair.

EMPLOYING A NANNY

When Matthew was eight months old Nicole hired her first full-time nanny. The cost, for someone on her salary, was appalling. She also realized that, although she got a bit more sleep, most of the time she found it impossible to stay in bed and leave it to the nanny when she heard Matthew crying. "It may have been that his asthma made me over-protective, or it may simply have been that I didn't like sharing my home with a relative stranger – whatever the reason, after two months I asked the nanny to leave, and deciced to look after Matthew on my own."

This helped ease the financial situation, which by that point had become quite critical. It was still hard for Nicole to go out, because she couldn't afford to spend money on a babysitter and an evening's entertainment. She realized, nearly a year after the birth, that she hadn't been out socially since having the baby.

A LIFE OF HER OWN

"That was when I had the idea of having my first post-Matthew dinner party. About eight friends came around, each with a home-made dish, and we had a fabulous evening without waking Matthew once. Having the dinner party made an enormous difference to me. It was the first time I felt as though I was a social being again, rather than just a single mother. About a week later I managed to come off the tranquillizers permanently."

Two months after Matthew's first birthday Nicole arranged day care so that a nanny looked after him three days a week, and he stayed with his grandmother one day a week. "This was the first time that things seemed to calm down enough for me to enjoy being a parent. I got used to the asthma attacks, and no longer panicked unduly. My job was more under control and I even began to nurture an infrequent social life. I no longer feel any guilt about having Matthew on my own, because I know he is well looked after and that he receives a huge amount of love."

NAME *Matthew Killen*

AGE *18 months*

MEDICAL HISTORY *Asthma diagnosed when 6 months old.*

ORGANIZING YOUR LIFE

Learning to look after your new baby in the first weeks can be overwhelming, so look after yourself, too.

- *Get your partner to help out with the baby so you can have some time to yourself*

- *Don't expect to be a perfect mother straight away. You have a lot to learn, and your baby is learning too*

- *Let the housework go. Do only the essential tasks, and get someone else to do them if you can*

- *Low potassium levels can contribute to a feeling of exhaustion. Eat plenty of potassium-rich foods, such as bananas, tomatoes, dried apricots, and plain yogurt*

- *Don't be surprised if you get the "baby blues" – up to 80 per cent of mothers do, and it will pass after about ten days. If depression persists, however, you should seek help very quickly*

As any mother knows, the physical, emotional, and social demands on your life seem to multiply unendingly with the arrival of a new baby. Interrupted nights and hectic days coupled with the psychological pressure of taking responsibility for a new person, combine to heap unexpected stresses onto a new mother.

Organization can be the key to survival. Pregnancy is the ideal time to sit down and take stock of the situation before you are swept away by the joys and traumas of parenthood. No matter what stage you are at, however, it is never too late to organize your time so that you get more out of it.

When you are planning your post-baby life, try dividing up things you have to think about into three or four areas: baby-related, work-related (house and/or office), partner-related, and you. This fourth category is usually under-valued, but happens to be one of the most important. If you aren't happy, your baby won't be happy. There are certain things that you will find helpful to think about in advance. For instance, if you are a working mother, have you spoken to your manager about if and when you want to return to work? Have you considered going back but doing reduced hours? Is it possible for you to do a job-share?

If you will be working part-time, will any of your working rights be affected? They shouldn't be, but you should check now rather than finding out later on. You don't want to discover that you might be facing a wage cut when you've already committed yourself to expensive child care.

Establishing a routine A lot of the work you do in caring for your baby involves repetitive tasks, and these will be much easier to manage if you can work out some sort of timetable. Your routine should follow your baby's needs, not vice versa, so you won't be able to establish it straight away; it will take your baby three to six weeks or longer to settle into a pattern of feeding and sleeping.

Time out
Make sure that you allow a little time every day to relax and indulge yourself; it's in everyone's interests that you do.

Be careful not to confuse organization with regimentation. You don't want your life to be inflexible, as the needs of a young child can change hourly. What is important is that the routine you create for yourself doesn't either bore you or ignore you.

TIME FOR YOURSELF

You are your child's universe, so it's best for him if you're not irritable, grumpy, and jaded. While you must make every effort to meet your baby's needs, you must also look after your own needs.

Plan at least half an hour each day to devote entirely to yourself – you may want to have a bath, read a book, watch television, write a letter, meditate, exercise, listen to music, manicure your nails, or give yourself a facial. Before the baby arrives, finding half an hour for yourself seems simple, but once he is born it can seem like an impossible task.

If you are to make some space for yourself, the first thing you must do is learn to accept offers of help graciously. Too many mothers feel they are failures if they don't personally attend to their child's every need. This can be a dangerous route to go down. It is based on unrealistic expectations and eventually leads to nervous exhaustion or even breakdown.

GETTING AWAY

If you and your partner have already discussed how you are going to share the new workload (see **Equal parenting**, p.231), the next stage is discussing how you can make some time for each other once the baby has arrived. Try to arrange for a baby-sitter to come at least once a month, or better still once a week, so that parenting doesn't take over every single waking second of your lives.

Look into the possibilities of nanny sharing (see p.241) or, if you are not working full-time, see if you can arrange a "baby-swap" with another mother. Find out about courses or activities that offer a crèche. This is an ideal way to meet friends, take up an interest, or increase your qualifications while your child is cared for and socializes with other children his own age.

Spending time apart from your child doesn't necessarily make you a worse parent – in fact, in most cases it makes you a better one. If you spend all your time with your child he'll develop unrealistic expectations of relationships in general, and is likely to become overly demanding of friends and teachers alike.

Moreover, although your child needs a close and loving relationship with you, it is a mistake to think that he needs your company every second of the day. He will gain confidence and valuable social skills by learning to interact with adults and other children.

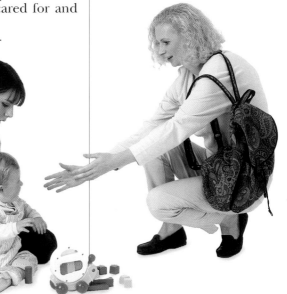

Handing over
Your baby doesn't need you every minute of the day, so let someone else take care of him now and then while you go out.

YOU AND YOUR PARTNER

When your baby arrives your relationship with your partner changes immediately. All the common interests and experiences that previously held you together (your social life, your sex life, hobbies, holidays, and so on) suddenly go out of the window overnight. You are likely to be so exhausted that your partner's needs are the last thing on your mind.

The discipline that a new baby imposes on your life makes keeping excitement and sparkle in a relationship a great effort. That's why many couples feel it's just never the same – and they're right. Sometimes it's better than it ever was before, but problems arise when one partner, inevitably the father, feels excluded.

YOUR PARTNER'S FEELINGS

Although it is widely acknowledged that a mother undergoes huge upheavals during and after pregnancy, there is less appreciation of the effects a new baby has on a father. Most fathers that accompany their partners through labour are in some state of shock after the birth. They are often traumatized by seeing their partners in considerable pain and distress. In fact, research has shown that nearly one in ten fathers suffers serious post-natal depression. One of the reasons suggested is that parental roles have changed so much in the last 20 or 30 years, making it more difficult than ever for fathers to adjust to parenthood.

Unless you make an effort with your partner, he may start to feel that "three's a crowd" and that he's being pushed out of the picture. It is unwise to let this type of situation develop, not just because you need your partner's help, but because he should spend as much time as possible with your baby at an early age. This will help him to build a close and loving relationship which lasts throughout your baby's childhood.

THE "REJECTED" FATHER

Be aware that barriers between you and your partner are likely to spring from the fact that, as one psychologist put it, "although men and women become parents at the same time, they don't become parents in the same way". There are many sociological, financial, and environmental reasons for this, but the result is often straightforward resentment or jealousy.

A man can quickly feel isolated within the family unit. He suddenly finds his partner's time monopolized by the new addition, and unless he is taking an active role in caring for the baby, he's no longer sure where he fits in. It is quite common to find a father becoming jealous of his own child. This situation may be exacerbated if there were differences of opinion about having the child in the first place (men often complain of being "pressurized" into having a baby).

TIPS FOR MOTHERS

Your partner will quickly start to feel he is neither wanted nor needed if you give all your attention to the baby.

• *Always ask your partner for help – you can't expect him to know how much you need it unless you tell him*

• *Involve him with the day-to-day care of the baby as early on, and as much as possible*

• *Don't refuse help when it's offered even if you feel you might do better on your own – it's his child too*

• *Do your best, no matter how unsociable you feel, to give your partner some of your attention and your affection*

• *If he is turning out to be a reluctant father and you are at the end of your tether, leave him a phone number, hand him the baby, and go out for the evening – he'll soon realize how much hard work it can be!*

Sharing feelings
Always make time to talk to your partner so you can avoid misunderstandings.

Your partner may find these feelings particularly difficult to deal with if he also feels rejected on a sexual level. Often men take a new mother's diminished sex drive as a personal rebuff. If it's not too late, discuss the effects this may have on your relationship before the baby arrives.

POSTNATAL SEX

If you haven't lost your desire for sex, that's wonderful and you should make the most of it. There is no reason to wait for your first six-week check-up to have sex if you feel physically fit enough. For some women, however, especially those that have had episiotomies, sex is not on the agenda.

After the baby arrives, your partner may share your lack of interest in sex, but if he doesn't, one sure way to make him understand your reluctance is to let him feel your episiotomy scar – most men will be very sympathetic.

A reduced sex drive is natural in that nature is doing her best to furnish you with the most reliable contraceptive of all – abstinence. After all, the last thing any new mother wants is to find that she's pregnant – imagine trying to cope with an eight-week-old baby and morning sickness.

Try to impress upon your partner, however, that there may be emotional as well as physiological reasons for your not wishing to have sex, and he needs to respect these equally.

COMMUNICATION

During the initial months of parenthood, both of you should make real efforts to keep the lines of communication open between you. No matter how exhausted or disorientated you may be, it is essential that you find the time to explain your feelings to each other.

Having a child changes things forever. If you are the one to spend most time with your new baby, you will be distracted from the fact that you have temporarily lost your lover. The same cannot necessarily be said for your partner – if he is not so involved in the day-to-day care of your baby, it is only natural that he feels the change in your relationship more keenly.

Let your partner help as much as possible in the care of your child (see **Tips for mothers**, left). Too often women involve their partners by giving them tasks that are only indirectly linked to the baby. When a mother says, for example, "I'll get Samantha ready while you run the bath", or "You heat the food up and I'll feed her", she is sharing some of the work, but not the child. Try reversing some of these options so that your partner spends sufficient time with the baby, and make sure that both of you consider the advice given in the columns on the left and right.

An active father
A father who helps care for his child will feel needed by both his partner and the baby.

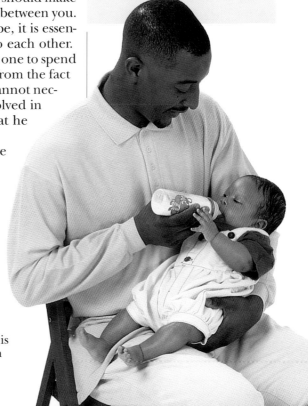

FEEDING

You must decide how you want your baby to be fed while you're out at work.

If you begin working before he is four months old, – that is, before any mixed feeding – you will need to plan. Introduce a routine so that feeding times are predictable and constant. If you feed your baby at breakfast and around 6 p.m., the person who looks after him during the day need give only the expressed milk or milk formula for the other two daytime feeds.

If you don't want your baby to take any milk substitutes, freeze expressed breast milk; it will keep for up to six months in the freezer. It should take around two weeks to get into this routine. You will need to run down your daytime milk production before returning to work or you will be most uncomfortable during the day.

RETURNING TO WORK

In the UK, you must go back to your job by the time the baby is 29 weeks old or your employer is no longer obliged to keep your job open for you. When it's time for you to return to work you may realize that you have not given yourself enough time to re-adjust after pregnancy. It is always a good idea to consult your doctor, as there are health factors to consider about which she can advise you. Some mothers find that they cannot bring themselves to leave the baby, while others – even though they adore the baby – are climbing the walls and have to "escape".

If you have taken the decision to return to work, be assured that as long as you arrange good child care (see below), you will not be neglecting your child. There is no danger of your young baby forgetting who you are, or transferring his affection to his daytime carer. The really important thing is that when you get home you spend quality time with your child.

I know from my own experience as a working mother that guilt pangs are inevitable. I felt certain, however, that my baby would instinctively know I was his mother. I was reassured when I later came across research showing that very young babies are quite able to single out their parents (whether biological or adoptive) due to the loving, interested attention that only parents can give. Similarly, it has been shown that premature babies can distinguish between the touch of their parents' hands through an incubator and the more matter-of-fact handling of nursing staff.

The important point is that it is the quality of the time you spend that counts more than the quantity. Love isn't measured in time: love is what you put into time, no matter how short.

CHILD AND CAREER

The job you face at home is twice as demanding as the one you face at work, and your terms of employment are worse. After all, you are expected to work seven days a week, 365 days a year. You will be frowned upon if you don't cook, clean, iron, entertain, and provide advice, nursing care, and sympathy continuously for at least 18 years, if not indefinitely. Your efforts will go largely unnoticed by society and, of course, you won't get paid a penny. In fact you will have to pay for the privilege of being a parent – but as most parents will tell you, despite the job description, it's a privilege worth paying for!

Your child's first step, first smile, and first word are all priceless personal achievements. Helping to mould a tiny baby into a thoughtful, well-adjusted individual is a task requiring sacrifice, responsibility and, above all, love. It also yields huge emotional dividends. To my mind this makes parenting one of the most important and rewarding jobs in the world.

Given this, it is disturbing to see the low status attached to parenting, particularly for women, who shoulder much of the burden. Being a good parent involves helping your child's personality to develop in a positive sense, and being a good role-model. If you want your children to grow up and work hard, then the fact that you work hard at your own job sets them an excellent example.

Having to combine the role of principal parent with full-time career is not easy, but women are doing it with imagination and sheer hard work. The rise of the mythical "super-mum" has meant that we are often expected to do it all without any help. There *are* a lot of "super-mums" around: they are the ones that manage everything day after day, at home and in the office, without failing to give love and energy to their children.

CHILD CARE

You should start looking for reliable child care about six weeks before you plan to return to work. Currently most governments do not give the priority they should to providing child-care schemes for women, which makes things more difficult.

Unfortunately, Britain has fewer nursery places for preschool children than any other country in Europe except Portugal. Nonetheless, things are gradually changing. Some companies now provide crèche schemes.

Friends and relatives Letting a relative help can be the perfect solution for many mothers, but consider the situation carefully before asking someone. You can start to feel uncomfortably indebted, or conversely, they can feel taken for granted.

Because you don't have a "professional" relationship, it may be difficult to stipulate rules and guidelines that they don't take quite as seriously as you; disciplining problems, for example, can soon become frustrating, particularly if your views on child-rearing diverge. On the other hand, if these problems are confronted early on, you can benefit immeasurably from the security, flexibility, and low cost of this type of arrangement. If you ask a friend, rather than a close relative, to help on a regular basis and you pay her, she must by law be registered with the local social services department as a childminder.

Childminders
You will be able to tell from your child's reaction whether he feels loved and secure with his childminder.

CHOOSING CHILD CARE

Your baby doesn't only need to be changed and fed: he needs the kind of loving attention that you would give him yourself if he is to learn to interact and become a sociable child.

Childminders *These are usually mothers themselves, and must be registered with the local social services department. Your local council will provide a list, but you arrange payment and hours with the childminder.*

Day nurseries *Run privately or by local authorities, these often have long waiting lists and usually only a small number of places for babies. You may get priority if you are a single parent.*

Nanny or mother's help *This kind of help can be expensive, but you might consider sharing a nanny with another family. You can find one through agencies, or by advertising locally, or in a newspaper or magazine. Parents' groups may be able to put you in touch with other mothers interested in sharing a nanny.*

Crèche *Perhaps you are very lucky and have enlightened employers who make it possible to take your baby to work with you. This means you can continue breastfeeding and have your baby close by all day. If there's a crèche at your work-place, ensure you arrange a place well before your baby is born.*

241

SEPARATION AND DIVORCE

A recent study suggests that children are better off with two unhappy parents than with divorced parents.

However, the research gives no indication of the different divorce situations which are critical in determining the effect on the child. An amicable divorce may be barely damaging and its effect entirely different from that of a bitter, acrimonious divorce. The main reason for this is that in an acrimonious situation, each parent usually does his or her best to turn the children against the other parent. This has a very negative and damaging effect on children, and should be avoided at all costs.

At some stage in every relationship, problems arise. In rare cases couples live happily ever after but the vast majority don't. This doesn't necessarily reflect a lowering of moral values; it is more an indication of the complexities and pressures of modern life. Support systems are weaker and expectations higher.

Statistics show that today two in three divorces are initiated by women, many of whom feel they are asked to do too much without adequate support from their partners. The average marriage lasts eight years – a depressing fact of life for growing numbers of children brought up without two parents.

PERIODS OF CHANGE

The problem for nearly all couples is that in the long term people change. Although this can be difficult, it can also be invigorating and constructive. If you learn to develop together, you will prevent boredom and stagnation building up in your relationship.

At the end of periods of change, which are often fraught with emotional insecurity, you will either grow together or grow apart. Whatever happens, it is vital that your children feel secure of their future at all times. For young children, change within a family unit (or fear of that change) is very damaging. Children do not have the defence mechanisms to protect themselves from the severe emotional insecurity that a breakup can cause.

EXPLAINING TO YOUR CHILDREN

A young child is like a sponge that soaks up emotional signals, whether or not they are directed at her. If you are happy, the chances are your child will be happy; if you are sad, she will be sad. Although it is always worth making an effort "for the sake of the children", don't fall into the trap of thinking they won't know what is going on. They usually sense when something is wrong, whether or not you have a smile on your face.

Because of this it's always best to explain, at least partially, what is going on. If you don't, children will invent their own explanations, mistakenly blaming themselves for problems in the family. This is because children under five only conceive the world in relation to themselves. If you don't give a plausible explanation of why you and your partner are arguing or splitting up, they may come up with explanations which are inconceivable to an adult, but make perfect sense to a child, such as: "Daddy has left because I don't clean my room properly", or "Mummy is upset because I wet the bed/I'm clumsy/I lost my pocket money". Feelings of guilt are severely damaging, especially for a child already struggling to come to terms with the emotional turmoil and insecurity that marital breakups can trigger. Doubt is one of the worst fears in a child's mind, so never leave your child in any doubt that you love her and that you will continue to look after her.

DIVORCE

If you reach the point where the only option left is divorce or separation, do not assume automatically that your children will be devastated. Some will be, but the effect on your child will depend greatly on age, personality, the circumstances of the divorce, and the prevailing social attitudes in the school and community.

I know of one primary school class in London, for instance, where out of 35 children, only five had parents who were still together. They were regularly teased by the others from "broken homes" who saw these five children as materially disadvantaged: the children whose parents were still together only got one set of presents on their birthday or at Christmas and they only had one house.

Although having divorced parents is nothing to boast about, many of these children did. This may be deeply shocking to a lot of people, but it is just one more indication of the different times that our children are growing up in.

MOVING OUT

If the time comes when you have to leave, it is vital to let your child know that you are not taking your love with you, and that you will continue to be an active parent. Let your child know specifically when you plan to see her and, no matter how difficult it is, try never to break these arrangements.

If you are the parent left with full-time responsibility for your child when your partner has moved out, try not to be upset if she misses her father or mother. Don't try to make her forget that the other parent exists, and don't speak abusively about the other parent as this will only confuse your child further.

Even if your child appears to be unaffected by a marital split, keep a close eye on her and ask her teachers if they notice any difference in her behaviour at school. Some children have fewer questions than others and keep their feelings of insecurity to themselves, but they may still need extra attention and love. Increased bedwetting, thumb-sucking, and general "clinginess" are all signs that your child is in need of reassurance and special care.

Grandparents can be a great boon at the time of the divorce. If possible, do encourage your child to see both sets. Don't let bad feeling act as a cut-off. Think of your child first – she needs continuity, security, and reassurance, and grandparents are second to none at providing these, as long as they don't bad-mouth either parent. Grandparents will also act as a mainstay during access periods and will show your child the unconditional love that every child needs if their parents are divorcing or separating.

Ask your children about their worries and anxieties and give them space to voice them. Listen and take them seriously. Act upon them. They will almost certainly be things of which you haven't thought, or would dismiss as trivial if you did.

ACCESS

Whatever your feelings are about your partner, it's best for your child if you're easy-going and generous about access.

Don't be stingy and don't be confrontational – it causes your child such anguish. Hand her over somewhere civilized like one of your homes, not somewhere like a park or shopping mall, or your child will feel like a commodity.

Plan well ahead, don't break promises at the last minute, and if your partner is late be breezy about it, otherwise your child will worry about both of you. Don't make it an opportunity to denigrate her father or mother; be off-hand, and keep your child calm: "Oh, I expect the traffic's bad" or "Shall we have a game of snap till he gets here?"

If your partner is consistently late or unreasonable, arrange a separate meeting to discuss this, out of earshot of your child. The only time to consider preventing your ex-partner having any access to your child is if you think she's at risk of being kidnapped or otherwise harmed. In such cases it is best to seek professional advice, either through counselling services or a lawyer.

New mothers are often surprised at the amount of work involved in caring for a newborn, and this is even more true for mothers who have multiple births.

• *Many mothers of twins don't realize how much help they will need, though mothers who have already had one baby tend to be more realistic about this. Don't underestimate the task of caring for twins, and don't for one minute imagine that asking for help reflects badly on your adequacy as a mother*

• *You may qualify to have a home help for the first few weeks from the social services department of your local council. Investigate this as soon as possible; ideally as soon as you find out you are expecting twins. Mothers of triplets or more may qualify for help until the children are of school age*

• *Helpers can create extra work. This is particularly true of a friend or relative who moves in to "help" you and then expects you to cook for her every evening, so consider this carefully before accepting long-term help*

• *You may find that everyone wants to help with the babies and no-one wants to do the housework. They're your twins, and you must learn to mother them yourself, so don't be afraid to be firm about what help you need*

MULTIPLE BIRTHS

Twins are by far the most common multiple births. Identical (mono-zygotic or uniovular) twins are formed by the splitting of a single fertilized egg: the two babies develop from one egg and one sperm, and share a placenta. Twins that develop from the fertilization of two eggs by two sperm and have a placenta each are called non-identical, fraternal, dizygotic, or binovular. Multiples can occur in any combination of identical and fraternal.

PREGNANCY AND BIRTH

Early rapid weight gain is a common sign of twin pregnancy. The minor complaints of pregnancy can become more uncomfortable and there are a few clinical conditions which are relatively more common in multiple pregnancies, such as anaemia or fluid reten-tion. Make sure you eat well and get plenty of rest.

A twin birth follows the same course as the birth of a single baby except there's a gap between the delivery of the first and second babies, which may be anything from a minute or so to a half an hour. The first stage is the same as for a single birth but, depend-ing on the time-lag between the two births, you may go through pushing twice. Twins are more likely to be premature.

FEEDING

There are some special considerations if you are trying to feed twin babies and, while I would always advocate breastfeeding, you may want to consider the pros and cons set out in the chart below. When you come to establishing daily routines there are several

BREAST	BOTTLE
• *You can feed both at once*	• *Difficult to feed both babies simultaneously unless they are propped up on chairs*
• *You need to devote time to eating and resting to produce enough milk*	• *Being tired and busy does not affect supply*
• *Difficult to feed two babies discreetly in public*	• *Babies can be fed anywhere and by anyone*
• *Physically tiring, but you can express and let someone else feed*	• *Tiring, but others can help*
• *Eating well may cost a little more than your normal diet*	• *Cost of formula milk for two babies can mount up*
• *Requires planning if you want to wean babies from breast to bottle to go back to work*	• *No physical adjustment is need-ed for you or babies if you are going back to work*

ways in which you can try to get your twins to feed and sleep at similar times, though initially one may wake early and want feeding and the other may simply sleep on. You could feed the baby who wakes first while waiting for the second, then reverse them; or feed both at once and spend time talking or playing afterwards.

SHOULD THEY SLEEP TOGETHER?

Twins are sometimes put in the same incubator after the birth, with the idea that they have been together since conception and would miss one another if apart. You could try putting your twins together in the same crib or cot to help them settle and sleep. Some twins do seem to sleep better this way – perhaps they derive security from each other's presence – but others simply kick and keep each other awake. Twins can usually be left to sleep in the same room together or side by side in cribs or carrycots. They rarely wake or disturb one another; it seems as if they are immune to each other's crying. For twins who have been tightly pressed together before birth, swaddling (see p.121) may give them a greater sense of security.

NAPPY CHANGING

When twins are small they may seem fragile and it may take longer to build up enough confidence to see to them efficiently and speedily. You do a very great deal of nappy changing with twins so you want to make the maximum use of disposable nappies. If you have a good supply of fabric nappies left over from an older child it can make economic sense to stick with them, though you may decide that whatever the relative costs you do not want to add washing and drying to the task of changing two sets of nappies. Your babies may fit into the newborn-sized disposable for some weeks or months. Some parents cut ordinary fabric nappies in two, using one half on each baby. If you do this, plastic pants with ties are probably best.

IMPORTANCE OF PLAY

Because of the demands they make on your time, your twins are likely to receive far less stimulation through play and physical contact than singletons. Loving interaction with you, however, is not a luxury for them – it's essential to their physical, mental, and social development.

You could pick a set time for play every day, or arrange the babies' sleeping times so that they are awake in the evening when both parents can play with them. When one twin is asleep, give the other baby your complete attention. Even five minutes of play will be of great value to him. If you have older children you may have even less time for your babies, but the older children can take your place.

THE FATHER'S ROLE

Most fathers want to be closely concerned with the care of their babies and so will enjoy looking after either or both of them to give you a break.

A father can help with feeding, changing, bathing, playing, reading the twins bedtime stories, and taking them out. Many fathers assume responsibility for shopping, and sometimes for cooking, and housework too. They can take time off work if necessary for doctor's appointments, check-ups, visits to the dentist, and so on, and should be able to relieve you so you can catch up on sleep or have time to yourself.

Helping out
With the amount of work involved in looking after twins, your partner's help will be indispensable.

BEING A TWIN

Twins have a close and intuitive understanding of each other and enjoy the companionship of a child of the same age. Having the support and approval of another person can be very reassuring as they grow and encounter new experiences.

PHYSICAL DEVELOPMENT

If twins are premature their growth and development will lag somewhat behind full-term babies. Don't make the mistake of expecting them to do too much too soon and, whatever you do, don't compare them to other babies of the same age.

There's no way of knowing how much more slowly your babies will develop, but if, for instance, they are five weeks premature you can probably expect them to focus some weeks later than if they'd been full-term. They may sit up, walk, and talk anything from three months late depending on how prematurely they were born, but they will still reach milestones in the same order as other babies (see pp.150–213). Don't worry that your babies will never catch up. A large study of twins carried out in the US showed that twin babies had caught up in height by four years and weight by eight.

Other factors affect the rate at which children develop. If your twins are identical they'll probably grow to much the same weight and height; if they are non-identical, and especially if they are boy and girl twins, one of them may grow and develop more quickly than the other.

TWINS AS INDIVIDUALS

When twins are hungry it's often easiest to sit them next to one another and feed them together with the same food; they may sleep in the same cot (see p.245) when they are small, and they may prefer to play at the same time with the same toys. When your twins are of the same sex, look alike, or have similar temperaments then it's easier to treat them very much alike, but I think it's best to treat twins as individuals right from the start. Don't choose names that sound alike, and try to distinguish your babies' differing needs and responses. It can be particularly difficult for people outside the immediate family to treat twins as individuals in their own right, especially if they are identical, but it's very important that they should. It's easier for others when the twins themselves show their different personalities and you encourage them to do so.

Individuality
Encourage each twin's sense
of identity and individuality
by dressing them differently.

DRESSING TWINS

Many parents wish to dress twins alike, especially if they are identical, and this can look very appealing.

You should, however, think of your twins as individuals from the start. Being recognised for one-self and being called by one's own name are powerful ways in which our sense of identity is established. If you dress your twins differently you can help to ensure that they are treated as individuals. Relatives, friends, and teachers can get to know who wears what.

As your twins get older I think it's much better to let them decide for themselves what they wear, and if you've always dressed them differently they will probably continue to do so themselves.

THE SPECIAL BOND

Being one of a close-knit pair of twins has advantages and disadvantages. Twins often become very close to each other and are central figures in each other's lives. The relationship between them can seem far stronger and more influential than any other. It is based on many feelings and experiences in common and a profound, intimate knowledge of each other. Their closeness gives twins an unusual opportunity to see how things look to someone else – an opportunity that singletons have only rarely. These close ties can give twins great security and are in many ways a source of strength. On the other hand, some twins struggle very hard for separateness and seem actively to reject one another, despite having abilities and attitudes in common.

TALKING TO TWINS

When single babies start to talk, adults or older children notice and encourage them. With twins, each child is given less attention so twins usually talk and listen to one another and may even invent a private language. Although twins' speech may start late and develop slowly, in time their ability to hold a conversation improves. If you want to speed that improvement it probably helps if you talk to your babies separately. It's easy to forget to talk to young children if you are very tired and feeling overworked, and peace and quiet may be precious. It's through taking part in play and learning to talk with you and your partner, however, that children learn language and how to use it.

BECOMING SOCIABLE

Because twins have each other for company they seem to be quite happy not mixing with other children. For the same reason your twins will be quite happy left alone together with comparative strangers, or at a playgroup. The more twins play exclusively with each other, however, the more difficult it is for them to make friends and play with other children. They may be overconfident and rough in a new group, appear to want to take the group over, and upset the balance of relationships. Some may tend to remain apart from groups formed by other children. These difficulties sometimes arise when twins first go to school and have to adjust to other children in the class. Make sure your twins feel at home with any social group, be it family, friends, or toddlers, from a very early age.

Because they have each other, twins are usually less afraid when first separated from you, and this gives everyone the impression that they are confident children. But when one twin is left without the other she may suddenly appear to be anxious and worried. This is because twins often mask each other's vulnerability. Twins, however, are just as much in need of your support and presence in new situations as a single child. A local playgroup can help your twins develop separate identities and learn the skills of making and keeping friends. The ideal would be for your twins to attend different playgroups or the same one on different days. Alternatively, ask the staff to encourage the twins to play separately.

SIBLINGS

Older children may feel doubly displaced by the arrival of twins. The needs of twins, especially if they are demanding, can drain the rest of the family and leave you with little time or energy.

If you've had to go into hospital several times during your ante-natal care it may take quite a long time to get to know your children again and to regain their trust and security. They may feel angry and upset that you left them and then came home with two new babies.

Older siblings can become more grown up when twins arrive. Others may feel the need to revert to babyhood, and a child who was dry may need nappies once more. Your children are upset. They feel dethroned and don't understand why you have less time for them than before. From the age of about two they miss having your full attention and resent your preoccupation with the two newcomers.

Do whatever you have to do to ensure that each of your children has at least half an hour a day of your undivided attention without any distractions. Then he will feel a valued member of the family. It's a good idea for you and your partner to take the children out on their own so that they have you entirely to themselves, and feel secure in your love despite the two new interlopers.

CHILDREN WITH SPECIAL NEEDS

There are many reasons why a child may need more care and attention than his peers. Your child may have a chronic condition such as asthma; a learning disorder, such as dyslexia; a developmental disorder, such as autism; or he may simply be very advanced for his years. Whatever the case, he will need extra support and consideration in order to maximize his potential. This may take the form of special medical treatment, home care, or special education. The same goes for a very bright child who might outstrip older brothers and sisters and even parents. This can put a unique strain on your family, so get specialist help so that your child is given the chance to fulfil her potential.

Early identification of special needs is very important. A severe condition such as cerebral palsy will be apparent soon after birth, but others, such as dyslexia, can go unnoticed for years. Never be afraid to act on your suspicions; seek professional advice if you are at all worried. Diagnosis of a chronic condition or learning disorder may nevertheless come as a shock. Make sure you seek out any help or advice that is available; you are still your child's main carer, whatever his needs, and the better informed you are, the more you can do for him.

THE SPECIAL CHILD

Although all children develop at different rates and the range of what doctors and psychologists consider "normal" is wide, a small number of children fall at either end of the developmental spectrum. At one end of the spectrum are children who are unusually advanced for their age, in terms of both motor and intellectual skills; at the other end are children who haven't acquired basic skills such as language and children who learn very slowly. In between there are also children with specific developmental or learning disorders such as autism and dyslexia.

Perhaps surprisingly, very advanced children have similar needs to children who have a learning disorder – lots of stimulation, attention and love. You might say that all children need these things – and you'd be right – but without them, children with special needs will suffer more. If such children do not receive the correct stimulation, they may not turn out to be "just average"; they could develop serious behavioural problems.

RECOGNISING THE SIGNS

If your child does have special needs, an early diagnosis is very important so that he can have help. Some learning disorders are difficult to spot, especially if they are characterized by behaviour that may be considered positive, such as quietness, little crying, or excessive sleeping. Autistic children, for example, are often described by their parents as well-behaved before other signs of their illness emerge. A gifted child, on the other hand, may be disruptive and not do well at school, making it hard for teachers to recognise his potential.

The lists below give some of the signs which might indicate that your child has special needs. Bear in mind, however, that children vary enormously in their rate of development and in personality, so what you regard as delayed speech in your child, for example, could be just a normal variation in development. If you are at all concerned, you should consult your doctor.

Developmentally delayed child
- Not speaking by the age of two-and-a-half years.
- Failure to interact with other people – to join in appropriately in conversation, for instance.
- Repetitive routines or habits beyond the normal age, such as asking the same question over and over again without responding to the answer.
- Problems reading and writing, inability to tell left from right, and poor co-ordination.
- Overactivity and short concentration span.

Gifted child
- Very early and fluent language skills.
- Very independent behaviour, or a preference for the company of adults.
- Tendency to be bored by repetitive tasks.
- Precocious development accompanied by bad behaviour such as temper tantrums.
- Unusually long concentration span.

If your child has special needs, don't think that he is incapable of learning, or – if he's gifted – that he can just wait until the other children "catch up". He requires teaching methods tailored to his individual needs, whether he is gifted or slow to learn.

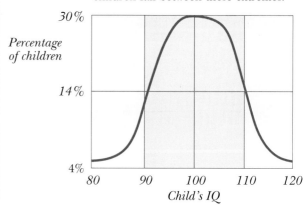

IQ chart
The few very gifted children appear at the extreme right of the curve. At the left is the small group of children with impaired mental abilities. Most children fall between these extremes.

Percentage of children

30%

14%

4%

80   90   100   110   120

Child's IQ

GIFTEDNESS

A gifted child is one who has advanced cognitive (understanding) skills and motor skills for her age. She can walk, talk, and reason earlier than average. She will be a high achiever in most areas, and she may have an IQ over 150.

Having a gifted child is rare. Although many children may be advanced for their age in a particular skill at a particular time, only about 2 per cent of the population are truly gifted. If your child is gifted, however, it is likely that you as a parent will be the first to notice.

DIAGNOSIS

Diagnosing a gifted child becomes easier as the child gets older, but one of the first signs is early language acquisition, particularly speaking fluently before the age of two. Early reading may be another sign of giftedness: many able children learn to read at the age of three or four, and 6 per cent learn to read before the age of two. Other possible qualities of gifted children are as follows:

• Good powers of reasoning.

• A good memory for places and names.

• A strong creative and imaginative drive.

• Sharp powers of observation.

• Being curious and always asking questions.

• More at home with adults than with children.

• An ability to grasp abstract ideas.

• Independence.

• Ability to solve problems or puzzles.

• Having an extensive vocabulary.

• Assimilating facts very quickly.

• Long concentration span.

• Ability to describe events, people, and situations accurately and vividly.

• Eagerness to spend time studying or learning.

• A specific talent, such as artistic ability.

• A high IQ.

SPECIAL NEEDS

Although you may perceive giftedness as an asset rather than a problem, your gifted child may not always be provided for adequately at school and she will have specific emotional needs that are different from those of the average child.

The gifted child may find it hard to relate to her peers. She may be impatient with other children for being slow and this may make her unpopular. Although your child may be condescending towards other children she will probably still want to be part of their group and this may lead to frustration and isolation. Alternatively, your child may try to conceal her talents in order not to seem different, so that she will be accepted by other children.

Interacting with adults can also be a problem. Teachers may treat gifted children as arrogant, precocious, or cheeky. Gifted children are likely always to know the answers to questions and to be able to point out inconsistencies, and question the reasons for doing something. The gifted child does not mean to be attention-seeking or trouble-making and the negative response she gets from adults can make her withdrawn and antisocial.

A gifted child who is denied the chance to exploit her potential may show a confusing mixture of intellectual prowess and immaturity. She may sulk and have temper tantrums; she may be bored by basic school subjects; and, if she's restless and inattentive, her teachers, far from recognising her talents, may believe that she is of low ability. You may have to intervene and discuss with your child's teacher the kind of specialized or accelerated learning your child requires and make sure that she gets it.

CAN GIFTEDNESS BE CULTIVATED?

Intelligence is wholly innate and overrides all cultures and backgrounds; cleverness is partly innate and partly environmental.

Although you can provide an environment that is conducive to intellectual development it is unlikely that you can "create" a gifted child. Evidence suggests that some gifted children come from relatively affluent homes with educated parents who spend time stimulating and encouraging their children; the extra boost can turn a very bright child into a gifted one. Being overly pushy as a parent will not help to cultivate giftedness in your child, however. You can help her fulfil her potential, but you cannot change that potential.

HOW YOU CAN HELP

It is important to know that your child is gifted since it may help to explain a lot of her behaviour, especially behaviour that is construed as deviant: social withdrawal, aggressiveness, tantrums, moodiness, and so on. It is also important in that it means you can start to cater for your child's specific needs. If you have a gifted child, don't adopt the attitude that she can simply wait until others reach her level. Gifted children need lots of intellectual stimulation and they will be deprived if they don't get it.

If your child is of school age, you should enlist the help of her teacher. If a teacher doesn't understand that your child is gifted, then he or she may perceive her as a threat or a problem. A sensitive teacher , however, will help your child to integrate with other children and will prevent her becoming isolated. Some schools have provisions for gifted children and in some areas there are enrichment programmes that will supplement your child's learning. You can contact the National Association For Gifted Children (see p.344) for more information.

As a parent, it is important that you treat your child sympathetically. Although she may be very advanced in some ways, she will still be emotionally immature, so avoid treating her as a "little adult". You can provide plenty of intellectual stimulation for your child in the following ways:

- Provide toys that promote interactive learning. Limit television viewing, as it is a passive way of learning.

- Give your child freedom to play and try not to intervene too much, unless she asks for your help.

- Encourage any specific talents such as painting.

- If you have a particular talent of your own, share it with your child and try to communicate your enthusiasm to her.

- Send your child to summer schools and introduce her to other gifted children.

- Encourage her to ask questions and, if you don't know the answer to a question, help her to look up the information in a book.

- Read her stories that will enrich her imagination.

- Involve her in your everyday tasks.

UNDER-ACHIEVEMENT

Whereas gifted children acquire skills very early, underachievers or developmentally delayed children acquire skills at an unusually slow rate. Some of the first indications that your baby is "behind" are docility, quietness, and sleeping for very long periods. Your baby will not make much noise, will not interact with his environment in the same way as the average child, and will be late in smiling, responding to sounds, and learning to chew.

When you try to engage your child in activities he will have a short attention span, and he will spend brief periods doing lots of different things rather than devoting all his energy to one task or game. As he grows older he may demonstrate a tendency to be overactive and he may have a lower than average IQ.

DIAGNOSIS

A developmentally delayed child will be later than usual in achieving some of the important developmental milestones (see below). It is important, however, to eliminate the possibility that your child has a physiological problem such as partial deafness or blindness. You should also find out whether your child has a severe developmental disorder, such as autism (see p.258), or whether he is simply developing at a rate that is below average. Ask your doctor to refer your child to a psychologist for assessment. Your child may need remedial help.

BEHAVIOURAL MILESTONES

There are various clues or signs that your baby or child is developmentally delayed or underachieving. Although children vary in the speed at which they develop, behavioural milestones do exist – if your child has not reached the following stages then he may have a learning or developmental disorder.

Hand regard Your baby becomes aware of his hands at about the age of eight weeks, shortly after he begins to play with his feet. Between the age of 12 and 16 weeks your baby will stare at his hands and waggle his fingers – he's discovering that he can control his hand movements. Hand regard may go on for as long as 20 weeks, however, in developmentally delayed children.

The grasp reflex If you put your finger (or any object) into a baby's palm he will close his fingers around it in a tight grip. This reflex usually lasts about six weeks after birth, but will persist longer if your child is developmentally delayed.

Mouthing At about six months your baby will put everything that he can into his mouth. This behaviour will last until around a year in a normal child and longer in a developmentally delayed child.

Casting Children up to the age of 16 months will throw objects out of the pram – a behaviour called casting. Developmentally delayed children may continue to do this for much longer.

Dribbling Slobbering and dribbling should stop at around one year. Developmentally delayed children may still be dribbling at the age of 18 months.

HOW YOU CAN HELP

Intellectual development is determined by both nature (inherited qualities) and nurture (things such as physical and social environment, and diet). Your child's IQ is decided before birth, but it can flower through the stimuli that your child is exposed to after birth. If your child is not encouraged to interact with other people from an early age, and he is not encouraged to engage his senses in the world around him, the chances are he will not reach his full potential, even if that potential is limited.

If you suspect that your child is lagging behind, spend lots of time reading aloud and talking to him, playing with him, taking him out, showing him new things and new people, and encouraging him to play imaginative games with his toys. Give him toys that are educational and plenty of colourful books and pictures to look at.

Behaviour modification techniques may be helpful. Put simply, this means rewarding your child's responses with praise and affection and being patient with his efforts, however slow they are. If you punish him for slowness, he may become discouraged and lose his incentive to learn.

DYSLEXIA

This is a learning disorder that affects reading, spelling, and written language. These difficulties may be accompanied by problems with numbers, poor short-term memory, and clumsiness. Although dyslexia particularly affects your child's mastery of written symbols – letters, numbers, and musical notation – he may have difficulties with spoken language too. Dyslexia is a specific neurological disorder and is not the result of poor hearing or vision, or low intelligence. One in 20 children is dyslexic (three times more boys than girls), and if you or your partner is dyslexic then your child is 17 times more likely to suffer from the disorder.

DIAGNOSIS

Many bright children are dyslexic, and the condition is often diagnosed earlier in these children since parents become aware of the gap between their child's obvious intelligence and her level of achievement in specific areas. The main symptoms of dyslexia are difficulty in reading and writing. Your child may have problems perceiving letters in the correct order, or she may confuse similarly shaped letters such as b and d, and p and q. The following may help you to recognise dyslexia in your child:

- Poor spelling.
- Poor co-ordination.
- Difficulty in remembering lists of words, numbers, or letters, such as the alphabet or tables.
- Difficulty in remembering the order of everyday things, such as days of the week.
- Problems telling left from right.
- Jumbled phrases, such as "tebby dare" instead of "teddy bear".
- Difficulty learning nursery rhymes.

Although not widely available yet, a new test exists for preschoolers. It involves repeating nonsense words, matching a series of pictures, identifying rhyming words, and testing balance and reaction.

Labelling a child dyslexic if she is not is just as harmful as failing to recognise it if she is. A correct diagnosis can only be made by an expert.

EFFECTS OF DYSLEXIA

The problems listed above may occur in children who don't have dyslexia. The difference is that dyslexic children will suffer more severe symptoms and won't grow out of them.

Recent research suggests that as well as having problems with literacy, dyslexic children also have problems with distinguishing different sounds, and with memory and balance. For example, dyslexic children will find it much more difficult to balance on one leg than non-dyslexic children.

A dyslexic child's strengths are likely to be sensitivity, intuition, and impulsiveness. Skills associated with the left side of the brain, such as dealing with written symbols, responding to instructions, and putting things in order, are weak in the dyslexic child. Some dyslexic children may be very creative and have an aptitude for drawing and painting.

SPECIAL NEEDS

One of the main problems that dyslexic children face is incorrect diagnosis. It is common for children to attempt to learn to read and write, fail to do so, and then be labelled "slow" or even disabled. This is very demoralizing for the child and is bound to affect her school performance overall. Parents and teachers often confuse dyslexia with a low IQ, but in fact most dyslexic children have an average or above-average IQ.

If dyslexia is recognised early, remedial education is very effective. If a child is diagnosed as dyslexic at the age of four or five, when she goes to school, she will probably only need about half-an-hour's extra tuition a day for a period of six months to bring her reading and writing up to normal standards. If dyslexia is not diagnosed until she's seven or eight, she will have a lot of catching up to do.

HOW YOU CAN HELP

You can do three things to help your dyslexic child at home. First – and this is sometimes overlooked – acknowledge that your child actually has a problem. If you are told that your child will catch up or will learn to read eventually, don't listen – dyslexia is a specific learning disorder that will respond only to the appropriate remedial treatment. Second, be supportive and positive, especially if your child is having problems at school. Third, play lots of learning games with your child.

Emotional support If your child is at school and is lagging behind other children, her self-confidence may be low and it is very important that you make her feel successful at home. Don't show any impatience. Encourage her to do the things that she is good at and help her do things for herself.

Give her self-help aids, such as left and right stickers on her tricycle, and, if she finds a particular task difficult tell her to take it slowly. The British Dyslexia Association (see **Useful addresses,** p.344) gives advice on coping strategies and remedial education for children with dyslexia.

Home learning games Playing games with letters, words, and sounds can be very useful. The following are all ways in which you can have fun and enhance your child's learning:

- Say nursery rhymes aloud together or make up rhyming poems or limericks. This will familiarize your child with the concept of rhyming words.

- Teach your child rhymes or songs that involve sequences of things such as days of the week.

- Play "Simon Says". This will help your child to follow instructions.

- Play "Hunt the Thimble". This will encourage your child to ask questions involving relationships such as under, on, and inside.

- Introduce the concept of left and right.

- Ask your child to lay the table at mealtimes.

- Play clapping games. Give one clap for each syllable of a word and get your child to repeat it. Clap a rhythm to her name.

- Give your child groups of words and ask her to pick the odd word out.

- Get your child to think of as many words beginning with a particular letter as she can.

- Play "I Spy". If your child has difficulty with letter names, make the sound of the letter instead.

- Encourage your child to trace words and letters, or to make letters out of plasticine.

ADD
(ATTENTION DEFICIT DISORDER)

This is one of the most common childhood disorders seen by psychologists. It is characterized by over-activity from birth and has elements in common with hyperactivity. Children with ADD behave impulsively, are highly distractable, and have trouble separating relevant from irrelevant information. They become frustrated easily and are susceptible to mood changes. Four times as many boys as girls have ADD, and it is caused by both genetic and environmental factors.

WHAT CAUSES ADD?

The current theory about ADD is that it is a disorder of perception and understanding. In the past, problems such as ADD and hyperactivity were thought to have a dietary origin. Diets high in chemical additives and lacking in essential vitamins and minerals were thought to cause aberrant behaviour in some children, though this has proven not to be so. Some treatment programmes for ADD and hyperactivity aim to eliminate chemical additives from the child's diet, usually to no effect, and this approach should no longer be advocated.

Some hyperactive children have benefited from cranial osteopathy – a very gentle yet effective technique. Cranial restrictions can arise at the time of birth as a result of obstructed labour, forceps, or ventouse intervention. If a hyperactive child had a difficult birth then it is possible that releasing any cranial restrictions will help to calm the child.

EFFECTS OF ADD

Your child with ADD may be unpredictable and disruptive. Even before he goes to school he may have problematic relationships with adults and have acquired a reputation for rebelliousness. This has a negative effect on his self-esteem, so that when he does go to school he starts off on an unequal basis with other children. The performance of your child may be variable: one day he might be quite compliant; the next he won't be able to sit still for more than a few minutes and will fidget incessantly. He may become a low achiever at school, with a reputation for poor concentration, and he may be thought to have a low IQ, though he doesn't.

There are certain early physical symptoms associated with ADD and hyperactivity. In babies these include colic (your child may be very difficult to feed either by breast or bottle), excessive dribbling, and thirst. In children they include poor appetite and sleeping problems.

Boys with ADD seem to suffer more than girls with ADD, in that girls are likely to be better adjusted socially and more achievement-orientated. Boys in particular may be criticized for overactivity and this can make the problem worse.

SPECIAL NEEDS

If your child is having problems at school – if he is irresponsible, careless, disorganized, and suffers from poor concentration and motivation – then you need to eliminate the possible causes. Consider the possibility that he is dyslexic (see p.253) or gifted (see p.251). If his behaviour has started recently, has he experienced a traumatic event? Does he have other behavioural problems such as lying (see p.218) or resistance to school (see p.227)?

Your child may need to be referred to an educational psychologist who will be able to diagnose ADD and decide on appropriate action to meet your child's individual needs. Discuss your child's problems with his teacher.

HOW YOU CAN HELP

It is important for a child with ADD to have an orderly home life and a structured, well-disciplined routine. If your child knows that he has to do certain things at set times of the day he is less likely to be unruly. You should also remember that, if your child has problems with self-control, he probably has a low self-esteem, because he meets with adult disapproval all the time. Always praise him for good behaviour and he will learn that certain types of behaviour win your approval, while others don't.

Parenting a child with ADD can be very demoralizing, since your child may have a reputation for being a troublemaker. Many parents feel isolated because their child is rejected by playgroups and nursery schools, and even banned from friends' and relatives' homes. Don't blame yourself for your child's behaviour. Organizations such as the Hyperactive Children's Support Group (see **Useful addresses**, p.344) can offer help and advice.

STAMMERING

When your child is learning to talk it is normal for him to stumble over words, repeat words, and hesitate. It is only when hesitations dominate your child's speech and cause him considerable distress that he is said to have a stammer. Whereas normal hesitation is the relaxed repetition of a word at the beginning or the end of a phrase, a child with a stammer will get stuck on a word, and repeat one of its syllables over and over again.

IS IT SERIOUS?

When children are learning language they are not always able to convey their thoughts in words as quickly as they would like to. Your child lives very much in the present and he will want to convey the intensity of his feelings immediately – when his vocabulary is not wide enough or his language skills aren't advanced enough, he may stammer in his rush to get the words out.

Most children stammer at some stage. Your child may stammer on some days and not others; he may stammer when he is tired, excited, or in a particular situation or environment. It doesn't matter, though, unless he stammers in a lot of situations and gets very upset because of it.

Occasional stammering is a natural part of language acquisition that will disappear and should never be made an issue of or treated as a problem. Making a fuss about it may cause your child to become anxious and so lead to a true stammer.

HOW YOU CAN HELP

You can influence your child's speech by the way you talk to him. If you speak very quickly and you appear distracted, your child may feel that he has to keep up and that you are not interested in what he has to say. Always try to speak slowly and appear attentive and interested. Look at your child and, if possible, talk to him on the same physical level. Use language that is simple and talk about very immediate things that can be seen. Avoid asking too many questions – instead describe your own feelings or experiences; this will encourage your child to contribute. Above all, never react negatively to your child's stammer or he will become more self-conscious and the stammer will get worse. When your child is struggling with a sentence try not to complete it for him or supply a word.

If your child is very anxious about stammering talk to him about it. If he knows that you understand, this will lessen his sense of suffering alone. If you don't talk about his stammering, your child may feel that it is something to be ashamed of. If your child is very young and is having problems with speech, return to games and activities that involve looking or listening rather than speaking. If your child is at school, try discussing the following strategies with his teacher:

- Your child may need extra help with reading. If he is worried about particular words this can cause him to stammer. Reading aloud in unison with another child may reduce stammering.

- Children tend to be more fluent when they are talking about something personal or a subject that they know a lot about. This should be encouraged whenever possible.

- If a teacher is observant about what encourages fluency and what increases stammering she can prevent your child feeling embarrassed. When she needs information from your child it may help if she asks questions that require a "yes" or a "no" answer, particularly if your child is distressed.

- Some methods of speech promote fluency and should be encouraged. These include saying words that have a rhyme or a rhythm, saying words that have actions to go with them, reciting lists or counting, acting, or singing.

- It may be a good idea for your child's teacher to broach the subject of stammering with him in a matter-of-fact way, since your child will then feel that it has been noticed by a sympathetic adult and that he doesn't have to hide it.

WHAT CAUSES STAMMERING?

If your child is to become a fluent speaker then he needs to be supported and encouraged to boost his confidence. A combination of the following three conditions can cause a stammer to develop:

• Parental demands that overestimate the child's ability, such as asking lots of questions; insisting on clear speech; and expecting fast replies and grown-up behaviour.

• Your child wanting to perform well to impress people before his vocabulary is large enough.

• Stressful situations in which your child is tired, anxious, or frightened, or where people are talking very fast, or there are lots of interruptions.

Stammering is not inherited. A stammering child believes that speaking hesitantly is in some way wrong or bad. Your child becomes acutely self-conscious and focuses on the way he speaks, and this leads to worse stammering. He may avoid situations that involve speaking, especially to new people, and if your child is of school age he may pretend that he doesn't know answers to questions to avoid having to speak in front of other children.

SPECIAL NEEDS

If your child has a severe stutter he may need the help of a speech or language therapist. A therapist may visit your child at school or liaise with parents and teachers. The Association for Stammerers (see **Useful addresses**, p.344) provides contacts, advice, and a helpline.

DELAYED SPEECH

At the age of about 11 months your baby will probably be able to say simple words, such as "mama", "dada", "dog", and "cat", and by two years he will probably be able to form simple sentences, such as "daddy in garden". Speech will become progressively more sophisticated during the third and fourth year. As with all aspects of development, the age at which milestones are achieved varies widely, but if your child is very far behind other children of his age then there may be something wrong.

There are many causes of delayed speech, the most important being deafness – have your child's hearing tested at once if you suspect he may be deaf. Chronic glue ear (see p.285) can result in problems with hearing. Your child may be late in speaking because he has not received the correct stimulation – this can happen to children who have been institutionalized or children whose parents simply don't talk to them enough. Boys are more prone to delayed speech than girls, and twins may speak later than average (see p.247).

Very occasionally, delayed speech is due to a physiological defect or a disease of the speech muscles, larynx, or mouth. There are also disorders that affect the part of the brain that controls speech.

Children vary in the age at which they begin to speak, but if your child is not talking at all by the age of two-and-a-half, you should seek medical help. If your child is deaf, he may need a hearing aid; if he has a severe speech defect he may need help from a speech therapist.

Tambourines or maracas can be used to beat out a rhythm

Improving fluency
Singing, or any kind of rhythmic speech, can reduce stammering, so tapping out a rhythm to rhymes and songs can help your child feel more confident.

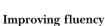

AUTISM

This is a condition in which a child is unable to relate to people and situations and may show an obsessive resistance to any change. Until quite recently, little was known about autism and there was a tendency to blame emotional deprivation or some negative aspect of the child's background or upbringing. Fortunately, we now know that autism has a physiological origin, in that it results from an abnormality in the brain. This abnormality may arise before, during, or after your child's birth and almost always before the age of three years. It may be caused by an illness during pregnancy, such as rubella, a deficiency of oxygen at birth, or a childhood illness, such as measles or whooping cough. There may also be a genetic cause. Autism is four times more common in boys than in girls.

DIAGNOSIS

Because autism is a developmental disorder it may take a while for you to become aware that your child is different from others. You may notice that your baby is uncommunicative in the first year of his life but you may not attach any significance to this until later, when other signs become apparent. Most parents know that their child is autistic or that "something is wrong" once he is two or three.

EFFECTS OF AUTISM

Children with autism vary considerably in their abilities, but there are three main traits that all autistic children share: problems with social interaction and communication, and impaired imagination. Many autistic children display repetitive behaviour, and some have very sophisticated memories.

Social interaction If autism is severe, your child will be indifferent to other people. In babies this manifests itself as crying that can't be appeased by holding and cuddling, quietness, poor eye contact, and failing to return or respond to gestures such as smiling, waving, or facial expressions.

Autistic children show a lack of interest in interacting with other people, particularly children. They don't make friends and, when they do approach people socially, they may behave inappropriately:

they may repeat snatches of conversation that have just been spoken, they may be aggressive, or they may use confusing language. In less severe forms of autism your child may accept social contact but will not be very responsive or respond in a stilted, and repetitive way.

Communication From an early age most children show a desire to communicate with other people. Even before they can form words they will communicate non-verbally using facial expressions and body language. Autistic children seem to lack this desire. Even if your child does speak he will tend to speak at people, rather than with them, or his speech may be restricted to conveying his immediate needs. Your child may exhibit echolalia (repetition of words that he has just heard), and he may use specific words or phrases in a repetitive or inappropriate way. It is common for autistic children to be confused about when to use "I", "you', or "he".

Imagination An autistic child doesn't use his imagination when he is playing with toys and, rather than perceiving things in their entirety, he may become overly interested in a small detail of a toy, person, or object. When playing with a toy train, for example, he might concentrate on one small part, such as a wheel or the buffer, rather than using it as a make-believe train.

Some autistic children do pursue activities that engage the imagination, such as reading, but these tend to be repetitive and stereotyped. For instance, your child may read one book again and again.

Repetitive behaviour Repeated tapping, rocking, head banging, teeth grinding, grunting, screaming, finger flicking, spinning objects, and standing up and jumping from the back foot to the front foot are some of the behaviours that often occur in autism. The type of repetitive activity that your child indulges in is dependent on his level of ability. More sophisticated types of behaviour include arranging objects in complex, repeated patterns, and collecting large numbers of a particular object. Your child may be interested in a particular topic and will ask the same questions about it and demand the same answers over and over again. You may also notice that your child likes repetitive routines, even inappropriate ones, to be observed without fail. For example, he may want exactly the same sequence of activities carried out when he goes to bed each night.

Memory Some autistic children are able to store a memory and retrieve it exactly as it was first perceived and the results can be very impressive. An autistic child may, for example, draw perfectly from memory a building he has seen or repeat whole conversations or lists of information.

SPECIAL NEEDS

The severity of your child's condition depends on several factors: whether he has any other learning disorders (such as dyslexia, see p.253); whether he has any accompanying physical disorders (such as epilepsy, see p.270), the type of education he has access to; and his personality or disposition, which will affect how he reacts to his disabilities. It is important to diagnose autism and associated disorders as early as possible so your child's needs are met.

The National Autistic Society helps parents with autistic children, offers various publications on care and education, and also organizes conferences and workshops (see **Useful addresses**, p.344). Depending on the severity of your child's autism, he will either be able to go to an ordinary school where he may receive extra help (about one in six autistic children go to an ordinary school), or he will need to go to a specialist school for children with learning or developmental disorders.

Using sign language
If your child finds talking a problem, you can use a sign language to communicate – it can help to clarify your language to her.

Signs can be used to complement speech but not replace it

HOW YOU CAN HELP

You will probably find that your child's behaviour is most problematic between the ages of two and five, and there may be an improvement between the ages of six and 12. As he grows up, your child will probably become more responsive and sociable. Although no cure exists for autism, there are many different therapies designed to improve the behaviour and adjustment of your child:

Behaviour modification This therapy concentrates on replacing dysfunctional behaviour (tantrums, head-banging, aggressiveness, and so on) with desirable behaviour, using a system of rewards.

Relaxation and massage The child is taught how to relax using massage, music, touching, and verbal cues. Later, the verbal cues can be used on their own when the child shows signs of tension; because he associates them with feeling relaxed, they should dissipate the tension. Massage helps autistic children bond to people through touch.

Holding therapy This involves giving the autistic child plenty of hugs and cuddles, regardless of his indifference. The theory is that if you insist on holding your child, he will be comforted and reassured without the problem of having to initiate the interaction in the first place.

Speech therapy Some cases of autism are diagnosed by speech therapists, because poor language development is often the first sign. Speech therapy can also improve your child's communication skills. If your child doesn't speak or his speech is very limited, it may help to teach him a sign language such as Makaton, which complements rather than replaces speech.

Psychotherapy This involves working with all the family so that parents understand the behaviour of the autistic child and its consequences. In some cases, the child himself might receive individual psychotherapy.

LIVING WITH CHRONIC CONDITIONS

The word "chronic" is used to describe an illness, such as cerebral palsy or asthma, that is long-lasting, where the symptoms are present on a daily basis, or where they flare up occasionally. In contrast, an acute illness, such as tonsillitis, comes on suddenly, and the duration of symptoms is quite short. Chronic conditions may be life-long and you, your family, and your child will need to make some changes in your lifestyle in order to cope with the condition on a day-to-day basis.

DEALING WITH ILLNESS

The most common emotional reaction to the news that your child has a chronic condition is anxiety, combined with fear, bitterness, and possibly guilt that you yourself have done something to cause the condition. After the initial shock, many parents become very involved in learning about their child's condition and how to manage it. The first thing you need to know is what the treatment programme entails – this may be daily injections, occasional blood transfusions, or just making sure that your child always carries a ventilator. You will also need to familiarize yourself with the symptoms of an attack or the possible dangers to your child, and learn what to do in an emergency.

When your child first shows signs of a chronic condition, apart from the physical unpleasantness of being ill, he will most likely find the experience of visiting doctors and hospitals quite stressful. Stay calm in front of your child and don't fuss and panic. He'll see your anxiety and interpret it in his own way; he may even become terrified that he is going to die. Talk to your child rationally about his condition and explain what is happening to him. If he doesn't understand what's wrong with him this can be more frightening than the illness itself.

Because you are worried about your child's health it is quite natural for you to pay special attention to him. You should be careful, however, that you don't exclude other members of your family, especially if you have other children.

Research is conducted into chronic conditions and management programmes are becoming progressively more advanced – in most cases your child will be able to live a near-normal life. (For self-help groups see **Useful addresses**, p.344.)

ASTHMA

About one in seven children in the UK has asthma. Hospital admissions for asthma have been increasing steeply in young children and admission rates have doubled since the mid-1970s.

A child who has asthma will suffer recurrent attacks of breathlessness with wheezing when she tries to exhale. These attacks are caused by narrowing of the bronchioles (the small airways in the lungs). They vary greatly in severity but even a mild attack can be frightening in a young child. Over 50 per cent of children affected by asthma grow out of the condition by adulthood.

Risk factors The reasons for the increase in rates of asthma are not entirely known, although parental smoking, pollution, viruses, low birth-weight, and bottlefeeding instead of breastfeeding are possible factors. Smoking is the only proven factor, particularly if you smoke during pregnancy, and you or your partner smokes during your child's early years. Boys are twice as likely as girls to have asthma.

The rising levels of air pollution caused by factories and vehicles are increasingly being blamed for the growing numbers of asthma sufferers. Vehicle exhaust fumes, for example, have increased by 75 per cent since 1980.

There is no simple way of preventing asthma. Breastfeeding is often recommended for a number of very good reasons, but has not been shown to prevent the onset of asthma. At best there is a delay in the onset of symptoms.

DIAGNOSIS

Most young children have wheezing episodes at some time, but this doesn't make them asthmatic. It's the pattern of symptoms that develops over time that shows whether a child has asthma or not. It can be quite difficult to spot asthma in very young children for three reasons. First, a third of all children will have at least one attack of wheezing during their first five years. Most of these children will never have breathing problems again, so doctors probably won't want to use the term asthma. Second, doctors use a variety of words to describe asthma, such as wheezing, wheezy bronchitis, chesty coughs, or colds. Third, a "peak-flow meter", the device normally used to measure how well the lungs work, can only be used with children who are over five years of age.

Before reaching a diagnosis your doctor should wait and see how the pattern of your child's symptoms develops. It is this pattern, not individual symptoms, which dictate the diagnosis of asthma. Typical symptom patterns are as follows:

- Repeated attacks of wheezing and coughing, usually with colds.

- A persistent cough.

- Many restless nights caused by attacks of wheezing or coughing.

- Wheezing or coughing between colds, especially after exercise or excitement, or when your child is exposed to cigarette smoke and allergens such as pollen or house-dust mite droppings.

Diagnosing asthma
A doctor will need to monitor the pattern of your child's symptoms over time before he can diagnose asthma.

Many people believe that wheezing is the only symptom of asthma, but for young children a dry and irritating cough may be the only symptom. Healthy children do not cough persistently.

Children under the age of one year are most likely to suffer from wheezing, which is set off by virus infections such as a cold or a runny nose. In fact viruses are an almost universal trigger for young children. Breastfeeding may help improve a child's resistance to viruses.

TRIGGERS

If your child does suffer from asthma, you will find that certain substances or activities can trigger an attack. Once you have identified triggers, you should take measures to protect your child from coming into contact with them.

Smoking Help your child avoid cigarette smoke because it's especially harmful to growing lungs, and can trigger asthma attacks. Never smoke around children and encourage visitors to your home not to do so. If you do smoke, and you are planning to have another child, you should give up smoking before becoming pregnant to reduce the risk of your baby developing asthma.

Cold air You may notice that your child coughs or wheezes initially on going out of doors. Keeping your child indoors, however, is not the answer. A dose of reliever medicine (see p.262) just before going out may be all that's needed.

Activity If laughter, excitement, or exercise trigger asthma in your child, it is a sign that the asthma is not properly controlled. You should consult your doctor, since it is very important for children to join in the fun and enjoy themselves. The symptoms of activity-induced asthma may be prevented if your child takes a dose of reliever medicine beforehand. Your child should warm up before playing games – several 30-second sprints over 5–10 minutes will allow her to exercise for up to an hour or so. Swimming provides an excellent form of exercise for children who are suffering from asthma and it seldom provokes an attack unless the water is very cold or heavily chlorinated.

Allergies If there is a family history of allergies you should minimize your child's exposure to potential allergens, such as mites, pollen, and fur.

TREATMENT

Your doctor can prescribe medicine that will control your child's symptoms, though they can't cure asthma. Most medications come in the form of an inhaler ("puffer"). There are two types: preventers and relievers. Children should always use their inhalers with a device called a spacer.

Relievers When an asthma attack occurs, a reliever, or bronchodilator, makes breathing easier by relaxing the tiny muscles around the narrowed airways and allowing them to open up. A child who suffers occasional asthma attacks must have a reliever medicine to hand at all times.

Preventers Your child will probably have to take a preventer if he usually needs to use a reliever more than once a day. These stop asthma from starting by building up resistance in the lining of the airways and making them less sensitive to irritants. Preventers must be taken regularly, even if your child is well. They take about 7–14 days to become effective from the time they are first taken. Once the symptoms are under good control your doctor may reduce the treatment. If your child uses a preventer as well as a reliever, label the puffers clearly.

Spacers Only about 10–20 per cent of asthma medicine actually reaches the lungs. A young child needs to use his inhaler with a spacer to ensure that the correct dose gets down to the airways where it's needed. Spacers can be obtained on prescription. A mask should be used with a spacer for children before the age of four or until the spacer mouthpiece alone is effective. Alternatively, there is a very small spacer called an aero-chamber that is suitable for children of all ages and fits all inhalers. You should carefully wash and dry your child's spacer from time to time.

Drug is forced into mouth by pump mechanism

Pressurized container delivers a metered dose

Aerosol puffer
A metered dose is inhaled directly into the lungs. This is the most effective method of delivery.

Dry-powder inhalers
Sometimes children over three years old will be given dry-powder inhalers. These are good for giving preventer medicines but they cannot be inhaled very well when the child is wheezing or is tight chested. An aerosol may still be needed for relieving these symptoms.

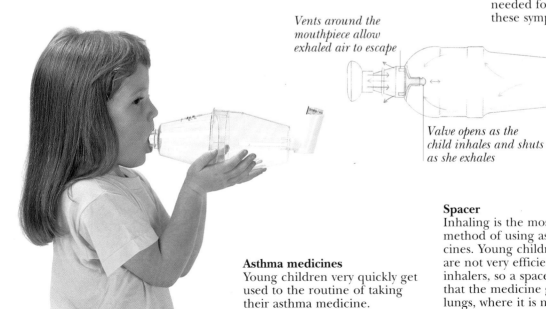

Vents around the mouthpiece allow exhaled air to escape

Valve opens as the child inhales and shuts as she exhales

A metered dose is sprayed into the spacer

Asthma medicines
Young children very quickly get used to the routine of taking their asthma medicine.

Spacer
Inhaling is the most effective method of using asthma medicines. Young children, however, are not very efficient at using inhalers, so a spacer ensures that the medicine gets to the lungs, where it is needed.

If your toddler finds it hard to take inhaled medicine use the spacer when he is asleep. If he knocks the spacer away from his mouth, gently wrap his arms around his chest. For an older child, turn the spacer into a toy by putting stickers on it, or play games in which you count out loud as your child takes five breaths from the spacer.

Some very young children need a nebulizer, which produces a very fine mist of medicine. For most children, however, spacers are the best solution.

HOW YOU CAN HELP

Although there is no known cure for asthma, modern asthma management can effectively reduce a child's symptoms and allow him to lead a full and active life. Regular contact with your doctor and close monitoring of your child are important.

Your doctor will develop an asthma management plan with you, and explain when to use the preventer and reliever, and what to do if your child's symptoms get worse. This should be written down for you to keep at home. A vital part of any plan is a review meeting with a doctor or nurse every few months. You should monitor your child's symptoms closely and consult your doctor if you notice any of the following:

- Wheezing and coughing in the early morning.

- Increased symptoms after exercise or exertion.

- Waking at night with a cough or a wheeze.

- Increased use of reliever therapy.

An emergency plan Any asthma attack can be life-threatening, so have an emergency plan of action agreed with your doctor for very severe attacks.

- At the start of the attack give your child his usual reliever. Wait about ten minutes and if there is no improvement send for an ambulance.

- Repeat the treatment until the breathing symptoms improve or until help arrives.

- Give your child steroid tablets if they've been prescribed by your doctor.

- Keep your child in an upright position.

- Call your doctor or an ambulance or take your child to the nearest hospital.

CYSTIC FIBROSIS

An inherited condition that affects mainly the lungs and the pancreas, cystic fibrosis (CF) is also known as mucoviscidosis because it produces thick and sticky mucus in the lungs and the pancreas. CF is the commonest inherited disease of its kind in the UK and affects approximately one in every 2,500 children, though in differing degrees. Recently the gene responsible for CF has been discovered and there is now a chance that there will be a cure by the time your child reaches adulthood.

WHAT CAUSES CF?

The disease occurs when both parents carry the gene for the disorder. One person in every 25 is a carrier of CF, but an affected gene will be masked by a normal gene from the other parent, and even where two carriers of CF have a baby, there is only a one-in-four chance that the baby will have CF. These chances apply anew for each pregnancy. They do not change the more pregnancies you have. CF affects girls and boys in equal numbers.

DIAGNOSIS

All babies born in the UK have a sample of blood taken when they are one or two weeks old, usually from a prick in the heel. These spots of blood are tested for the signs of several diseases, one of which may be CF.

Another test, carried out when a child is at least three months old, measures the amount of salt in the sweat; children with CF have more salt in their sweat than normal children. (Some parents comment that their child tastes salty when they kiss him or her, even though children with CF do not sweat more than other children.) This sweat test is carried out on any baby who has recurrent bouts of pneumonia or fails to thrive, and on the brothers and sisters of a child with CF.

Your feelings Once the diagnosis is made, you may have trouble accepting it, especially if your child seems well. You may feel angry, or guilty, but very soon you will realize that no one is to blame. Recriminations are not only pointless, they will do great harm to relationships within the family and to your CF child.

You may seek a second opinion or even consider alternative therapies. You should discuss this with your doctor. Write down the questions you want to ask as you think of them, in case you forget later. Doctors will be happy to provide a second opinion, particularly if you have not yet had the chance to visit a special clinic for CF.

There is no evidence that any other therapies can do anything to help CF. It is essential for the future health of your child that conventional medicines are given in the prescribed way. Provided this is the case, then additional treatments should do no harm.

It's important to try not to overprotect your child. Remember she is a normal child who happens to have CF. She will be naughty and have all the same emotions as other children, and there's no reason to treat her differently in relation to discipline, education, or physical activities. If you do, you will not only be doing her a disservice, but also creating problems for yourselves in the long run. A child with a chronic illness can greatly strain a relationship, so always talk openly with your partner.

Learning about CF Much of the treatment for CF is carried out at home, and to be as effective as possible, you should try to understand as much as you can about the disorder. CF is a complicated condition, however, and each child will be differently affected, so other people's experiences may differ from yours. Bear in mind that you can't expect to know everything immediately and no one will expect you to. Moreover, you will be given a huge amount of information and advice from various sources, some of which will be conflicting.

DIGESTIVE PROBLEMS

The pancreas, a gland in the abdomen, produces insulin, which passes directly into the blood, and digestive juices or enzymes, which pass into the intestines where they help with the digestion of food. In CF, the small channels down which these juices flow to reach the intestine become blocked with sticky mucus and the enzymes therefore build up in the pancreas, which becomes inflamed, resulting in the formation of cysts and thickened tissue, which is known as fibrosis.

Treatment Most of the missing digestive enzymes can be replaced with pancreatin, which is given in a powder or a capsule form. For a young baby the powder can be mixed with a little cooled boiled water or milk, and given before each feed from a spoon or feeding bottle. It should not be mixed with a whole bottle of milk, because it will curdle the milk. Once your baby is on solids, she should eat whatever the rest of your family is having. Vitamins are not well absorbed in CF, so your child will need a dose of vitamin drops each day.

RESPIRATORY PROBLEMS

Inside the lungs there are lots of tiny tubes, the bronchi, down which air passes to reach specialized airsacs, the alveoli; here, oxygen enters the bloodstream and carbon dioxide leaves the blood to be breathed out. CF children have normal lungs at birth, but the mucus produced in them is abnormally thick, so it blocks some of the smaller airways and leads to infection, and later to lung damage.

Treatment The aim of treatment is to keep the lungs as normal as possible, and there are two components to this:

• Clearing the sticky mucus with physiotherapy, breathing exercises, and physical exercise.

• Prevention and prompt treatment of chest infections, usually with antibiotics.

HOW YOU CAN HELP

Even with pancreatin, a child with CF may not absorb all the nourishment she needs in order to grow normally. Your child will therefore need more calories, so high-energy snacks between meals, such as milkshakes, are helpful. It's important to be sure that your child is growing well as this shows she's absorbing nourishment; you can plot her measurements on the charts on pp.318–25.

You can only learn how to clear the thick mucus from your child's chest from a physiotherapist and with lots of practice, so don't be afraid to ask for help. You should start the physiotherapy from the time of the diagnosis, and it's important to get into a routine early on. You will need to do it twice a day when your child is well, and more often when she has a chest infection.

You should liaise very closely with your doctor about the prevention and treatment of chest infections. Should an infection occur your child will need extra physiotherapy and antibiotics.

WHEN TO SEE THE DOCTOR

Your CF child is very vulnerable to chest infections, so it's important to seek medical help promptly, either from your doctor or your child's regular hospital clinic, if you think something is wrong. The following symptoms may indicate that a doctor's visit is needed:

• Decreased or poor appetite.

• Weight loss.

• Tummy aches.

• Frequent or loose stools.

• Increased or frequent cough.

• Vomiting.

• Increased sputum.

• Change in the colour of sputum.

• Breathlessness.

• Unwillingness to exercise.

• Fever.

• Cold symptoms.

IMMUNIZATIONS AND CF

Babies with CF are particularly at risk from the common childhood infectious diseases, especially those that may affect the lungs.

A child with CF must stick rigidly to the normal immunization schedule (see p.283), and injections should only be postponed in very exceptional circumstances and after consultation with your doctor. Having a cold or a cough is not sufficient reason to delay immunization. CF children over four years should also be immunized against flu every winter.

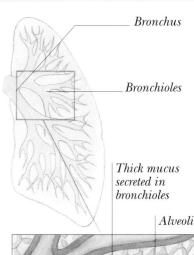

Bronchus

Bronchioles

Thick mucus secreted in bronchioles

Alveoli

Physiotherapy
To clear the thick mucus from your child's chest use physiotherapy twice a day, and more often during chest infections.

Slapping the back with cupped hands loosens the thick mucus in the lungs

Blocked airways
Thick mucus blocks the airways, starving them of oxygen and ultimately causing parts of the lung to collapse.

Your child should lie on a comfortable support during physiotherapy

DIABETES MELLITUS

A chronic disease, diabetes mellitus in children is due to a lack of insulin from the pancreas. Insufficient insulin results in an increase in blood glucose concentration (hyperglycaemia), causing excessive urination and constant thirst and hunger. An accumulation in the body of chemicals called ketones occurs when there is a severe lack of insulin. A high sugar level is not in itself dangerous, but high ketone levels are.

The onset of diabetes can be swift and may take some time to stabilize. Most diabetic children need insulin injections and a strictly controlled diet.

IS THERE A CURE?

Diabetes occurs because cells of the immune system attack the insulin-producing islet tissue in your child's pancreas. Any cure must therefore replace the damaged tissue in some way. For this reason, transplantation offers the only viable therapeutic approach, but rejection of the transplanted tissue poses a serious problem.

There is promising research going on that suggests we might be able to graft tissue into the body that will not be recognised as foreign. Already this approach has worked experimentally and has been used to reverse diabetes in a number of animal models, without the need for anti-rejection therapy. It is quite possible that diabetes will be cured with transplants in your child's lifetime. Progress has also been made with genetic research, and the recent discovery of two new genes has opened up the possibility that the condition could be prevented.

ADJUSTING TO DIABETES

It can be quite frightening when you're told that your child has insulin-dependent diabetes (Type I diabetes), but the disease will not prevent your child from leading a full and active life.

How you and the family handle your child's diabetes helps to determine the way in which your child accepts or denies the disease and becomes a balanced, mature person. You will soon know a lot about diabetes itself, the need for insulin, the technique for injection, and about the importance of proper food intake and exercise. You will also need to know how to look out for, detect, and treat an insulin reaction.

Subcutaneous injection
Pinch the skin gently and insert the needle at 90°. A ½-inch (1 centimetre) needle will deliver the insulin to the layer of fat just below the skin.

Injection sites
To avoid scarring, vary the injection sites. Suitable sites include the upper arms, thighs, buttocks, and stomach.

CONTROLLING DIABETES

The aim of diabetes treatment is to keep blood sugar levels as near to normal as possible. Too high a level (hyperglycaemia) can lead to fatigue, excessive urination, constant thirst, weight loss, and an increased level of ketones in the body. Too little blood sugar (hypoglycaemia) can lead to weakness, dizziness, confusion, and even seizures. Proper levels are achieved by a combination of dietary control, with particular attention paid to the intake of sugar and carbohydrates, insulin injections, and regular physical exercise. Speak to your doctor about blood glucose self-monitoring, because you and your child can do this at home, and it will help you both to manage his disease.

Perfect control is too much to hope for. Even if your child is completely trustworthy about insulin and food, he will still occasionally have a raised blood sugar. If your child eats sweets occasionally, this act of breaking the rules isn't life-threatening, so don't make too much fuss.

One bite of chocolate will not make any child sick, not even a child with diabetes. Even if your child has followed your advice, you will have to accept that blood-sugars can sometimes be a little high or a little low. Be realistic.

HOW YOU CAN HELP

You will need to exercise skill to help your child accept his condition with the minimum of fuss. You should supervise invisibly while giving your child responsibility, to learn self-care and control.

Children with diabetes tend to worry more than children without the disease, and this is only to be expected; they have to assume important responsibilities and they know, or will come to know, that diabetes can do some very unpleasant things. Diabetes makes children feel tired and confused, and can make them lose consciousness. A child who is diabetic has to plan ahead when leaving home, and remember to take along some sweets or sugar and insulin and syringes if the trip is a long one. Your child is threatened both physically and psychologically by diabetes, so you need to be sympathetic without becoming over-protective. As your child grows older, however, he will gain mastery over the situation, learn self-care, and understand what needs to be done.

BLOOD GLUCOSE SELF-MONITORING

A system is available that enables you to measure your child's blood sugar level accurately at any time. Precise monitoring and testing of blood sugar may reduce and even reverse some of the complications of diabetes.

You begin by obtaining a drop of blood from a tiny finger-prick. The blood is dropped onto a chemically sensitive strip and then after a simple processing operation the blood sugar level is read on a digital display meter. Another method relies on comparing the strip visually with a colour-coded chart. Each method gives accurate results.

Blood glucose self-monitoring allows you to measure your child's blood sugar levels frequently and accurately without visiting the doctor and waiting for lab results; with it you can respond promptly to a low blood sugar count by giving high-carbohydrate foods, or to a high blood sugar count by giving an insulin injection. Your doctor can recommend the proper insulin dosages or other medications according to blood glucose levels.

While it involves a small element of pain, blood testing is more accurate than urine tests, since there is a delay between the rise of blood sugar and the time it shows up in the urine. Another problem is that urine tests only show high glucose readings when the levels are well above acceptable limits.

Blood samples
Use lancets and a machine for pricking your child's finger to obtain a drop of blood. You may prefer to use the sides rather than the tips of the fingers as they're less sensitive. Place a drop of blood on the pad on the strip.

Testing strips
The strip will change colour to indicate your child's glucose level. Read the blood glucose level by comparing the strip with the colour chart on the side of the strip container.

CEREBRAL PALSY

In the UK each year roughly 1 in 400 babies are born with or develop cerebral palsy. It is a disorder which affects both boys and girls from all races and social backgrounds.

WHAT CAUSES CEREBRAL PALSY?

Cerebral palsy is caused by an injury to the brain, usually before, around, or soon after the time of birth. Causes of such injury include a difficult or preterm birth, perhaps because the baby fails to breathe properly; cerebral bleeding, which may occur in preterm babies; or bleeding into cavities of the brain (intraventricular haemorrhage), which may also occur in preterm babies; or an infection in the mother during the first weeks of pregnancy – German measles or cytomegalovirus, for example. Occasionally, the brain is formed abnormally for no obvious reason, or the disorder is inherited even if both parents are healthy.

TYPES OF CEREBRAL PALSY

If a child has cerebral palsy it means that part of the child's brain either is not working properly or has not developed normally. The affected area is usually one of the parts of the brain that controls the muscles and certain body movements; the disease interferes with the messages that normally pass from the brain to the body. In some children cerebral palsy is hardly noticeable at all; others are more severely affected. No two children will be affected in quite the same way. There are three different types of cerebral palsy:

Spastic cerebral palsy Here, the cortex, which is the outer layer of the brain and controls thought, movement, and sensation, is affected. Tight and sometimes jerky muscle movements result.

Athetoid cerebral palsy This type involves the basal ganglia, groups of cells lying deep within the brain. The basal ganglia promote organized, graceful, and economical movement, so an abnormality can cause movements that are bending and wave-like.

HOW YOU CAN HELP

It's difficult to predict the effects of cerebral palsy, particularly on a young child. It does not become more severe as your child gets older, though some difficulties may become more noticeable, and your priorities will change: when your baby is young, for example, you might concentrate on helping her to sit up, but later you will be more concerned with communication skills and talking.

There is no cure for cerebral palsy, but if children are lifted, held, and positioned well from an early age, and encouraged to play in a way that helps them to improve their posture and muscle control, they can learn a lot and lead fulfilling lives.

There's no question that you're going to have to work very hard with your child and there will be difficult moments when you feel that it's all too much. These feelings are natural, and most parents feel that they gradually get less severe. Indeed, many parents say they find bringing up a child with cerebral palsy a challenging and fulfilling task.

Children with cerebral palsy often tend to lie or sit in certain ways, because their muscles are sometimes in spasm, and cause problems with their joints.

Having physiotherapy as soon as cerebral palsy is suspected can help reduce the risks of these complications developing.

- Your child may get stiffer and have more muscle spasm when she's lying on her back, so lie her on her side or tummy instead, supporting her with a cushion if necessary. It's also a good idea to change her position every 20 minutes or so.

- Help your child to learn to use her hands right from the start by letting her feel things with different textures, and encouraging her to hold toys and other objects. Toys securely strung over her chair can be useful.

- Enable your child to learn shapes by showing her different simply-shaped objects, and encouraging her to handle them and play with them.

- A cerebral palsy child of three or four years may want to help with everyday tasks around the house like any child her age. Explain to your child what you're doing, let her watch you, and if possible let her join in.

Ataxic cerebral palsy This indicates that the cerebellum, which is located at the base of the brain, is affected. Because the cerebellum is responsible for co-ordinating fine movement, posture, and balance, an abnormality can result in an uneven gait and difficulty in walking.

EFFECTS OF CEREBRAL PALSY

Some children with cerebral palsy will have difficulty talking, walking, or using their hands, and most will need help with everyday tasks. The child with cerebral palsy may suffer slightly or severely from slow, awkward, or jerky movements, stiffness, weakness, floppiness, or muscle spasms. Some children are prone to involuntary movements.

There are a number of disorders associated with cerebral palsy, due either to poor muscle control or to other abnormalities in the brain.

Eyesight The most common eye problem is a squint, which may need correction with glasses or, in severe cases, an operation.

Hearing Children with athetoid cerebral palsy are more likely to have severe hearing difficulties than other children. This is not so for children with other forms of cerebral palsy. It is important that hearing difficulties be diagnosed early (see p.178). An affected child may be able to wear a hearing aid.

Speech The ability to control the tiny muscles in the mouth, tongue, palate, and voice box is necessary for speech. Difficulty in speaking and problems with chewing and swallowing often occur together in children with cerebral palsy. Speech therapists can help with both sorts of difficulty.

Spatial perception Some children with cerebral palsy cannot perceive space and relate it to their own bodies; for instance, they're not able to judge distances or think in three dimensions. This is due to an abnormality in a part of the brain that is not related to intelligence.

Epilepsy About one-third of children with cerebral palsy are affected by epilepsy (see p.270), but it is impossible to predict whether, or when, your child may develop seizures. In some children they start in infancy; in others, not until adulthood. If your child does develop epilepsy it can be controlled with medication.

Learning difficulties People who are unable to control their movements very well, or to talk, are often assumed to have a mental disability. Some people with cerebral palsy do have learning difficulties, but this is by no means always the case; many people with cerebral palsy actually have a higher than average intelligence.

The feet should be manipulated so they don't become stiff

A straight back helps in turn to straighten the hips and legs

Wedge support
A child who is not ready to sit needs support so that she can use her hands. A wedge allows her to lift her head, straighten her back, and reach forward. The ultimate aim is to reduce the support that the child needs so that she can sit in a chair.

The child can reach forward and use her hands to play

CHOOSING AND USING TOYS

Despite their difficulties with movement, children with cerebral palsy need stimulating play as much as any child, but choosing toys can be problematic. Most toy companies make goods suitable for children with cerebral palsy. If you are planning to buy an expensive toy, ask your physiotherapist or occupational therapist for advice. Better still, join a toy library and experiment to find out which toys your child will find most rewarding. Wedges (see p.269) and standing frames can greatly help children with cerebral palsy to enjoy their toys. Once again, your occupational therapist will be able to help.

- When your child is playing let him choose from two or three toys, then put away the ones he doesn't want. If he's surrounded by lots of toys, he will easily be distracted.

- Always show your child how a new toy works, not once but many times.

- Help him to use his imagination by telling him stories about his cuddly toys while you play with him, for example, or encourage him to have a tea-party with them.

- If your child doesn't seem to want to play, start showing him how much fun it is by starting to play with his toys yourself, and ask him to join in.

CONDUCTIVE EDUCATION

This intensive learning system is designed to help adults and children with certain kinds of learning disabilities, including children with cerebral palsy, to become much more independent individuals.

It was developed at the Pëto Institute in Hungary and in some cases has helped children to gain skills that their parents never believed possible.

The aim of conductive education is to help people to function normally – intellectually, physically, and socially – without the need of a wheelchair or other special services or equipment. It is based around a consideration of the child as a whole person, intensive group work with parents and children, and the encouragement of every small movement towards gaining independence.

In the UK, Scope (see Useful addresses, p.344) is establishing a network of schools where parents and their preschool children can learn the basics of conductive education together.

EPILEPSY

The most common disease of the brain in the UK, affecting 1 in 200 births, epilepsy tends to run in families. The normal electrical impulses in the brain are disturbed, causing periodic seizures which can be very minor or severe.

EPILEPTIC SEIZURES

There are several forms of epileptic seizure. One, called "grand mal", involves recurring attacks of convulsions with loss of consciousness followed by stiffening of the body lasting a minute or less, and then a series of rhythmic jerks of the limbs, clenching of the teeth (when your child might bite his tongue), possible urination or double incontinence, and frothing at the mouth. When the convulsion is over your child will lapse into sleep and wake up without any memory of the fit.

In another form, called "petit mal", there are no convulsions, only a second or two of unconsciousness, very much like day-dreaming. Your child's eyes will glaze over and he appears not to see or hear anything. This kind of epilepsy is not easily recognised, and may go undiagnosed. Although not so dramatic as grand mal, petit mal seizures can interfere with a child's normal life, particularly with school attendance and performance, and with certain physical activities where loss of control could pose a danger, such as skating or cycling.

Epilepsy is not to be confused with febrile convulsions (see p.281), which are fairly harmless and are caused by a high temperature preceding or during an infectious illness.

HOW SERIOUS IS IT?

Epilepsy is by no means life-threatening. Most children grow out of the petit mal form by late adolescence, but those who suffer from the grand mal form may need special attention throughout their lives, even though the condition is controlled by drugs. They will need supervision during activities like swimming or cycling.

It can take time to establish the level of medication required, and a young child may go through times when the epilepsy is not absolutely controlled by drugs. Consult your doctor, who can raise the dose for better control. If your child has a convulsion of any kind, consult your doctor immediately.

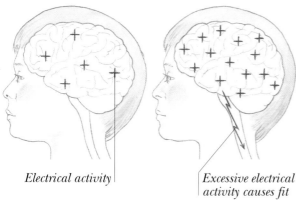

Electrical activity

Excessive electrical activity causes fit

Normal brain activity
The level of electrical activity in the brain is relatively low.

Brain activity in a seizure
When an excessive level of electrical activity builds up, signals are sent to the body which cause a seizure.

WHAT TO DO DURING A SEIZURE

- Remove any furniture, so that your child's jerking limbs don't hit any solid objects.

- Loosen the clothing around his neck or chest.

- Don't try to hold your child's teeth apart if they are clenched, or put anything into his mouth.

- As soon as your child stops moving violently, put him in the recovery position (see p.329).

- During a petit mal seizure, guide your child to safety and stay with him until it has passed.

- Make a note of what happens during your child's seizure so you can tell your doctor.

TREATMENT

If your child has a convulsion your doctor will ask you about it and examine him to decide what form of seizure he's had. If his convulsions are recurrent he'll be referred to hospital for an examination that may include an EEG (electro-encephalogram), blood tests, and a brain scan.

Epilepsy can be controlled, but not cured. Anticonvulsive drugs taken on a daily basis will reduce the frequency of grand mal seizures and eventually eradicate them. Selective drugs are now available that target a precise area of the brain and do not cause the side-effects associated with older drugs.

Your child's condition will be reviewed periodically by your doctor, and if there are no seizures for a year or two, he may try phasing out the drugs.

Surgery may be used if drugs are not effective and if damage to a single area of the brain is thought to be the cause. Your doctor will advise you as to whether this might be appropriate.

HOW YOU CAN HELP

It could be a shock to realize that your child has epilepsy, but you must try to remain calm. You and your child will both need to get your confidence back. You can do this with the help of your doctor, who can advise you on how to cope with the seizures.

It is important to observe your child's condition so that you can report back to your doctor. Make a note of the frequency of your child's seizures. If he's on medication, watch him carefully and report any mental or personality differences that may be caused by the drugs. You should never stop your child's medication without seeking medical advice first. To do so could result in a severe, prolonged convulsion after a few days.

Treat your child as normally as possible all the time. Tell his friends and teachers about the condition so that they're not frightened and shocked if your child has a convulsion when they're there. Your child should always wear a bracelet or medallion engraved with information about his epilepsy.

When your child is old enough, teach him to recognise the signs of an oncoming attack. Many sufferers of epilepsy experience sensations such as an unpleasant smell, distorted vision, or an odd feeling in the stomach just before a convulsion. If your child can identify these sensations as warning signs he may be able to avoid having an accident.

THE OUTLOOK FOR YOUR CHILD

The aim of caring for a child with epilepsy is to control the seizures with a minimum of side-effects and enhance his quality of life as he grows up. Seizure control should never be established at the cost of drug side-effects, as they may result in cramping of important brain functions that allow your child to develop normally.

Monitoring your child's condition is very important. Don't rely on your doctor to do this; establish a plan of action that involves regular visits and if your child has more than one or two seizures, visit the doctor immediately for reassessment; the medication may need to be adjusted.

SICKLE CELL DISEASE

This inherited disease is most common in people of African or West Indian descent, but may also occur in people from the Indian subcontinent, the Middle East, and the eastern Mediterranean. A child with sickle cell disease (SCD) will be prone to bouts of pain and may be at risk from other disorders, but most of the time he will be quite well.

TYPES OF SCD

Sickle cell disease is caused by an abnormality of haemoglobin, the oxygen-carrying substance in red blood cells. There are three main types of SCD: sickle cell anaemia, haemoglobin SC disease, and sickle beta-thalassaemia.

Sickle cell anaemia When oxygen levels are low, the abnormal haemoglobin (known as type S) becomes crystallized, making the red cell fragile, ridged, and sticky. These sickle cells – so called because of their characteristic sickle or crescent shape – can then become trapped in the blood vessels, causing a blockage which prevents blood flow. This accounts for the excruciating pain that is characteristic of an SCD attack. Sickle cells last only about 20 days in the body, as opposed to the usual 120 days for normal red cells, and the death of red cells leads to anaemia.

Sometimes aplastic crises occur, where the blood-forming activity in the bone marrow is reduced temporarily, decreasing the level of red-cell production and shortening the life of the red cells. As a result, the bone-marrow may become inactive, which can be life-threatening.

Haemoglobin SC disease In this form of SCD there are two abnormal haemoglobins – type S and type C. The disease appears later, and in a milder form, than sickle cell anaemia.

Sickle beta-thalassaemia This is similar to sickle cell anaemia in that there is an abnormality in the haemoglobin that results in abnormally shaped cells. Sufferers inherit a sickle cell gene from one parent and a thalassaemia gene from the other.

SICKLE CELL TRAIT

Sickle cell trait is found in areas where malaria was or is endemic, and offers some protection against malaria during the first years of life. It's not surprising, therefore, that around 10 per cent of Afro-Caribbeans, 25 per cent of Nigerians, and a smaller but significant number of Middle Eastern and Mediterranean people have the trait.

A child can only inherit sickle cell disease if both parents pass on the abnormal trait, and even then the chances are only one in four. If only one parent passes on the trait then the sickle cell gene will be masked by a healthy gene from the other parent. A carrier is unaffected, but the trait shows up in blood tests.

EFFECTS OF SCD

Apart from the anaemia caused by the death of affected red blood cells, SCD can cause other problems, including infections, stroke, jaundice, and acute pain attacks called "crises".

Infections Children with SCD are particularly vulnerable to infections, especially of the lungs, to salmonella infection, which is especially dangerous in SCD because it can spread to the bones and blood, and to meningitis. An overwhelming infection can cause a dramatic loss of blood cells in the spleen or liver, resulting in a massive drop in haemoglobin levels which is potentially fatal if treatment is not given immediately.

Pain crises When sickle cells block a blood vessel there may be oxygen starvation of tissue supplied by that blood vessel; this can occur nearly anywhere in the body, although the feet and hands are particularly vulnerable.

These crises are one of the most distressing aspects of SCD; the pain is violent and unpredictable, and as a parent it is very difficult to watch your child in pain and be unable to help him. The crisis can be treated with painkilling drugs, however. Sometimes crises are brought on by infections, strenuous exercise, low temperatures, or dehydration caused by vomiting or diarrhoea.

Jaundice The rapid breakdown of red cells can result in increased levels of a pigment called bilirubin (see **Jaundice**, p.25). This causes a yellowish appearance in the whites of the eyes, which often increases with the severity of the crises.

Development Children with SCD may experience slowing down of their growth (both height and weight) and possibly lateness in achieving bladder and bowel control. They may exist in a permanent state of chronic anaemia leading to a rapid decline in their condition when ill.

SCREENING

Genetic and support counselling are essential for couples at risk or with SCD in their families. In some areas, all babies are screened for haemoglobin abnormalities regardless of ethnic origin. Early detection means the condition can be managed properly right from the start, and in particular that treatment with penicillin can begin promptly, to minimize the risk of lung infections.

Antenatal screening is available to find out if a baby's haemoglobin is normal and can be carried out at the time of amniocentesis (usually about 16 weeks into the pregnancy). Screening is advisable for pregnant women who are aware that they have sickle cell trait. Couples will be offered counselling to clarify the risks of having a baby.

TREATMENT

If your child has SCD, he'll need frequent doses of penicillin to nip bacterial infections in the bud. This should be given from the time of diagnosis until the child is at least eight years of age, and usually

until after adolescence. If your child has chronic anaemia he will need folic acid supplements. He should drink plenty of fluids to prevent dehydration – at least 1 litre (1³/₄ pints) daily – and should always keep warm, to encourage normal circulation. Although over-exertion can cause problems, your child should exercise regularly and find his own energy tolerance level – exercise will improve the health of his heart and circulation. Pain and symptoms of infection should be treated promptly.

Where millions of red blood cells have been destroyed, exchange transfusion in hospital will be necessary. Sometimes many exchange transfusions will have to be given. Although this is a lengthy procedure, it will allow your child a near normal life.

HOW YOU CAN HELP

Although knowledge about the disease is incomplete, it is important that you are as well informed as possible, so that you can help your child avoid pain crises. Counselling will give you a safe, confidential way of exploring your feelings, and provide a source of encouragement and support (see **Useful addresses**, p.344).

When your child starts school, you should inform his head-teacher and class-teachers of his condition, making them aware of the problems it can impose on education. Your child may miss out on classes, for example, because of hospital admissions or a crisis. Reassure your child and encourage him to express his feelings and anxieties.

Your child's feelings must be given great consideration. Many children with SCD can experience difficulties with their classmates at preschool and school. Your child's teachers should educate the other children about SCD so that your child does not suffer from feelings of alienation or isolation – as he might if, for example, they thought they could catch the disease from him.

Once they can speak, many SCD children express a fear of dying or being deformed. Others feel different and alienated, thinking they're the only ones who are suffering from this condition and that nobody understands them. Yet others are afraid of expressing when they are in pain in case nobody believes them. You can help enormously by making sure that your child feels assured of your understanding, sympathy, and care whenever he needs it.

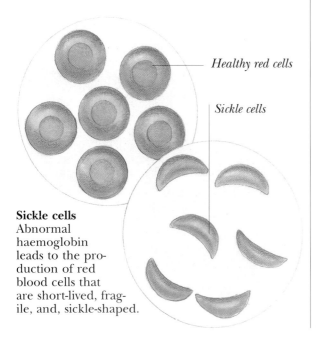

Healthy red cells

Sickle cells

Sickle cells
Abnormal haemoglobin leads to the production of red blood cells that are short-lived, fragile, and, sickle-shaped.

CHAPTER SIX

MEDICINE AND HEALTHCARE

*Most childhood illnesses are minor and others are easily pre-
ventable; inoculations are effective against most infectious
diseases. In a baby, however, seemingly minor illnesses can
cause complications: a cold that develops into a throat
infection, for instance, may cause breathing difficulties.*

*You will be understandably anxious if your child is
sickening for something, is ill, or has had an accident.
Sometimes deciding whether to seek medical help can be
equally stressful. Even if your child's symptoms appear
commonplace, you may worry that they are indicative of
something more serious. You should never worry that you are
being too cautious – if you find yourself wondering whether
it is worth consulting a doctor, then you probably should.*

*The main cause of death in young children is accidents, but
fortunately many injuries are preventable. You can reduce
the likelihood of accidents by making your home safe and
taking precautions when your child is away from home. You
should also learn first aid so that you know how to help
your child in an emergency. Don't just read this book; attend
an approved first aid training course (see p.327) and learn
the emergency procedures on pp.326–33 by heart.*

Dealing with illness

It's fairly easy to recognise when your child is ill: she'll be pale, listless, and off her food. You should be able to treat her successfully at home for most things. If you're ever worried or in two minds, however, call your doctor. Some symptoms always require immediate medical attention: these are listed on p.277.

Even when you are quite sure your child is ill, you may be unsure what is wrong with her, and you will need your doctor's help in deciding what the matter is. To help him, you should observe everything you can about your child's symptoms; the more accurate information the doctor has, the better his chance of making an accurate diagnosis.

Warning symptoms

It is usually apparent when your child is falling ill, and signs that you should monitor closely are your child's temperature, appetite, and breathing rate.

Temperature The normal body temperature for a child is 37°C (98.6°F). When your child's temperature rises above 38°C (100.4°F) she has a fever, and when it falls below 35°C (95°F) she has hypothermia. (These figures are based on rectal readings.) In both cases you should seek medical help. Your child's temperature does, however, vary according to how active she has been and the time of day. Her temperature is lower in the morning than during the day, and higher in the evening. It will also be higher if she has been running around a lot and expending a lot of energy.

Diarrhoea Loose, watery bowel movements mean the intestines are inflamed and irritable, and there is not enough time for water to be reabsorbed from the stool. Diarrhoea always indicates a problem in the gastrointestinal tract. Gastroenteritis is the most common cause, but occasionally it is caused by gastric flu or some other infection. Diarrhoea is always serious in babies and young children because it can lead to dehydration.

Vomiting You should consult your doctor if your child has been vomiting intermittently during a six-hour period or more, especially if the vomiting is accompanied by diarrhoea or fever. Vomiting is usually caused by food which does not suit or gastroenteritis. Occasionally, there may be a more serious cause; your doctor will make a diagnosis.

Taking your child's pulse

A rapid or undetectable pulse may indicate that your child is unwell. The pulse rate varies according to health, age, and physical exertion.

The average pulse rate for a young baby is 100–160 beats per minute; this slows to 100–120 for a one-year-old, and 80–90 for a seven-year-old.

When taking your child's pulse, use the first two fingers, not your thumb. Count the number of beats over a 15-second period and multiply this figure by four to get the rate per minute. Do not use your thumb, as it contains a pulse of its own.

Checking heartbeat
For a child under a year, the best way to take a pulse is to put your palm on her chest at the level of the nipple and count the number of heartbeats (you'll also find a pulse in her arm, see p.328).

Radial pulse
In a child over one year, it should be relatively easy to find the pulse on her wrist. Place your middle and index fingers on the spot on the wrist immediately below the thumb, and count the beats.

Use your index and middle fingers, not your thumb

Pain You should see your doctor if your child complains of headaches, particularly after she's bumped her head or if the headache comes on a few hours after the head injury, or if there is blurred vision, nausea, dizziness, or stomach pain, particularly on the lower right side of the abdomen.

Breathing Difficulty in breathing is a medical emergency and requires immediate help. Breathing may be laboured and you may notice that your child's ribs are drawn in sharply each time she takes a breath. If your child's lips go blue you should treat this as an emergency and send for an ambulance.

Appetite Sudden changes in appetite may indicate underlying illness, especially if your child has a fever, even a mild one. Your doctor should be alerted if your child refuses food for a day and seems lethargic, or, if she is under six months old, has a poor appetite, and doesn't seem to be thriving.

CALLING THE DOCTOR

It is only natural for a new mother to be anxious, and you may worry because you are not sure whether your baby is genuinely poorly. Along with many doctors I quickly learned that the one person whose opinion cannot be dismissed is the mother's. So your guideline should be, whenever in doubt, call a doctor. Don't feel shy about asking your doctor questions if something is worrying you, however trivial it may seem.

What to tell your doctor In order to make a diagnosis a doctor will need the following information: a description of your child's symptoms; when they started; in what order they occurred; how severe they are; and whether anything precipitated them (eating something poisonous, for instance). In addition to this, your doctor will need to know your child's age and medical history.

Be prepared to give details of any injury or accident. Did your child lose consciousness? Has she had anything to eat or drink (in case she needs an anaesthetic)? Was she bitten by an insect or animal? What was it and what were her symptoms? If she has swallowed a toxic substance or plant, keep it to show to the doctor.

The specific questions your doctor may ask about an illness are: Has your child vomited or had diarrhoea? Does she have any pain? Where is it? How long has it lasted? Have you given her anything for it? Is her temperature raised? How quickly did the fever come on and what was her highest temperature? Has she lost consciousness at any time? Have you noticed swollen glands or a rash? Has she had any dizziness or blurred vision? The doctor will also ask general questions about your child's appetite and sleeping patterns.

What to ask your doctor If your child is prescribed drugs, make sure that you know when drugs should be taken (some need to be taken on a full stomach), how long they should be taken for, and whether there are any side-effects. Find out how your child should be nursed and how soon her symptoms can be expected to go away. Ask your doctor about preventive measures for a child who has a recurring condition like cold sores.

With an infectious disease you'll need to know whether it's safe to have visitors, how long your child will have to be off school, and whether the illness has any long-term effects.

EMERGENCIES

Some situations demand immediate medical attention. You should call an ambulance or take your child to the nearest casualty department by car should any of the following potentially life-threatening situations happen:

- A bone fracture or suspected fracture (see p.339).

- A severe reaction to a sting or bite from an insect or animal (see p.341).

- Pale blue or grey skin around the lips and under the fingernails.

- A burn or scald (see p.336) that is larger than the area of your child's hand.

- Poisoning or suspected poisoning (see p.334).

- Unconsciousness (see pp.327–29).

- Severe bleeding from a wound (see p.335).

- Contact with a corrosive chemical, especially involving the eyes (see pp.334 and 338).

- Laboured breathing or choking (see p.333).

- Any injuries to the ears or eyes (see pp.284, 287 and 338).

- An electric shock (see p.334).

- Inhalation of toxic fumes such as smoke or gas.

TEMPERATURE

Whenever you suspect that your child is ill you should take his temperature. A raised temperature shows that the body is fighting off an infection. When your child's temperature is over 38°C (100.4°F), he has a fever (see p.281), which you should try to reduce.

TAKE CARE

Until your baby is two years old you should take his temperature rectally using a thermometer lubricated with petroleum jelly, baby cream, or oil; after this you can take it under the armpit.

Don't put a mercury thermometer in your child's mouth until he is at least seven; he may bite it and swallow mercury, which is a poison.

THERMOMETERS

There are several types of thermometer. The most accurate is a mercury thermometer, in which a narrow column of mercury expands in response to heat and moves up to a point on a calibrated scale.

Other types include liquid crystal (strip) thermometers and digital thermometers.

Strip thermometers are less accurate than others, but simple to use; digital thermometers are accurate and unbreakable, but more expensive than other kinds.

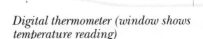

Digital thermometer (window shows temperature reading)

Mercury thermometer (to be used rectally or under the armpit)

Strip thermometer (a glowing panel indicates your child's temperature)

Using a strip thermometer
The thermometer is easy to use; just hold it against your child's forehead for a minute or so.

TAKING YOUR CHILD'S TEMPERATURE

Under the armpit
Position the bulb of a mercury or digital thermometer in your child's armpit and fold his arm over his chest. Hold the thermometer in place for about three minutes. The armpit temperature is 0.6°C (1°F) below actual body temperature.

Rectal temperature (1)
Lay your baby on his back, remove his nappy, grasp his feet, and insert the lubricated tip of the thermometer about 2.5 centimetres (1 inch) into his rectum. Hold it in place for one or two minutes.

Rectal temperature (2)
Lay your baby over your knees, place one hand on his back to keep him from wriggling, and insert the lubricated tip of the s thermometer about 2.5 centimetres (1 inch) into his rectum.

MEDICINES

Most medicines for children come in syrup form with either a spoon, dropper, or syringe to administer them. Your child may be quite compliant when it comes to taking medicine, but he may resist.

If your baby refuses medicine, get your partner to help you, or wrap him up in a blanket so that you can hold him steady. Droppers and syringes are the best ways to give medicine if your child can't yet swallow from a spoon. Older children may be cajoled into taking medicine by the promise of a favourite food or drink to take the taste away.

GIVING MEDICINE

Dropper
Hold your baby in the crook of your arm, put the dropper into the medicine and draw up the right amount by squeezing the teat at the top. Place the dropper in the corner of your baby's mouth and gently release the medicine by squeezing the teat.

Spoon
The spoon should be sterilized with boiling water or sterilizing solution. Hold your baby in a semi-reclining position, pull his chin down with your finger, and place the spoon on his lower lip. Raise the angle of the spoon so that the medicine trickles into his mouth.

Finger
Measure out the correct dose of medicine into a small container. Dip your finger in it and allow your baby to suck it off your finger. Continue until he has taken the whole dose.

APPLYING DROPS

Eye drops
Lay your baby on his back and tilt his head in the direction of the affected eye. Gently pull his lower eyelid down with your finger and let the drops fall inside the lid. Release the lid.

Nose drops
Lay your baby on his back with his head tilted backwards. Let two or three drops fall into the nostrils.

Ear drops
Lay your baby on his side. Using a dropper, let the eardrops fall into the centre of his ear.

NURSING YOUR CHILD

You don't need any special skills or medical knowl-edge to look after your sick child. It helps if you relax the rules and try to hide your anxiety from her. Don't insist that she eats while she is ill, but do encourage her to drink lots of fluids.

GENERAL NURSING

As well as whatever treatment the doctor recommends, the following routines will help your child to feel more comfortable while she is ill:

• Air your child's room and bed at least once a day.

• Leave a bowl by your child's bed if she is vomiting or has whooping cough.

• Leave a box of tissues by your child's bed.

• Give small meals frequently; your child may find large portions off-putting.

• Sponge your child down with tepid water if she has a fever.

• Give paracetamol elixir for pain relief.

SHOULD YOUR CHILD BE IN BED?

At the beginning of an illness when your child is feeling quite poorly she will probably want to stay in bed and she may sleep a lot. As she starts to feel better she will still need bed rest, but she will want to be around you and she may want intervals of playing. The best way to accommodate this is to make up a bed on the sofa in a room near where you are working so that she can lie down when she wants to. Don't insist that your child goes to bed just because she is ill – children with a fever, for instance, don't recover faster if they stay in bed. When your child is tired, however, it is time to put her to bed. But don't just leave her alone. Make sure that you visit her at regular intervals (every half an hour), and find the time to stay and play a game, read a book, or do a puzzle.

When she's on the road to recovery make sure that enough happens in her day to make the distinction between night and day. If she hasn't been watching television, let her watch it before bedtime.

GIVING DRINKS

It is essential that your child drinks a lot when she's ill – when she has a fever, diarrhoea, or is vomiting – because she will be dehydrated and will need to replace lost fluids. The recommended fluid intake for a child with a fever is 100–150 millilitres per kilogram (1½ – 2½ fluid ounces per pound) of body weight per day, which is the equivalent of 1 litre (2 pints) per day for a child who weighs 9 kilograms (20 pounds).

Encourage your child to drink by leaving her favourite drink at her bedside (preferably not sugary, fizzy drinks such as cola), by putting drinks in glasses that are especially appealing, and by giving her bendy straws to drink with.

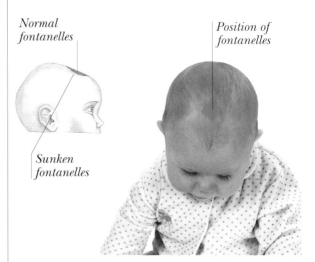

Normal fontanelles

Position of fontanelles

Sunken fontanelles

Dehydration
If your baby is under 18 months and has been vomiting or has had diarrhoea she may be dehydrated. One sign of dehydration is sunken fontanelles, which indicate that your baby needs immediate medical attention.

OCCUPYING YOUR CHILD

Illness is an occasion when you can completely indulge your child. When she is not resting, spend time playing games and talking to her. Relax all the rules and let her play whatever games she wants to, even if you've previously disallowed them in bed. If your child wants to do something messy like painting, just spread an old sheet or a sheet of polythene over the bed. If you can, move a television into her room temporarily – this will keep her entertained and make her feel special as well.

Let her do some painting; read aloud to her; get out some of her old toys and play with them together; buy her small presents and let her unwrap them; sing songs or make up a story together; ask her to draw a picture of what she is going to do when she feels better; and, unless she has an infectious illness, let some friends visit her for a brief period during the day. As your child gets better let her play outside, but if she has a fever discourage her from running around too much.

VOMITING

Your child will probably find vomiting a distressing experience and you should try and make her as comfortable as possible. Get her to sit up in bed and make sure there is a bowl or a bucket within easy reach, so that she doesn't have to run to the toilet. Tie back long hair, and when she's being sick hold her head and comfort her. Afterwards help your child to clean her teeth, or give her a peppermint to suck to take the taste away.

When your child hasn't vomited for a few hours and she's feeling hungry, offer her bland foods, such as mashed potato, but don't encourage her to eat if she doesn't want to. More important than eating is maintaining a constant level of fluids. Give your child lots of water, and add a half teaspoonof salt and four teaspoonfuls of glucose per pint to replace lost salts and minerals. Avoid giving her drinks such as milk, and give her plenty of fruit juice diluted with water.

TREATING A HIGH TEMPERATURE

The first sign of a raised temperature is often a hot forehead, but to check that your child is feverish take her temperature (see p.278). Call your doctor if the fever lasts more than 24 hours or if there are any accompanying symptoms. Temperatures over 38°C (100.4°F) should be taken very seriously in children under six months.

Try to cool your child down by taking her clothes off and getting her to lie in bed. Sponge her all over with tepid water and keep taking her temperature every minute until it has stabilized at 38°C (100.4°F). Never use cold water to sponge her since this causes the blood vessels to constrict and the temperature to increase. Cover her with a light cotton bedsheet and take her temperature every five minutes to check that it doesn't go up again. Changing the sheets on your child's bed regularly will help to keep her comfortable.

When sponging with tepid water fails to lower your child's temperature try giving her paracetamol elixir (aspirin is unsuitable for young children). It's still important for her to drink lots of fluid as she will be perspiring a lot.

FEBRILE CONVULSIONS

The most common cause of convulsions in babies is a raised temperature that accompanies a viral infection. This sort of convulsion is most common in children between six months and four years, and is known as a febrile convulsion.

During a convulsion the muscles of the body twitch involuntarily due to a temporary abnormality in brain function. Possible symptoms include loss of consciousness, loss of bowel and bladder control, rhythmic jerking of the limbs, with sleepiness and confusion on coming round. You should clear a space around her so that she doesn't damage herself. Wait until her body has stopped jerking and then place her in the recovery position (see p.329).

You will need to sponge your child with tepid (never cold) water to reduce her temperature. Don't leave her alone, don't try to restrain her, and don't put anything in her mouth. Call a doctor as soon as your child has come round. Should the convulsion last more than 15 minutes, call an ambulance.

Treating convulsions
Your priority should be to lower your child's temperature by sponging her with tepid water (see above).

Sponge your child all over to cool her down

HOSPITAL

At some point in your child's life she may have to go into hospital. This could be because she has an accident, a childhood illness, a chronic condition such as thalassaemia (see p.272) which necessitates regular blood transfusions, or she needs an operation. Given a little forethought on your part, a stay in hospital does not have to be upsetting or frightening for your child.

TEACHING YOUR CHILD

If you don't like hospitals and you convey this attitude to your child you may inadvertently make her stay in hospital more difficult than it has to be. Try to teach her that a hospital is a friendly place where people go to get better. Whenever the chance arises – if you have a friend or a relative in hospital, for instance – take your child along when you go to visit and be matter-of-fact, not gloomy, about their illness. If a child's first experience of a hospital is when she becomes sick, it will seem more alien than it would otherwise.

If you know that your child is going to hospital read her a story about a child who goes into hospital, and role play doctors and nurses with toy stethoscopes. Be as honest as you can about why she's going to hospital, and emphasize that it's to make her better. Reassure her that you will be with her as much as you can, and if she is old enough to understand, tell her when she'll be well enough to come home.

If your child requires an operation she'll probably be curious about what's going to happen to her. Answer her questions as honestly as you can – if she asks you whether the operation will hurt, don't pretend that it won't, but tell her that doctors have medicines to make the pain go away quickly.

WHAT TO TAKE

You can help your child prepare for a stay in hospital by packing a bag with her. One of the most unsettling things for her will be the unfamiliar surroundings and the change of routine, so let her have some of her own things with her: a personal stereo and tapes or a radio, travel games, cuddly toys, and a photograph for her bedside. On a practical level, for a short stay pack the following items:

- A toilet bag containing a hair brush, comb, soap, flannel, toothbrush, and toothpaste.
- Three pairs of pyjamas or three nightdresses.
- A dressing gown and a pair of slippers.
- Three pairs of socks.
- Three pairs of pants.

IN HOSPITAL

Many hospitals allow parents to stay with their children 24 hours a day. Whether yours does or not, try to spend as much time as possible with your child, especially at first, when her surroundings are unfamiliar. Let her know when you are going to come, and always keep your promises about visiting. Ask the nurses on the ward whether you can bathe, change, and feed your child. If she is well enough you can read to her and play games with her. If you can't stay at the hospital all the time, encourage your partner, friends, and relatives to visit at different times rather than all at once so that your child has someone she knows well with her almost all the time.

COMING HOME

Depending on how long your child has been in hospital, you may notice some changes in her habits. She probably woke up and went to sleep much earlier in hospital than she does at home, and these sleeping and waking patterns may carry on for a while. She may resent the discipline at home after having been spoiled and indulged a little, and she may be reluctant to go back to school. The best approach to these things is to be tolerant, as your child will soon adapt to life at home again.

IMMUNIZATION

The incidence of potentially fatal childhood diseases such as diphtheria has declined dramatically since the introduction of vaccination programmes, which provide immunity. Some vaccines are long-lasting (rubella), others need to be "boosted" at regular intervals (tetanus).

There are two types of immunization: passive and active. The former works by introducing already-formed antibodies into the body. The latter involves injecting a weakened bacterium that encourages the immune system to produce its own antibodies – this is why immunization can sometimes produce mild symptoms of the disease it is intended to protect against.

In the first five years of your child's life, she will need several immunizations: three DPT injections, one MMR injection, three Hib injections, and three polio immunizations (taken orally). Vaccines do not provide instant protection against disease; in some cases they take up to four weeks to be effective. Give paracetamol elixir to ease any discomfort.

IMPORTANCE OF IMMUNIZATION

Because immunization programmes have been so successful, it is easy to forget how prevalent diseases like whooping cough or polio once were. Many first-time mothers nowadays have never seen a child in leg-braces – a common sight in their parents' generation when the possibility of paralysis or even death from polio was a very real one.

Immunization protects both individuals and whole communities from infectious diseases. Every child should therefore be properly immunized. Some mothers are alarmed by stories about the side-effects of vaccinations, but these are actually quite rare. Your child shouldn't be vaccinated, however, if she has a fever or infection, or if she's had a severe reaction to a previous dose of vaccine. Your doctor or health visitor will advise you.

TETANUS INJECTIONS

There is a danger of tetanus with any deep penetrating wound. Tetanus bacteria only thrive where there is hardly any oxygen, so superficial wounds carry little risk. Tetanus bacteria and spores live in soil and manure, so it's dirty wounds that are dangerous. The bacteria produce a poison which attacks the nerves and brain, causing muscle spasm, particularly of the face – hence the common name lockjaw. Patients always require hospital treatment. Tetanus can be completely prevented by immunization. The first tetanus injection should be given before 12 months and boosters should be given at ten-yearly intervals up to a total of five doses. If your child has a dog bite or a deep, dirty cut and has not been immunized, she must have a tetanus injection straight away at a casualty department.

INJECTION	PROTECTS AGAINST	COMMENTS
DTP.	Diphtheria, tetanus, and pertussis (whooping cough).	Given as three injections at two, three, and four months.
Polio.	Polio.	Given by mouth at two, three, and four months. A booster dose is given at the age of five, and lasts for about ten years.
MMR.	Measles, mumps, and rubella.	Given to babies at about 13 months, or any time after this, and offers lasting protection.
Hib.	The bacterium Haemophilus influenzae type b (can cause bacterial meningitis, a severe form of croup, blood poisoning, and other infections).	Given at two, three, and four months.

COMMON COMPLAINTS

Any illness in a child is different from, and more serious than, the same illness in an adult because the immune system is not fully developed and because complications can occur. A throat infection in a child, for example, can easily spread to the chest because the airways are so short.

In this section I've described the most common childhood complaints, and given advice on when you need a doctor, and what you can do at home. Try to become familiar with the material in these pages; it'll help you to take prompt and appropriate action whenever your child complains of feeling ill.

EARS

Ear infections are common in children because their Eustachian tubes – the tubes that connect the middle ear to the throat – are short, so any throat infection can ascend quickly to the middle ear.

WAXY EAR

Ear wax is produced by glands in the outer ear canal and protects the ear from dust, foreign bodies, and infection. Children tend to produce more with a cold or sore throat, and if this dries and hardens, it can result in hearing loss. Although it's not usually serious, you should consult your doctor.

Symptoms Ear wax can become hard and compacted and cause impaired hearing, a ringing sound in the head, or a sensation of fullness in the outer ear. It may be possible to see the build-up of wax.

Treatment Syringeing with warm water, which will be done by your doctor, or ear drops may be effective. Drops are more likely to be used if the wax has formed a hard plug, as they will soften it, allowing it to come out overnight on soft cotton wool placed at the opening of the canal. Syringeing is painless and effective in expert hands. You should never try to insert anything into your child's ear, not even a fingernail or a cotton bud.

OUTER EAR INFECTION

The passage leading to the eardrum from the ear flap can sometimes become infected as a result of excessive cleaning or scratching, or the presence of a foreign body in the ear. This can be painful, but is not usually serious.

Symptoms Your child will complain of earache and her ear flap and outer ear passage may be red and tender. You may notice a pus-like discharge from the ear, and a dry scaly appearance. If your child is in great pain a boil may have developed within the ear canal.

Treatment Home treatment includes keeping the ear flap clean, giving paracetomol elixir to relieve pain and keep the temperature down, and covering the ear with a cotton pad. Your doctor may prescribe antibiotics or ear drops. Any foreign body or boil in the ear must be dealt with in hospital.

MIDDLE EAR INFECTION

Otitis media or infection of the middle ear is quite common in children and is associated with recurrent tonsillitis. In fact, one of the main reasons for removing tonsils (and adenoids) is chronic middle ear infections. Infections are caused by bacteria entering the middle ear from the nose and the throat via the Eustachian tube. If middle ear infections are left untreated, they can result in permanent hearing loss. Recurrent middle ear infections are often linked with glue ear (see p.285).

Symptoms The most prominent symptoms are severe earache and loss of appetite. Your child may also have a fever or a discharge from the ear, and there may be some hearing loss. A baby with a middle ear infection may be distressed and pull and rub her ear, which will be very red; in fact the whole side of her face may be inflamed.

Treatment The usual treatment is a course of antibiotics and pain-relieving medication. At home you should keep your child comfortable and cool and give lots of drinks as well as her medicines. An ear, nose, and throat specialist should treat repeated middle ear infections to avoid glue ear, and in some cases a tonsillectomy will be carried out.

GLUE EAR

If your child has repeated infections of the middle ear or throat, or tonsillitis, the middle ear can gradually fill with jelly-like fluid. As the fluid cannot drain away through the Eustachian tube it becomes glue-like and impairs hearing because the sounds are not being transmitted across the middle ear to the inner ear, where they are actually heard. It's important to deal with glue ear promptly or your child could be slow to speak and learn.

Symptoms Glue ear generally causes no pain, but partial hearing loss and a feeling of fullness deep in the ear may occur. A child with chronic glue ear may sleep with her mouth open, snore, and speak with a nasal twang. If glue ear is not treated it can cause permanent deafness, resulting in speech and learning problems.

Treatment After examining your child's ear with an otoscope, a doctor may prescribe antibiotics to clear the infection and vasoconstrictor drugs to allow the fluid to drain. In severe or recurring cases of glue ear, a minor operation may be necessary to insert a grommet – a plastic tube that drains off the mucus through the eardrum, which quickly heals after the grommet drops out. Grommets quite often drop out of their own accord and rarely have to be reinserted as all the fluid has drained. A child who has grommets fitted should take precautions to avoid letting water into the ears, and should only swim if snugly fitting earplugs are worn.

Ear drum

Cochlea
Grommet

Ear grommets
These allow mucus to drain away, relieving the congestion of glue ear. Grommets may fall out naturally or be removed by a specialist.

NOSE

A blocked nose, due to a cold, flu, or more rarely from an allergy, is quite common in childhood; so are minor nosebleeds. Neither is usually serious.

BLOCKED OR RUNNY NOSE

Excess mucus in the nose, which results in sniffing or a runny nose, is usually caused by a cold virus (see p.294). The mucous membranes lining the nasal passages become inflamed, swollen, and congested and hence block the nose. Other causes include allergic rhinitis (see p.293) or a foreign body, like a bead, lodged in the nose (see p.343).

Symptoms The secretions produced by a cold virus usually start off being clear and runny, but may become thick and yellow by the time the body's defences attack the infection. The mucus produced by a sinus infection is thick and yellowish-green.

Treatment Encourage your child to blow her nose frequently. Demonstrate how she should do it, clearing one nostril first, and then the other. Inhaled menthol in the form of a chest rub or drops on your child's pillow or clothes may help. Consult your doctor if a runny nose persists for more than three days. Your child may be prescribed nasal drops, or antibiotics if she has an infection or sinusitis.

NOSEBLEED

Most nosebleeds can be stopped quite easily. If a nosebleed is severe, lasts more than 30 minutes, or follows a blow to the head, you should take your child to the doctor.

Symptoms The bleeding usually comes from tiny blood vessels on the inner side of the nostril. A clot may form in the nose; it shouldn't be removed.

Treatment Sit your child down with her head forward over a bowl or a sink while you gently squeeze the bridge of her nose. Keep applying pressure for about ten minutes or until the bleeding has stopped. Your child shouldn't blow her nose for at least three hours after a nosebleed. Never put your child's head back, as she may swallow blood and be sick. If a nosebleed is severe, consult your doctor, who will probably pack the bleeding nostril with gauze.

THROAT

Throat infections such as tonsillitis and adenitis are rare in babies under one year. They are more common in children who have just started school and are being exposed to a new range of bacteria.

SORE THROAT

An uncomfortable or painful throat is usually due to infection by a bacterium such as streptococcus, or a virus such as the cold or flu viruses.

Symptoms Your child may tell you that she has a sore throat, or you may notice that she finds it hard to swallow. Depress her tongue with a spoon handle and tell her to say "aaahhh" so that you can look down her throat for signs of inflammation or enlarged red tonsils.

Treatment Give lots of drinks, and liquidize your child's food if she finds it difficult to swallow. Your doctor may prescribe an antibiotic if there is a bacterial infection or tonsillitis.

TONSILLITIS AND ADENOIDS

The tonsils, situated on both sides of the back of the throat, prevent bacteria which invade the throat from entering the body by trapping and killing them. This can sometimes result in the tonsils themselves becoming swollen and infected. The adenoids, which are situated at the back of the nose, are nearly always affected at the same time.

Symptoms Your child will complain of a sore throat and may find swallowing difficult. On examination, the tonsils appear red and enlarged, possibly with yellow and white patches. She may have a raised temperature, the glands in her neck may be swollen, and her breath might smell. If the adenoids are swollen, too, her speech may sound nasal.

Treatment Consult your doctor, who may take a throat swab and examine your child's ears and glands. The treatment for bacterial tonsillitis is the appropriate antibiotics. Removal of the tonsils is considered after many severe recurrent attacks or if the ears are badly affected too.

LARYNGITIS

An infection of the larynx or voice box may accompany any cold or sore throat. As long as it does not develop into croup (see p.296), laryngitis is rarely a serious condition.

Symptoms The most common symptoms are hoarseness or loss of voice. Your child may find it uncomfortable or painful to swallow, and may have a dry cough and a mild fever. Sometimes laryngitis develops into croup (see p.296).

Treatment Most cases of laryngitis are short-lived. Your child should rest, preferably in a humid environment in which the air can circulate. Give her lots of fluids and encourage her to rest her voice. If her temperature remains high she may need antibiotics. Make sure she doesn't overheat (see p.281) and should croup develop (see p.296), seek medical help as soon as possible.

LYMPH NODES

With a local infection, extra white blood cells are produced at the lymph nodes nearest the site of the infection, to mop up and kill the bacteria. The production of white cells causes lymph glands to become inflamed and sore.

Swollen glands
Lymph nodes in front of the ear and below the angle of the jaw swell due to throat infections. To feel them, run your finger down your child's neck from a point just below his ears; they feel like a string of beads.

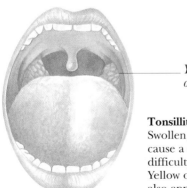

Yellow spots on tonsils

Tonsillitis
Swollen, infected tonsils cause a sore throat and difficulty in swallowing. Yellow or white spots may also appear on the tonsils.

Lymph nodes

EYES

The most common childhood eye problems are infections or inflammations that can be cured with good hygiene, and sometimes antibiotic eye drops.

BLEPHARITIS

This is inflammation of the eyelid margins, found in conjunction with eczema and cradle cap, and usually recurring. It is not serious and can usually be alleviated with simple self-help measures. Consult your doctor if your child's eyes become sticky or if the condition does not clear up within a week.

Symptoms The eyelid margins appear red, scaly, and inflamed and you may notice tiny crusts of dried pus on your child's eyelashes.

Treatment Using cotton wool dipped in a solution of warm boiled water and half a teaspoon of salt, tell your child to close her eyes and wipe each eye from the nose outwards. Use a fresh piece of cotton wool each time you wipe the eye, and do this every morning and night until the skin has healed. Your doctor, may prescribe an anti-inflammatory cream, or eye drops if there is an infection.

CONJUNCTIVITIS

In this common eye complaint the membrane covering the eyeball (the conjunctiva) becomes inflamed and red. There are three main causes of conjunctivitis: infection by a virus or bacteria, damage due to the presence of a foreign body, and an allergic reaction. Infective conjunctivitis is very contagious and if one eye is infected, the other one is likely to become infected too if you don't take precautions.

Symptoms Inflammation causes pain on blinking and your child may find it uncomfortable to look at bright lights – a symptom called photophobia. When conjunctivitis is caused by an infection the eye will be sticky and there may be a collection of pus in the lower eyelid. Allergic conjunctivitis produces clear, watery tears and swollen eyelids.

Treatment When a foreign body is visible remove it with the corner of a clean tissue. Always seek medical advice for a child who has a "red eye". For an infection your doctor will prescribe an antibiotic ointment or eye drops. Anti-inflammatory eye drops and antihistamines are used for allergic conjunctivitis. You should place a pad of cotton gauze over the affected eye to keep it closed and rested.

STYE

When the follicle of an eyelash becomes infected, a stye, or small abscess, develops on the margin of the eyelid. Rubbing the eyes may encourage them. A stye will require medical treatment because it's painful and obscures vision.

Symptoms At first the eyelid appears red and a bit swollen, then the swelling fills with pus and the stye may protrude noticeably from the eyelid.

Treatment First aid can only be done with an older, brave child. If pus is visible in the stye you can release it by plucking the eyelash from the infected follicle, using a pair of sterilized tweezers; then wiping away the pus using a cotton wool ball dipped in warm water. Should the eyelash not come out easily, stop, and get medical advice. Although styes are not as contagious as other eye infections, you should still keep your child's flannel and towel separate from the rest of the family's.

SQUINT

Your baby's eyes may appear to be pointing in different directions, sometimes convergent (towards each other) and sometimes divergent (away from each other). Until the age of about eight to ten weeks this is perfectly normal but if the baby's eyes have not aligned by three months you should seek advice. The usual causes of a squint are an imbalance in the muscles of the eyes, or one eye being long-sighted and the other being short-sighted.

Symptoms If you suspect that your baby has a squint, confirm by observing how light is reflected in her eyes. It should be reflected from exactly the same place in each eye; if not, then she almost certainly has a squint. Consult your doctor.

Treatment The usual treatment is to cover the strong eye with a patch, since this forces the muscles in the weak eye to become stronger. The eyes should become aligned within about five months, though it can take longer. If your child's squint is related to long- or short-sightedness she should get glasses from an optician.

MOUTH

Childhood mouth problems are generally minor; thrush is the only condition that needs immediate medical attention, since it does not respond to the usual self-help measures. Your child may refuse food when his mouth is sore. Give him liquidized bland foods that he can suck through a straw.

TEETHING PAIN

A child's teeth usually begin to come through at about six months and are complete by his third birthday (see p.175). During the period when the teeth are erupting, the gums are red and swollen.

Symptoms If you touch the swollen, red gums you may feel a hard lump beneath. Your baby will salivate and dribble more than usual and will chew objects. He may have trouble sleeping and be more irritable and clingy. Eating may be painful.

Treatment Medical treatment is not usually necessary. Don't think that other symptoms, such as loss of appetite or vomiting, are caused by teething. They never are. Consult your doctor.

The ring can be cooled in the refrigerator

Pain relief
Chewing on a cool teething ring – never frozen – or firm-textured foods such as carrot fingers or pieces of apple can ease the pain.

MOUTH ULCERS

Open sores in the mouth occur inside the lower lip, although they are common on the tongue, gums, and inside the cheeks. Aphthous ulcers are the most common kind and appear as round or oval yellow spots with an inflamed outline. They should go away by themselves in 10–14 days, but if they're recurrent, or prevent eating, see your doctor.

Symptoms All mouth ulcers are painful. Your child may have difficulty eating, especially food that is acidic or salty, and may refuse food.

Treatment If your child has an aphthous ulcer, try applying an antiseptic jelly (ask for something in orobase, a base which doesn't dissolve in saliva), to the affected area, and giving paracetamol elixir. Your doctor may prescribe an anti-inflammatory cream if the ulcer is severe. Avoid anything containing a local anaesthetic as allergies may occur.

Try to eliminate the underlying cause: ask your dentist to file down any rough teeth; discourage your child from biting his cheeks; or, if you are bottlefeeding your baby, try using a softer teat.

Whatever the type of ulcer, you should liquidize your child's foods, give him a straw to drink through, and avoid salty or acidic foods.

THRUSH

The mucous membranes can sometimes become infected by a fungus called *Candida albicans*. The growth of candida is usually kept in check by the presence of other bacteria, but when these bacteria are eradicated by taking antibiotics candida begins to multiply unrestrictedly. Alternatively, thrush can be passed on from a mother at the time of birth when the baby passes through the vagina. Although thrush is not serious, it can cause a young baby discomfort while he is sucking or feeding.

In children thrush may only be seen in the mouth, but it infects the whole gastro-intestinal tract and the anal area, where it is sometimes confused with nappy rash (see p.104).

Symptoms Thrush produces white, curd-like patches on the gums, cheeks, tongue, and roof of the mouth. If you attempt to wipe them off they become raw and may bleed. Around the anus thrush appears as red spots or a rash. If your child has nappy rash as well, there may be white flaky patches.

Treatment Thrush can be treated quickly and simply with anti-fungal medications, in liquid form for oral thrush, and cream form for anal thrush. These are available only on prescription.

Liquidized, bland, cold, or lukewarm foods are best if your child has oral thrush, particularly natural yogurt (not for very young babies).

Fungi flourish in warm, moist conditions, so if your baby has anal thrush you should keep him as dry as possible. Leave his bottom exposed to the air as much as you can and avoid using plastic pants. Be meticulous about hygiene, and always keep your child's hands clean.

SKIN

Childhood skin complaints may be caused by an infection, an allergy, or a response to very high or low temperatures. Most of them are minor and can easily be treated. Rashes occur with a variety of complaints, some of which are serious; if you are at all worried about a rash, consult your doctor.

CHAPPED SKIN

Chaps are little cracks in the skin, sometimes raw and deep. Exposure to the cold makes skin dry and prone to chapping, particularly the extremities where circulation is poor – hands, fingers, and ears. Damp skin around the lips chaps too. Failing to dry properly after washing, and washing so frequently that the skin's natural oils are removed can both contribute to chapping.

Symptoms Chapped skin has a dry, cracked appearance. If the cracks are deep there may be some bleeding and severe pain, and if they become infected you may notice pus and inflammation.

Treatment Unless chapped skin becomes infected or is very slow to heal, you can probably solve the problem with self-help measures. Apply rich emollient creams to your child's skin, use lip salve on his lips, avoid using soap (use baby lotion instead), and dress him warmly in cold weather. Avoid icy winds and sudden changes in temperature. Infected chapped skin should be treated by your doctor.

CHILBLAINS

Children who are sensitive to cold may get chilblains. Constriction of blood vessels in the skin is a normal reaction to cold, but in a cold-sensitive child the fine network of blood vessels beneath the skin may overconstrict, and then overdilate when your child returns to a warm environment. Where overdilatation occurs, a bump will form in the skin.

Symptoms A chilblain is a red or purple lump of any size. The main symptom is intense itchiness when the body starts to warm up after exposure to cold. Chilblains usually occur on the feet, the backs of the lower legs, the hands, the tip of the nose, and the edges of the ears.

Treatment Chilblains, although irritating, are not serious and usually heal themselves if kept warm. Your doctor may prescribe a vasodilator cream if they are causing your child a great deal of pain. It works by causing the blood vessels beneath the skin to remain open in the cold, thus improving circulation. A simple application of talcum powder or calamine lotion can often alleviate itchiness and discourage your child from scratching.

If you know your child is susceptible to chilblains make sure that he is dressed warmly when he goes out in cold weather, paying particular attention to the vulnerable areas of the body. As damp conditions increase the likelihood of getting chilblains, make sure that he has waterproof clothing to wear in wet weather.

COLD SORES

The virus responsible for cold sores is called herpes simplex and is a relative of chicken pox and shingles. All sufferers from cold sores carry the virus in their skin, where it lies dormant in the nerve endings. The virus is transmitted from parent to child during kissing. A rise in skin temperature due to intense sunlight, flu, a cold, stress, or overexertion can reactivate the virus and result in a cold sore. Cold sores are not usually harmful except near the eye where, rarely, they can cause ulceration of the conjunctiva (the transparent covering of the white of the eye).

Symptoms There is usually warning of an attack in the form of a hot, itchy, tingling sensation for 24 hours before the cold sore appears. The skin becomes red and then tiny blisters appear, usually around the lips or the nostrils. The blisters enlarge, join up, and then burst, revealing the classic cold sore. Fluid from the blisters then forms a crust, which gradually shrinks and falls off as the skin underneath heals. This takes 10–14 days. While a cold sore is at the blister and weeping stage it will be very painful and your child may complain of pain over the whole side of the face, earache, and pain when she chews because the facial nerves are inflamed by the virus.

Cold sores are very contagious, and your child can spread them to other parts of her face by touching them with her fingers.

Treatment Your doctor will give you an anti-viral cream to be applied every two or three hours as soon as the skin begins to tingle. This will prevent future cold sores from developing into their full-blown form. He may prescribe an antibiotic cream if the cold sore becomes infected.

Discourage your child from touching his face, from kissing other children, and from sharing his flannel and towel for the duration of an attack. Applying petroleum jelly may stop a cold sore from cracking and bleeding. Surgical spirit may help to dry the sore out, but it stings and I don't approve of its use on children.

It's helpful to identify the triggers that bring on your child's cold-sore attacks. For instance, if it is strong sunlight, your child should wear a high protection sunblock around his lips in summer.

BOILS

When a hair follicle becomes infected a red pus-filled swelling can result. Boils are rarely serious if they are treated appropriately, but they can cause pain, particularly if they are in an uncomfortable place such as the armpit or buttock. Boils rarely heal by themselves, and left untreated can form a carbuncle (a cluster of several boils).

Symptoms Initially the skin is red and swollen. As the swelling increases yellow pus collects beneath the skin. Boils usually appear singly, but, because hair follicles are so close together, it's possible for infection to spread and for a crop of boils to appear.

Treatment Consult your doctor if your child has several boils, if there are signs that the infection is spreading, if the boil is causing severe pain; or if it has not burst after a couple of days. Your doctor may decide to lance the boil to drain the pus away, which provides immediate pain relief. Crops of boils require antibiotics and investigation of the cause.

Don't try to burst or squeeze a boil at home; this will be excruciatingly painful and will spread infection. Instead, dab the affected area with surgical spirit or antiseptic and cover with a gauze dressing.

Infected follicle

Healthy follicle

Boil
A bacterial infection causes a pus-filled painful red lump.

IMPETIGO

The bacteria staphylococcus, which is present in the nose and on the skin, can sometimes cause a skin infection around the nose, mouth, and ears and elsewhere. Impetigo is characterized by a bright yellow, crusted rash or small pus-filled blisters; it is highly contagious and you should keep your child away from school until it has cleared.

Symptoms The first sign of impetigo is reddened skin. This is followed by the appearance of blisters full of pus, which burst leaving patches of oozing skin. The fluid dries into a yellow crust. Impetigo spreads rapidly if left untreated.

Treatment Take your child to see the doctor, who will prescribe an antiobiotic cream and dressings to keep the skin covered, and possibly antibiotic tablets. Be meticulous about hygiene – wash away crusted areas with warm water and pat dry with a paper towel. Use disposable flannels and towels to protect the rest of the family from infection.

INFANTILE ECZEMA

This inflammatory skin condition is caused by an inherited tendency plus a trigger factor such as an allergy or an infection. Occasionally it is simply a response to stress. The type of eczema that usually affects children is atopic eczema and it appears between two and eighteen months of age.

Seborrhoeic eczema can also affect children. This occurs on the scalp, eyelids, around the nose, ears, groin, and ear canal, where there are a lot of sebaceous (sebum-secreting) glands.

Symptoms Skin affected by atopic eczema is raw, dry, scaly, red, and itchy, and there may be small white blisters, like grains of rice, that burst and weep if scratched. Seborrhoeic eczema looks similar to atopic eczema but is less itchy and occurs in quite different places (see right). Itchiness is the most irritating symptom of eczema, causing severe scratching and sleeplessness.

Treatment If you suspect your child has eczema see your doctor, who may prescribe an anti-inflammatory cream and anthistamines to curb itching and combat any allergy. If the skin is infected antibiotics may be necessary. Your doctor will also try to identify the cause of the eczema: a pet, washing powder, or food, for example.

Affected area
Atopic eczema (above)
typically occurs on the
face, hands, neck, ankles,
and knee and elbow
creases. The grey areas
indicate the usual sites of
seborrhoeic eczema.

Keep contact with water to a minimum, and if you have to bathe your child, put unguent emulsificants in the bath. Stop using soap, and make sure that clothes are thoroughly rinsed and contain no trace of washing powder or fabric conditioner. Minimize your child's contact with potential allergens, use emollient cream on his skin, and keep his fingernails short so that he cannot damage the skin by scratching. Use cotton fabrics, never wool.

DERMATITIS

This is an inflammation of the skin that occurs in response to stress, to an allergy such as nickel sensitivity (contact dermatitis), or occasionally to light (photodermatitis). Seborrhoeic dermatitis (or seborrhoeic eczema, see p.290) affects the face, especially the nostrils, eyebrows and eyelids, and scalp.

Symptoms Dermatitis, no matter what type, is a red, itchy, and scaly rash, sometimes with blisters. In contact dermatitis the rash usually appears where the skin has been in contact with the allergen. Photodermatitis appears as clusters of spots or blisters on skin that has been exposed to the sun.

Treatment If dermatitis is very severe your doctor may prescribe a weak steroid cream. Make sure that your child keeps the affected areas clean, doesn't scratch them, and doesn't expose them to defatting agents such as soaps and detergent.

HEAT RASH

A hot, poorly ventilated environment in which the skin can't cool encourages heat rash; the body responds by sweating excessively and the sweat glands become enlarged and red. Heat rash is quite common in babies as their sweat glands are primitive and can't switch off as ours can.

Symptoms A faint red rash appears on parts of the body which get hot easily and where sweat glands are most numerous. Typical areas include the neck, the face, and skin folds such as the groin, elbows, and behind the knees.

Treatment Don't over-dress or swaddle your baby. Bathe him in tepid water and pat him dry, leaving his skin slightly damp. Make sure the temperature of his room is not too high and keep air circulating by opening a window slightly. Consult your doctor only if the rash has not cleared up after 12 hours to exclude other possible causes.

SUNBURN

Spending too much time in the sun or being exposed to sunlight that is too intense can cause sunburn. All children should be protected by a high-factor sunscreen, a hat, and clothes. If your child is fair-skinned or unused to being in the sun you should be especially cautious about letting him play outdoors. Children should be gradually acclimatized to sun, especially if abroad (see p.147). Although sunburn can be painful it is not generally serious unless it leads to heatstroke (see p.340). In the long term, however, sunburn can lead to skin cancer, particularly in fair-skinned people.

RASHES

Infectious diseases like chickenpox, German measles, or measles, as well as allergies and blood disorders may all cause rashes.

A rash may be discrete or blotchy, flat or bumpy, it may disappear on pressure or not, and it may contain blisters. If your child has a rash, check to see if he has a fever (this may indicate an infectious disease), and consider whether he has been exposed to any potential allergens (see p.292). An itchy rash between his fingers may indicate scabies.

A rash which doesn't disappear on pressure, such as purpura, is nearly always serious and can result from a fault in the blood clotting mechanism or from bacterial toxins, as in meningitis. You can spot purpura by pressing a drinking glass to your child's skin to see if the rash remains visible through it. If it does, see your doctor immediately.

Symptoms The affected skin is hot, inflamed, red, and tender. Sometimes the skin looks "bubbly" and blistered. After a few days the dead skin will flake and peel, at which point your child may complain of itchiness. If sunburn is severe, particularly on the back of the neck, look out for symptoms of heatstroke: fever, vomiting, and dizziness, and if they are present, seek medical help immediately.

Treatment Immediate relief can come from applying calamine lotion and cold sheets or towels to the affected areas. Paracetamol elixir may also be helpful to keep your child's temperature normal. Treat sunburnt skin very gently; let your child go without clothes indoors, and cover the skin with loose-fitting clothes and bare skin with total sunblocks if he is going outdoors. A hat should cover the nape of the neck. Your doctor may prescribe an anti-inflammatory cream for sunburn.

WARTS AND VERRUCAE

Warts may occur singly or in great numbers. Most disappear without treatment after two years. There are more than 30 different types of wart virus. Children usually get common warts on the hands or areas subject to injury, such as the knees, and verrucae, which are warts on the soles of the feet. Although contagious, warts are not at all serious.

Symptoms Common warts, such as those found on the hands, appear as firm, flesh-coloured or brown growths. They are composed of dead skin cells. Although they may look unsightly, common warts should not be painful unless cracked and bleeding. Verrucae are flat warts on the sole of the foot. Unlike other warts, they may be very painful because they are pressed into the sole of the foot.

Treatment Unless warts are painful, unsightly, or at risk of being passed on to other children, don't worry since they may disappear spontaneously. If you do decide to treat a wart at home, there are several products available over the counter in pharmacies. Never use these on the face or the genitals, as they are too harsh and can scar delicate skin. If you consult your doctor, he may refer your child to a wart clinic to have the warts or verrucae removed. If you suspect that your child has genital warts consult your doctor straight away. Verrucae should be kept covered at all times to prevent them from being passed on to others.

ALLERGIES

An allergy is an abnormal response of the immune system to a specific chemical or substance. The most common form is hay fever – an allergy to pollen, but children may be allergic to a range of things, from foods and plants to light and drugs.

URTICARIA (HIVES)

An allergic skin rash which takes the form of itchy, raised red blotches with white centres, urticaria is most commonly caused by a nettle sting (nettle rash), but can be the result of an allergy. Histamine (a chemical found in cells throughout the body) is released in response to contact with an allergen or nettles and it causes fluid to leak into the skin from the blood vessels, leading to the typical weal. Newborn babies sometimes have an urticaria rash (see p.14).

Symptoms The skin is extremely itchy and there are raised white lumps (weals) surrounded by a flare of inflammation. The weals are small and circular or large irregular patches. The rash usually appears on the limbs and the trunk, although it can appear anywhere on the body. Urticaria lasts a few minutes, disappears, and then reappears at a different site. It can be accompanied by facial swelling (angioedema) which is a reason to consult your doctor without delay. Occasionally urticaria can affect the mouth, tongue, and throat, and cause difficulties with breathing (anaphylaxis). This should always be treated as an emergency.

Urticaria rash
Raised white lumps form, surrounded by inflammation. Sometimes these join together forming large patches on the skin.

Treatment Apply calamine lotion to your child's skin or give her a coolish bath. Your doctor may prescribe antihistamine tablets. With anaphylaxis your child should be taken to hospital, where she may be given an adrenalin injection.

HAY FEVER
(ACUTE ALLERGIC RHINITIS)

When the mucous membranes are exposed to an allergen (usually pollen) they become inflamed and the child suffers the symptoms of allergic rhinitis (see below). The condition usually occurs in the spring and summer months when the pollen count is high. Hay fever is relatively unusual under the age of five, it tends to run in families, and it may disappear spontaneously.

Symptoms Hay fever symptoms include sneezing, a runny nose, and red, itchy, watery eyes. Hay fever is distinguishable from a common cold in that it is seasonal and there is no fever.

Treatment It is impossible to prevent your child being exposed to the allergen unless you stop her going outside in the summer months. However, you can note the pollen count each day and discourage your child from playing outside if it is high.

Your doctor may carry out skin tests to identify the allergen and give a course of desensitizing injections or prescribe an antihistamine and a steroid nasal spray if her symptoms are severe.

CHRONIC ALLERGIC RHINITIS

Chronic or perennial allergic rhinitis is just like hay fever, but happens all year round. It starts in the same way as hay fever (see above) but the culprit is usually house-dust mite rather than pollen. Other causes are feathers and cat and dog fur.

Symptoms The symptoms of chronic or perennial allergic rhinitis are the same as those of hay fever – runny nose, watering of the eyes, itchy nose and eyes. Diagnosis is confirmed by skin tests.

Treatment The most effective treatment is avoidance of the allergen or allergens, which show up in skin tests. You may have to get rid of a favourite pet, change bedding or vacuum clean frequently.

Antihistamines and other drugs help prevent symptoms occurring. Intra-nasal steroids, given in very small, safe doses, often bring rapid relief.

PHOTOSENSITIVITY

This condition is an allergy to light, or rather to certain wavelengths of light. A very rare form is inherited, but more commonly photosensitivity is caused by swallowing a photosensitizing substance or applying it to the skin. Examples of such substances are some drugs, dyes, chemicals, and plants.

Symptoms Photosensitivity usually shows as a rash, easily distinguishable because the skin which is covered by clothes is free of inflammation and there is a clear line demarcating the skin which has been exposed to sunshine.

Treatment The photosensitizer and/or sunlight should be avoided until the rash clears. A susceptible child should cover up and wear total sunblock.

FLEA BITES

Children quite often get one flea bite, develop an allergy to it and then come out in a crop of spots that resemble the first bite. These spots may be mistaken for more bites but are in fact an allergic rash which is very itchy but will subside in 10–14 days.

Treatment The family cat or dog will have to be sprayed for fleas. You will also have to spray any carpets or soft furnishings, which may harbour flea eggs. Your doctor may prescribe an antihistamine medicine to contain the itching and scratching.

DRUGS

The commonest drug allergy is to penicillin or any of its derivatives. Once diagnosed, your child should wear a bracelet or medallion stating he is allergic to penicillin so that he won't be given it again. Any drug at any time, however, can cause an allergy, particularly if there's a family history of allergies, eczema, and asthma. The worst form of drug allergy is anaphylaxis, in which blood pressure drops and the tongue and throat may swell up; it requires emergency treatment.

Symptoms A rash appears up to ten days after exposure to the drug, possibly with swelling of the face and tongue. In severe cases there may be problems with breathing, vomiting, and diarrhoea.

Treatment For mild allergies antihistamines are usually sufficient. Once a drug is identified as an allergen it must be avoided for life.

COLDS AND INFLUENZA

Infections with cold or flu viruses are common in childhood because children have not yet developed immunity to specific viruses. There are roughly 200 cold viruses producing similar symptoms – your child will never get the same cold twice.

COMMON COLD

Colds are not serious unless your baby is very young, or a complication such as bronchitis (see opposite) sets in. Colds are more frequent when your child starts nursery school, because she's suddenly exposed to lots of new viruses.

Symptoms Most cold viruses start with "catarrhal" symptoms (blocked or runny nose, cough, sore throat), fever, and listlessness. The nasal discharge is first clear and then thick and yellow as the body's defences take over. The rise in temperature that accompanies a cold can cause cold sores (see p.289), hence their name.

Treatment Only symptoms can be treated, not the virus itself; there's no cure for the common cold. If a secondary infection such as sinusitis or bronchitis supervenes, then your doctor will prescribe antibiotics; otherwise, home remedies suffice. Give your child plenty of fluids, encourage her to blow her nose frequently, showing her how to clear one nostril at a time, and apply petroleum jelly to her nostrils and top lip if they become sore or chapped. When congestion is severe, make sure that she sleeps with her head propped up with pillows, and try applying a menthol rub to her chest. Your doctor will prescribe nose drops if a blocked nose interferes with sleeping or feeding. Paracetamol elixir reduces the temperature and eases aches and pains.

SINUSITIS

The sinuses are cavities in the bones around the nose and cheeks and above the eyes, and are lined with mucous membranes. Mucus usually drains from them into the nose. Sinusitis occurs when drainage is impaired, usually with a cold or flu or if an infection spreads to the sinuses from the throat.

Clearing the sinuses
Get your child to inhale dissolved menthol crystals in boiling water. Cover his head with a towel to keep the vapours in.

Symptoms Nasal secretions are clear and runny at first with a cold. A change to a thick, yellow discharge is normal, but if it is persistent, sinusitis has probably developed. Other symptoms include a feeling of fullness and discomfort around the top of the nose, headache, diminished sense of smell, blocked nose, and sometimes fever.

Treatment Sinusitis can be treated with antibiotics, decongestants, and nose drops. At home, keep the atmosphere humid, prepare menthol inhalations for your child, and give her paracetamol elixir if she complains of pain in her face and forehead.

INFLUENZA

This is a viral infection similar to the common cold but it produces more severe symptoms. Influenza, or flu, can be very debilitating, and is potentially serious because it can weaken the body and make the ears, sinuses, and chest vulnerable to secondary infections by bacteria.

Symptoms Flu symptoms resemble cold symptoms, but in addition to the usual sore throat, runny nose, and cough, your child will have quite a high temperature, a headache, and backache, and she may complain of feeling hot, cold, and shivery. She will be lethargic and weak, and may feel nauseous.

Treatment The only remedies available for flu are symptomatic ones. Let your child rest in a warm, ventilated room, and give her paracetamol elixir and plenty of fluids. Take your child's temperature regularly – if it fails to come down, call your doctor. A persistent yellow nasal discharge (sinusitis) or earache (ear infection) requires medical help.

CHEST INFECTIONS

In very young children the air passages, the sinuses, ear, nose, and throat are really all one system because the tubes are so short. A chest infection can therefore develop from an infection elsewhere in the upper respiratory tract. Chest infections are always serious. The airways may become so narrow that breathing is impaired and pneumonia may develop. If your child's breathing is ever laboured you should seek medical help immediately.

COUGHS

The cough is a reflex action that clears the throat of any irritant such as mucus, food, dust, or smoke. A cough may be due to the irritation of a cold, sore throat, tonsillitis, or sinusitis. The cause should always be treated, not just the cough alone which is merely a symptom of an underlying condition.

Symptoms There are two types of cough: a productive cough, in which phlegm is produced, and a non-productive cough, in which there is no phlegm. The first has a "wet" sound, while the second is dry and hacking. Both will prevent sleep. In a small baby, mucus running down the back of the throat can cause vomiting. A cough may also be a nervous symptom. If a cough is hacking or croaking your child may have croup (see p.296). Coughing can be so distressing as to cause vomiting.

Treatment If you suspect that your child has croup (see p.296) or asthma (see p.260) you should seek medical help straight away. An underlying chronic infection like sinusitis or tonsillitis should be treated separately. As long as they don't stop your child from sleeping or eating, most other coughs can be treated at home. Discourage your child from running around, as breathlessness may bring on a coughing fit, and get her to lie on her stomach or side at night; this prevents mucus running down the throat. Give your child plenty of warm drinks, and if she is coughing up lots of phlegm use an expectorant elixir, and lay her over your lap and pat her on the back. Suppress a dry cough, but never suppress a productive cough.

Respiration
Air flows from the trachea through the bronchi to the bronchioles. Finally oxygen enters the blood via tiny vessels called alveoli.

Trachea
Bronchus
Bronchiole

BRONCHITIS AND BRONCHIOLITIS

The larger airways in the lungs are called the bronchi and the smaller are called the bronchioles. Bronchitis or bronchiolitis occur when a bacterial or viral infection causes the linings of these airways to swell and mucus to build up. The two can appear the same, but bronchiolitis is more serious because it can cause severe breathing difficulties and pneumonia may develop. Bronchiolitis is most common in babies and very young children. Bronchitis is not usually serious in children over a year old.

Symptoms Your child is pale and limp, and seems quite ill. The symptoms of bronchiolitis are a cough, laboured breathing, a raised temperature, a bluish complexion, and indrawing of the chest in the struggle to get air into the lungs. The symptoms of bronchitis are a dry cough that develops into a cough producing green or yellow phlegm, laboured breathing, raised temperature, and possibly loss of appetite. If phlegm is swallowed your child may vomit it up. Blue lips and tongue may indicate a severe infection or even pneumonia (see p.296).

Treatment You should consult your doctor if you suspect that your child has a lung infection. He will prescribe antibiotics as necessary. Laboured breathing and a grey or blue complexion should always be treated in hospital, where your child will be put in an oxygen tent to help her breathe.

Keep your child warm and rested, give plenty of fluids, and encourage her to cough up the phlegm. If she has a fever, sponge her down with tepid water (see p.281) and give her paracetamol elixir to keep her temperature down. Don't give her a cough suppressant as it is important to bring up the phlegm.

PNEUMONIA

This is a severe and serious inflammation of the lungs, caused by a virus or bacterium. Your child will be ill for two reasons: first because of the bacterial or viral toxins, and second because the affected lung is out of action. The initial cause of pneumonia is often a cold or flu. Conditions like asthma, cystic fibrosis, whooping cough, and measles increase the risk of pneumonia. Pneumonia is always serious and small children are often treated in hospital because oxygen is needed.

Symptoms Your child will be very ill and pale and he will find it difficult to breathe. Fever, chills, indrawing of the chest, pale damp skin, and a weak pulse are all classic symptoms.

Treatment Laboured breathing is always a reason for you to seek medical advice urgently. You should consult your doctor straight away if you suspect your child has pneumonia. Your doctor will prescribe antibiotics and may decide that immediate hospitalization is necessary if your child is in need of oxygen therapy.

CROUP

When a small child's air passages become inflamed and congested as a result of a cold, breathing can become difficult and croup can result. The croup sound is due to air being drawn in through swollen, inflamed vocal cords in the larynx, usually as a result of a viral upper respiratory infection. Croup usually occurs in children between the ages of one and four years. It can come on suddenly: your apparently well child will wake in the night with croup.

Symptoms The predominant symptom is a barking cough, accompanied by wheeziness. In severe cases your child may be fighting for breath and his face may turn grey or blue. Attacks occur at night and are often short-lived.

Treatment Stay calm. If your child is upset his breathing will become even more laboured. Make sure the air around your child is damp – get him to lean out of a window, or take him to the bathroom and run the hot taps.
   If your child's face turns blue, you must get medical help immediately. Even if croup is mild you should still report it to your doctor, who may prescribe antibiotics for the underlying infection.

PARASITES

Parasites are very contagious, so if your child has lice or worms the whole family should be treated. Inform your child's nursery, playgroup, or school of the infestation, and keep your child at home until it has cleared. Infestations can be uncomfortable, but they're not serious and can be eradicated.

LICE

Nits or head lice are common in children of school age. The louse is a small insect that lives on blood from the scalp, lays eggs, and cements them to the base of the hairs; the eggs become visible as the hair grows. Contrary to the belief that lice are a sign of uncleanliness, head lice prefer clean hair.

Symptoms Your child will complain of an itchy scalp, which feels worse in hot weather. You may see white eggs firmly attached to the hair near the scalp.

Treatment Keep your child away from school so that he cannot pass lice onto others. Several insecticidal shampoos are available over the counter, and kill eggs as well as adult lice: ask your pharmacist to recommend one. After treatment, comb your child's hair with a fine metal comb to remove the dead eggs from the hair shaft. Clean any combs, brushes, or headwear with the anti-louse shampoo. All members of the family should be treated.

Louse and nit

The adult louse lays its eggs (nits) at the root of the hair (right). The eggs become firmly attached and hatch after about two weeks. They can be removed if an anti-louse shampoo is used.

Adult louse

SCABIES

This is an infestation by a microscopic mite that burrows into the skin and lays eggs. Although it is not serious, it can be very itchy, especially at night, and it's highly contagious. A child can get scabies by physical contact with someone suffering from scabies or from infested bedding.

Symptoms The backs of the hands, finger clefts, feet, ankles, and toes are affected by an intensely itchy rash. Burrows are usually visible as grey, scaly trails across the skin with a black pin-head spot (the mite) at the end.

Treatment Your doctor will probably prescribe a lotion to treat scabies. This should stay on for 24 hours and the treatment should be repeated after a day. The whole family should be treated.

Mites can live independently of human skin for up to six days, so you should wash all your clothes and bed linen to prevent re-infection.

Scabies mite
The mite burrows into the skin and the opening of the burrow is visible as a grey, scaly swelling. The classic site of the rash is between the clefts of the fingers. The mite may be visible as a dark spot at the head of the burrow.

Typical site of scabies rash

THREADWORM

Threadworms are extremely common in children, but are not serious and are easily eradicated. If a child eats food containing worm eggs, they will hatch in the intestines. As the larvae mature, the females move down the intestine and lay eggs around the anus. This causes itchiness and a child can easily pick up the eggs on his fingers and transfer them to his mouth, thus beginning the whole cycle of infestation again.

Cycle of infestation
Threadworms enter the body through the mouth and lay eggs around the anus. A child can become re-infested by scratching the anus, then transferring the eggs to her mouth.

Eggs are swallowed and hatch into larvae inside the intestine

Female worms lay eggs around the anus at night causing itching

Eggs are passed from the anus to the mouth via the fingers

Symptoms The most distressing symptom is the intense itchiness around the anal area, which feels worse at night when your child is hot and can prevent him sleeping. There may also be tiny white worms present in the stools.

Treatment If you notice worms in your child's stools or find he's suffering from anal itchiness, consult your doctor, who will prescribe a medication for the whole family. Pay special attention to hygiene: encourage hand-washing often after using the lavatory, keep your child's fingernails short, and get him to wear pants in bed to discourage scratching.

ROUNDWORM

This type of worm is very rare in the West and is usually only brought in by people living in tropical climates, especially in areas where hygiene is poor. The parasite is a cylindrical worm approximately 15–40 centimetres (6–16 inches) long, and enters the body in egg form via contaminated food. Once in the body, the eggs hatch and the worms mature and lay new eggs, which may be passed in the stools.

Symptoms Roundworms inhabit the intestine and produce few or no symptoms. Sometimes the worms may be visible in your child's stools. Where roundworm is endemic it leads to poor growth and a failure to thrive.

Treatment Roundworm is treated with tablets that kill the worm. Laxatives may also be given so that the worms pass quickly and easily in the stools. Scrupulous hygiene is absolutely essential if treatment is to be successful.

AFTER TRAVELLING ABROAD

If you have recently been travelling in the tropics and your child is suffering from persistent diarrhoea he may have contracted amoebic dysentery.

This is caused by an amoeba – a tiny single-celled organism that lives in the large intestine – which is only picked up in tropical countries. It causes serious illness with symptoms such as fever, diarrhoea, and stomach pain. If you suspect amoebic dysentery, take your child and a sample of his stools to the doctor as soon as possible. He will need drugs to get rid of the parasite and possibly rehydration therapy if diarrhoea has been severe.

STOMACH AND ABDOMEN

Babies are affected by few of the conditions that cause abdominal pain in adults, like gallstones and peptic ulcers. Several causes of abdominal pain in infants are, however, potentially very serious so must call your doctor immediately if abdominal pain is accompanied by a temperature, diarrhoea, or vomiting.

Any tension in the house, between parents, between siblings, or at school can cause a child to feel nauseous, vomit, and suffer abdominal pain. When all other causes have been eliminated stress should be considered. Ask your doctor for advice.

COLIC

This type of abdominal pain usually occurs in the first four months of life, then clears spontaneously without treatment. It's thought to be due to spasm of the intestines, though there is no proof of this and the cause remains unknown. The condition is harmless, though distressing for parents.

Symptoms Your baby, who is otherwise well, will have bouts of pain when he screams and draws his legs up towards his abdomen.

Treatment No drugs are needed. Your baby may be soothed by any rhythmic activity such as rocking, swaying, being taken in the car for a ride, or being laid on his tummy on your lap while you rhythmically pat his back.

Often, nothing will calm a colicky baby. The important thing is to remain relaxed yourself. Since colic often occurs at the same time each day, typically in the evening, you should try to plan your day accordingly so as to reduce the stress on you.

GASTROENTERITIS

Inflammation of the stomach and intestine, usually due to bacteria or viruses in contaminated food, causes diarrhoea and vomiting; pain is a lesser symptom. There are various non-infectious forms of gastroenteritis caused by food intolerance, spicy foods, and antibiotics. The complaint is extremely common and fairly mild. It rarely lasts for longer than three days and the child tends to recover without any specific treatment other than replacement of fluid and minerals. A small baby, however, cannot tolerate dehydration, and if he vomits or has diarrhoea for longer than three hours you should contact your doctor without delay.

Symptoms The first symptom is going off feeds, followed by vomiting and colic or possibly diarrhoea. Your baby may become dehydrated in which case the fontanelles of his skull will be sunken (see p.280) and his mouth dry.

Treatment Mild cases can be treated at home by your doctor but if vomiting or diarrhoea continue your baby must be treated in hospital, where fluids will be given intravenously.

INTUSSUSCEPTION

In this rare condition, the intestine telescopes on itself forming a tube within a tube, usually causing a blockage of the intestine, which is very serious. It's commonest at the junction of the small and large intestines. We don't know why this telescoping of the bowel occurs.

Symptoms Your baby may scream intermittently and vomit, and there may be blood and mucus in his stools. The condition may be complicated by a ruptured bowel and peritonitis (inflammation of the lining of the abdomen) if left untreated.

Treatment Sometimes applying pressure to the bowel by giving a barium enema causes the intussusception to unfold. If it doesn't, then in practically all cases surgery is successful. In severe cases a segment of bowel may have to be cut out.

Twisted intestine
A section of the small intestine telescopes on itself, like a finger in a glove being turned inside out. Intussusception is rare, and very serious.

Large intestine

Blockage

Telescoped intestine

Small intestine

APPENDICITIS

Inflammation of the appendix, a small, finger-like sac at the junction of the caecum and the ileum in the small bowel, is a common cause of abdominal pain. The cause is not known, but it may be obstruction by a small piece of faeces or very occasionally by threadworms. The appendix becomes inflamed, swollen, and infected. Appendicitis is not a serious condition as long as it is diagnosed early. However, if the symptoms are mistaken for something else such as constipation, and there is any delay in treatment, the appendix can burst, and an appendix abscess or even peritonitis (inflammation of the abdominal lining) can result.

Symptoms The first symptom is pain around the navel which, after a few hours, shifts to the right lower side of the abdomen where it becomes intense. Your child may have a slight temperature and refuse food. The tongue may become coated and there may be vomiting, diarrhoea, or constipation.

Treatment Consult your doctor immediately. The appendix must be removed before it ruptures. If this is not done soon enough, it will perforate and cause an internal abscess. The abscess must then be drained and the appendix removed after treatment with large doses of antibiotics.

Site of pain
The first symptom of appendicitis is a slight ache in the navel area. This develops into a sharper, more localized pain which is usually most intense in the lower right-hand side of the abdomen.

Initial pain around navel

Sharper pain in lower right side

TYPE OF PAIN	OTHER SYMPTOMS	CAUSE
Sudden pain causing your baby to scream and draw his legs up.	*Common in babies under four months.*	*Colic (see opposite).*
Crippling abdominal pain that causes your baby to scream.	*Blood and mucus in the stools and vomiting.*	*Intussusception (see opposite).*
General mild abdominal pain.	*Vomiting and diarrhoea.*	*Gastroenteritis (see opposite).*
Severe pain near the navel that moves towards the lower right of the abdomen.	*Slight temperature, refusal of food, coated tongue, vomiting.*	*Appendicitis (see above).*
Generalized tummy ache.	*Anxiety, clinginess, tearfulness, aggression, and nausea.*	*Stress (see introduction opposite).*
Sudden crippling pain in the lower abdomen.	*Swelling and pain in the scrotum.*	*Torsion of the testis (see p.301).*
Generalized tummy ache.	*Sore throat, nasal congestion, and slight fever.*	*Throat infection (see p.286), common cold (see p.294), or middle ear infection (see p.284).*
Dull abdominal ache spreading round into the back or down into the groin.	*Pain on urinating, bedwetting when previously dry, and rarely blood in the urine.*	*Urinary tract infection (see p.300).*

UROGENITAL COMPLAINTS

Symptoms such as painful urination or blood in the urine may result from an infection of the bladder, a kidney disorder, or rarely an injury. Correct diagnosis is important in all such complaints so they don't become chronic. The commonest genital emergency is torsion of the testis (see opposite).

URINARY TRACT INFECTION

The urinary tract consists of the kidneys, where urine is produced from water and waste products; the ureters, which carry urine from the kidneys to the bladder; the bladder, which stores urine; and the urethra, which carries urine away from the bladder. The female urethra is much shorter than the male urethra, so bacteria entering the female urethra have a much shorter distance to travel to the bladder, increasing the likelihood of infection.

The most common cause of urinary tract infections is poor hygiene; the main type is cystitis, though only in girls. A tendency to repeated infections can be due to an anatomical abnormality of the urinary tract although this is quite rare.

Preventing infection
Urinary tract infections are usually spread from the rectum via the urethra to the bladder or kidneys. Girls should always wipe from front to back after passing a stool.

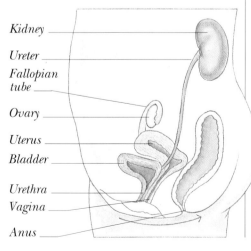

Kidney

Ureter

Fallopian tube

Ovary

Uterus

Bladder

Urethra

Vagina

Anus

Symptoms Urgent, frequent urination is the most prominent symptom of a urinary tract infection. Your child may complain of a burning or stinging sensation at the beginning and end of urine flow. This is due to the bladder muscle contracting down on the inflamed lining. Your child may also pass urine involuntarily, and start to wet the bed again at night. Pain in the lower abdomen and back is common. Severe back pain, fever and chills, refusal to eat, and headache mean your child has a kidney infection and will be very ill. Blood in the urine indicates a severe infection or kidney damage.

Treatment All urinary tract infections require medical treatment. Your doctor will take a sample of urine to confirm the presence of a bacterial infection and find the most suitable antibiotic to treat it. A bladder infection can spread upwards towards the kidneys, but if you seek treatment early on this should not happen.

If your doctor suspects that the urinary tract infection is due to an anatomical abnormality, your child will be referred to a paediatrician for assessment.

Give your child plenty of fluids to keep the bladder flushed out, preferably water with bicarbonate of soda added (one teaspoon to one glass of water) and fruit juice to taste. Encourage your child to urinate as often as possible. Paracetamol elixir and a hot-water bottle on the lower abdomen can help to relieve pain.

Show your daughter how to wipe herself from front to back after passing a stool. If you have a bidet use it every time she passes a motion. For the duration of an attack washing should be very gentle, as the urethra is sensitive.

BALANITIS
This is an inflammation of the foreskin and head of the penis as a result of bacterial infection. The foreskin is nearly always tight. Products such as washing powder can cause irritation and swelling.

Symptoms The glans (tip of the penis) and foreskin are red, swollen, and tender to the touch and you may notice pus coming from inside the opening. Your child won't let you retract his foreskin and he will have pain on passing urine.

Treatment Medical treatment is always necessary or your son could develop a stricture of the foreskin and it will become too tight to retract. Your doctor will give you an antibiotic cream and may suggest circumcision if the foreskin is tight – either now or if it doesn't stretch by the time he's six.

Things you can do yourself include changing nappies frequently, keeping the penis clean, applying antiseptic cream to any soreness, and applying a barrier cream to the entire genital area. Always make sure your child's clothes are thoroughly rinsed to remove any traces of detergent.

UNDESCENDED TESTES

Before a baby boy is born, his testes develop inside his abdomen, and descend into the scrotum (the pouch that hangs below the penis) shortly before birth. Occasionally, one of the testes fails to descend. The testes need to hang outside the body, where the temperature is lower, for efficient sperm production to take place; a testis at body temperature cannot produce sperm. When both testes are undescended their position must be corrected surgically to prevent infertility. A man is fertile with only one testis.

Retractile testes withdraw into the abdomen in response to cold or touch. This is normal in young children, and can persist into adulthood. It does not affect fertility.

Symptoms One or both testes are absent from the scrotum. This condition is otherwise symptomless and will not cause your child any discomfort.

Development of the testicles
In a fetus, the testicles grow inside the abdomen, near the kidneys. Not long before a boy is born, they move downwards into their normal position in the bag of skin called the scrotum.

Testis developing with the kidney

The testis travels to the scrotum from the kidney

The testis may fail to descend into the scrotum

Testis in scrotum

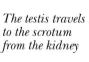

Treatment Often the testes descend during the first year of life. If they do not, corrective surgery may be carried out when your child is older.

TORSION OF THE TESTES

If one of the testes becomes twisted on its stalk the blood supply will be interrupted and it will become red, swollen and very painful. If left untreated the testis could be damaged so you should seek medical treatment straight away.

Symptoms The first symptom is severe pain. Later the testis becomes swollen and tender. Your son could feel sick and may vomit. The scrotum turns red, purple, and blue.

Treatment The testis must be surgically untwisted as soon as possible to restore blood flow. Occasionally, the testis will untwist spontaneously but you mustn't wait for this to happen.

BLOOD IN THE URINE

The medical name for blood in the urine is haematuria. It may be only a streak or sufficient to colour the urine deep red. The cause may be in any part of the urinary tract from the kidneys to the urethra. Cystitis (inflammation of the bladder) and urethritis (inflammation of the urethra) are two common causes. Nephritis (inflammation of the kidneys) is less common but more serious. A child with haemophilia may pass blood in the urine from internal bleeding.

If you notice any blood in your child's urine you should seek medical advice immediately. Although infections such as cystitis are not serious, they cause great discomfort and it's important to stop bacteria spreading from the bladder up to the kidneys.

Symptoms Slight bleeding may be invisible, and found only when urine is examined under a microscope, or when a special diagnostic dip-stick is put into the urine. The symptoms of a urinary tract infection (see opposite) may be present or your child may have a kidney infection or nephritis.

Treatment Since blood in the urine is only a symptom of an underlying disorder, your doctor will perform special tests to determine the cause and treat it. The urine must be cultured to find an infection and urinary tract X-rays performed to find any anatomical abnormalities.

Infectious diseases

An infectious disease is one that is caused by a micro-organism – that is, a bacterium or a virus. The infection is most commonly spread via the air or by direct contact, though it may also be spread via food, water, or insects, particularly in poor conditions. In countries where standards of sanitation are high, appropriate drugs are readily available, and health and nutrition are generally

Mumps
The salivary glands will swell up, changing the shape of your child's face; the swelling may appear on either or both sides of the face, just below the ears or the chin.

Disease	Possible symptoms
Chickenpox A common and mild viral disease.	Red, itchy spots that become fluid-filled blisters and then scabs. Headache and slight fever.
German measles A viral infection, which is usually mild in children.	Small red spots, first behind the ears, then spreading to the face and all over the body, slight fever, and enlarged lymph nodes at the back of the neck.
Mumps A fairly common viral illness which is seldom serious in children.	Tender, swollen glands below the ears and beneath the chin. Fever, headache, dry mouth, and difficulty chewing and swallowing. Less common symptoms are painful testicles in boys and swollen ovaries in girls.
Measles A highly infectious and potentially serious viral illness.	Brownish-red spots appear behind the ears and then spread to the rest of the body. White spots in the mouth (Koplik spots) are the diagnostic sign. The child is feverish, has a runny nose, a cough, and a headache. He may have sore eyes and find it hard to tolerate bright lights.
Whooping cough A bacterial infection that clogs the airways with mucus.	A cough with a distinctive "whoop" sound as the child tries to breathe, common cold symptoms (see p.294), and vomiting. Coughing may stop your child from sleeping.

good, infectious diseases pose far less of a threat than they once did. In addition, many serious infectious diseases have been virtually eliminated in the West by immunization (see p.283). The characteristics of many childhood infectious diseases are similar: a rash on the body, a fever, general malaise, and cold symptoms. If you notice a rash and your child's temperature is raised, consult your doctor. The dangers with most illnesses are that your child may become dehydrated from vomiting or refusing food and drink, have difficulty breathing due to constricted airways, or suffer febrile convulsions (see p.281), and some diseases can lead to complications if left untreated.

TREATMENT

Apply calamine to the rash, keep your child at home, and discourage scratching. Your doctor may prescribe an anti-infective cream.

There is no specific medical treatment. You can give your child paracetamol elixir if he has a fever and you should try and keep him in isolation.

There is no specific medical treatment. You should keep your child away from school, give him paracetamol elixir and plenty of fluids, and liquidize his food.

Keep your child in bed for the duration of the fever, keep him away from school, and give him paracetamol elixir and plenty of fluids. Your doctor may prescribe eye drops for sore eyes and antibiotics for secondary infections.

Your doctor may prescribe antibiotics, and in severe cases your child may need to go to hospital for oxygen therapy and treatment for dehydration. Encourage your child to bring up phlegm by laying her over your lap and patting her back as she coughs, don't let her exert herself, and keep her away from cigarette smoke.

COMPLICATIONS

In very rare cases chickenpox may lead to encephalitis (inflammation of the brain) and, if aspirin is taken, Reye's syndrome, a serious illness whose symptoms are vomiting and fever.

The biggest risk is to pregnant women who come into contact with a child with German measles, since it causes birth defects. There is a slight risk of encephalitis.

Occasionally, meningitis, encephalitis, and pancreatitis. Occasionally, one of the testes is affected, and decreases in size. If both testes are affected, this can lead to infertility, but this occurs very rarely.

Ear and chest infections, vomiting, and diarrhoea may occur a couple of days after the appearance of a rash. There is also a slight risk of pneumonia and encephalitis. The lungs and ears may be permanently damaged if antibiotics aren't given.

The main danger is dehydration due to persistent vomiting. Sometimes a severe attack of whooping cough can damage the lungs and make your child prone to chest infections. Secondary infections, which are rare, include pneumonia and bronchitis.

Applying lotion
The rash that accompanies chickenpox is very itchy. Rub calamine lotion in to soothe the itch; the spots may leave scars if they are scratched vigorously.

DISEASE	POSSIBLE SYMPTOMS
Hepatitis *A viral infection causing inflammation of the liver. There are two types, A and B. Type A is more common in children than B.*	*Loss of appetite, jaundice, and flu symptoms. In severe cases, your child may pass dark brown urine and pale stools.*
Meningitis *An inflammation of the membranes that cover the brain and spinal cord, resulting from a viral or bacterial infection. Epidemics of meningitis are caused by the meningococcus bacterium. The Hib vaccination (see p.283) protects against this form, which is very serious.*	*Fever, stiff neck, lethargy, headache, vomiting, intolerance of bright light, and bulging fontanelle (membranous gaps between the bones in the skull) in children under two. In meningococcal meningitis there may be a purple-red rash (purpura, see **Rashes**, p.291) covering most of the body.*
Scarlet fever *A bacterial infection whose effects are similar to those of tonsillitis, but accompanied by a rash. It is not very common, and rarely serious.*	*Enlarged tonsils and a sore throat, a high temperature (up to 40°C or 104°F), abdominal pains, vomiting, a rash of small spots that starts on the chest then spreads and merges, but does not affect the mouth area, and a furry tongue with red patches.*
Roseola *A relatively rare viral infection whose symptoms resemble those of scarlet fever.*	*A fever with a temperature of 39–40°C (102.2–104°F) for about three days. After this red or pink spots on the trunk, limbs, and neck appear. The rash fades after about 48 hours.*
Diphtheria *A serious and highly contagious bacterial infection. It is now very rare because of widespread inoculation.*	*The tonsils are enlarged and may be covered by a grey membrane. Your child may have a mild fever, a cough, a sore throat, breathing difficulties, and headaches.*
Tuberculosis *A highly infectious bacterial infection which most commonly affects the lungs, but can also affect the kidneys, meninges, joints, bones and pelvis if long-term.*	*Persistent coughing (with blood and pus in the sputum if the lungs are affected), chest pain, shortness of breath, fever (especially at night), poor appetite, weight loss, and tiredness.*

Checking the throat
Use a spoon or spatula to hold your child's tongue down while you check his throat. Enlarged tonsils and a sore throat may be symptoms of scarlet fever.

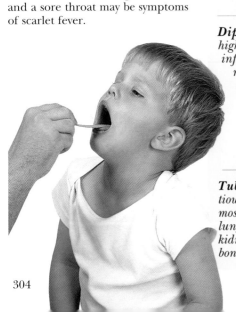

TREATMENT

Your child should be isolated and rest in bed for at least two weeks. Be meticulous about hygiene – hepatitis is highly contagious – and give her plenty of fluids. If she won't eat, add a spoonful of glucose to her drinks.

Intravenous antibiotics are used to treat bacterial meningitis, and painkilling drugs relieve the symptoms of viral meningitis. If a purple rash appears on the skin, your child should be taken straight to hospital.

Your doctor may prescribe antibiotics. Home treatment includes giving your child plenty of fluids and liquidizing food to make it easier to eat. Give paracetamol elixir to lower temperature.

Keep your child rested and sponge her down with tepid water to reduce her fever. Give paracetamol elixir to lower her temperature.

Diphtheria is very serious because of the possibility of breathing difficulties and your child should be hospitalized immediately. She will be given strong antibiotics and she may need a tracheostomy to help her to breathe – that is, a small tube will be inserted into the windpipe to bypass the blockage in the throat.

Tuberculosis is a serious disease if left untreated but is rare nowadays due to widespread immunization. The disease can usually be treated at home. Your doctor will prescribe antibiotics.

COMPLICATIONS

Some children suffer post-hepatitis symptoms for up to six months. These may include moodiness and lethargy.

Viral meningitis is not usually serious and clears up within a week. Bacterial meningitis is potentially fatal because of the risk of meningococcal septicaemia, and so should always be treated as a medical emergency.

If your child is sensitive to the streptococcus bacterium it may cause complications, including nephritis (inflammation of the kidneys) and rheumatic fever (inflammation of the joints and heart). These are rare.

If your child's temperature is very high, she may have febrile convulsions (see p.281).

Without treatment diphtheria can cause other serious complications: pneumonia and heart failure.

The main possible complications of tuberculosis of the lungs are pleural effusion (collection of fluid between the lung and chest wall) and pneumothorax (air between the lung and chest wall).

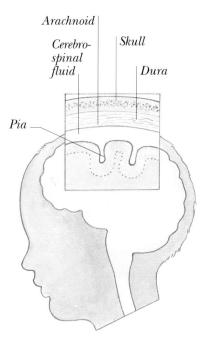

Arachnoid *Skull*
Cerebro-spinal fluid *Dura*
Pia

Meningitis
The three membranes that cover the brain and spinal cord – dura, arachnoid and pia – are called the meninges. Inflammation of the meninges results in meningitis.

SAFETY

Many apparently innocuous household items are dangerous to children. Every year a large number of children are admitted to hospital because they have fallen from windows, burned themselves on cookers or been scalded by hot drinks, choked on small objects, or swallowed household chemicals. Your child is naturally adventurous and inquisitive, and it is all too easy for you to underestimate the dangers presented to him as he explores his environment, especially in the light of his developing mobility and manipulative abilities.

FALLS

The causes of accidents from falling vary according to the age of the child. Babies under the age of one are most likely to fall from a pram or a pushchair, or from a raised surface, such as a table top, whereas children aged between one and four are more likely to tumble down stairs, fall out of windows, or topple off play equipment.

You can minimize the risk of your child's falling by careful supervision – make sure you never leave your baby unattended on a raised surface – and by making a few changes in your home, such as installing window locks and safety gates on the stairs. Check that the railings on balconies and banisters are no more than 10 centimetres (4 inches) apart or your child may fall through or get his head stuck between the rails. If you do not have a harness for your baby's high chair, pram, or pushchair, you should buy one. A built-in harness may not be adequate. Full harnesses are available from department stores and baby shops – look for one that is easy to fasten and adjust. Make sure you buy one and *use* it.

WINDOWS AND DOORS

The types of accidents associated with windows and doors include falling out of an open window, being cut by broken glass, and getting limbs and fingers trapped in closing doors. Various door slam protectors are available which prevent fingers being trapped in closing doors. The glass that is usually used for doors and windows is particularly dangerous as it breaks into long, sharp shards. Safety glass, on the other hand, is less likely to break and when it does break it does not form sharp pieces. Laminated

SAFETY EQUIPMENT

Smoke alarms
Your home should be protected with smoke alarms on each level. These alarms are inexpensive and easy to fit. They must be attached to the ceiling, not a wall, to be totally effective.

Light shows if battery is working

Fire extinguisher and blanket
The kitchen is the most likely place for a fire to start, so you should keep firefighting equipment there. Extinguishers need to be checked regularly for pressure, and may need to be replaced annually.

A dry powder extinguisher is most suitable for kitchens

Safety locks
Make sure that windows remain firmly closed, or can be opened only a little way, especially on upper storeys.

A mortice bolt can only be opened with a key

Stair gates
These can be installed at the top or bottom of the stairs. The bars should be vertical so that your child can't climb on them, and the gate should have a childproof lock.

An adjustable gate will fit most stair widths

glass stays in one piece when it is broken, and toughened glass shatters into small rounded pieces. A cheaper option is to use safety film but this can only be used on unpatterned glass that is completely flat, and, once applied, cannot be removed.

To prevent your child falling out of a window you can install window locks that only allow the window to open by 10 centimetres (4 inches). If you do this you will need to work out how you would escape from the window in an emergency – consider taping the key to part of the window frame.

FIRE SAFETY

House fires can be fatal if you or your child inhale smoke and toxic fumes. Fortunately, there are lots of ways that you can minimize the likelihood of a fire and lessen the damage that it can do.

- Don't smoke indoors.

- Don't leave pans containing hot fat unattended.

- Keep flammable liquids locked away.

- Use fireguards on any open or gas fire.

- Store matches out of your child's reach.

- Buy flame-resistant furniture.

- Replace fire extinguishers every year.

- Keep a dry powder extinguisher and a fire blanket in the kitchen.

- Fit smoke alarms, and check regularly that the batteries are working.

- Smother a chip pan fire with a fire blanket, damp cloth, or pan lid.

BURNS AND SCALDS

Scalds occur when a child is exposed to hot liquids – they usually affect the face, neck, chest, and arms. As a child gets older and his hand-eye coordination improves he will be able to pull saucepans, mugs, and kettles containing hot liquids off work surfaces. Another cause of scalding is putting a baby in water that is too hot, or leaving him unsupervised in a bathroom where there is a bath or sink full of hot water. A child can be scalded by less water, at a lower temperature, than an adult.

A good way to avoid scalds is to turn your hot water thermostat down to 54°C (129°F). At this temperature scalding will only start to occur after 30 seconds of exposure. When running a bath for your child put the cold water in first and then add the hot water afterwards; don't leave a young child unsupervised in the bathroom.

In the kitchen you can prevent your child pulling things off work surfaces by making sure that there are no trailing flexes. Try to buy coiled flexes for your kettle and iron or shorten the existing flex and use hooks to prevent trailing flexes. After you have finished with a mug, kettle, or pan full of hot fluid, empty it immediately. Fit a guard to your cooker, and, when cooking on the hob, use the back rings in preference to the front ones and always keep saucepan handles turned in.

ELECTRICAL SAFETY

Make your child aware of the dangers of electricity and cover unused sockets with heavy furniture or with socket covers. These are dummy plugs made of plastic that prevent your child from sticking his fingers or objects into the socket. Avoid brightly coloured socket covers, as these will only serve to attract your child's attention.

POISONOUS SUBSTANCES

Children aged between one and three years are most prone to accidental poisoning because they learn how to climb and open cupboards. Before the age of 18 months children cannot tell by taste whether something is likely to be bad for them. Common household poisons include bleach, paraffin, disinfectant, detergents, medications such as antidepressants and tranqillizers, and painkillers such as aspirin and paracetamol. Fortunately, only one in 500 incidents of accidental poisoning has very serious consequences.

Poisoning is largely preventable. You should keep all drugs and household chemicals in a high place out of reach of your child, or preferably in a locked cupboard. When using them, watch your child the whole time – this is when most accidents happen. Both prescribed and proprietary drugs should be kept in bottles with child-resistant lids – avoid taking medicines out of their original containers – and out-of-date or unused drugs should be thrown away.

Household chemicals, such as bleach, should also be stored in an inaccessible place, and you should never put chemicals into bottles that are familiar or attractive to children, such as lemonade bottles. Keep pet food bowls away from children, as they can harbour bacteria, and don't keep toxic plants or flowers, such as daffodils and irises, in the house.

SAFETY AT HOME

There are some general rules that apply to all rooms of the house. These include avoiding having trailing flexes, loose carpets, rugs, and flammable items of furniture, and choosing furniture that is child-friendly – for example, avoid tables with sharp corners. Keep all electric plug sockets covered, and have windows fitted with window locks. Teach your child from an early age that hot things such as fires and ovens are dangerous and that she should never go near them, but maintain safety precautions until your child is at least three years old.

When your child visits other people's homes, scan the room for potential dangers. If you are in a house where there are no children, carry out a quick check for breakable items, heavy ornaments that can be pulled off surfaces, open, low-level windows, and sharp objects.

KITCHEN

- Fit a guard to the cooker and always point sauce pan handles towards the back of the cooker.

- Keep matches out of your child's reach and fit a smoke alarm.

- Set the hot water thermostat to a maximum of 54°C (129°F) – at this temperature it will take half a minute for serious scalding to occur.

- Keep plastic bags out of reach.

- Store sharp knives and cutlery in a drawer with a child lock fitted.

- Don't use tablecloths . Your toddler can pull them and everything on the table on to her head.

- Don't leave hot pans or mugs containing hot drinks around.

- If you spill fat or liquid on the floor, mop it up straight away.

- Turn your washing machine and dishwasher off at the mains. Remove dangerous parts.

- If you are not using the iron, put both the iron and the ironing board away. Never leave your child unattended if the iron is on.

- Keep bowls of pet food out of reach to avoid bacterial infection.

- Never leave your child unattended while he is eating – he could choke.

HALL AND STAIRS

- Install a safety gate at the top and the bottom of the stairs.

- Don't leave objects lying on the stairs.

- The stairway should be protected on both sides by walls or banisters.

- The gaps between the banisters should not be more than 10 centimetres (4 inches) wide so your child can't get an arm or a leg caught in them.

- Stair carpets should fit the stairs exactly so that your child can't trip on them.

- Mend any loose or frayed carpet on the stairs without delay.

- Make sure that it is impossible for your child to get out of the front door and run into the street.

DANGERS IN THE HOME

Your child could pull a tablecloth on top of herself

Remove all harmful plants

Never leave objects on the stairs

BATHROOM

- Store medicines in a locked cabinet or on a high shelf and throw away unused or old medicines.

- Keep disinfectants and bleach locked away in their original containers, preferably with child-resistant tops, and make sure they are always out of reach while you are using them.

- Never leave a child alone with a filled bath.

- When preparing your child's bath always add hot water to cold, never the other way round.

- Use non-slip mats in the bath.

- Keep the lavatory lid closed.

- Fix heated towel rails out of your child's reach.

BEDROOM

- Cot toys should not have strings that are longer than 30 centimetres (1 foot).

- Never leave your baby with the cot side down.

- Never leave your baby alone on the changing table, even for a second.

- Put window locks on windows.

- Avoid lights with trailing flexes.

- Cot bars should not be too widely spaced (over 6 centimetres or 2 1/2 inches apart), as your child could get part of her body stuck between them.

- Don't use a pillow in your baby's cot until she's one year old.

- Choose furniture with rounded corners.

- Don't leave gas or electric fires on when your child is on her own.

LIVING ROOM

- When you replace the glass in patio doors choose laminated glass or toughened glass.

- Use a floor-standing or wall-mounted fireguard in front of the fire but always make sure that it's securely fitted to the wall. Don't put cups, mugs, or ashtrays on the fireguard.

- Use socket covers to stop your child poking objects into plug sockets.

- Avoid trailing flexes from lights, TV, stereo, and video equipment.

- Avoid poisonous houseplants (see p.311).

- Don't leave alcohol, cigarettes, matches, or lighters lying around.

- Keep fragile, breakable items out of reach.

- Don't place hot or heavy objects on low tables.

- All shelving should be securely fixed to the wall.

PLAY AREAS

- Keep older children's toys away from younger children's toys. Toys with small parts, modelling kits, and chemistry sets can also be dangerous to babies and toddlers.

- Store toys safely in a box and don't leave them lying around on the floor.

- Throw broken toys away.

- A playpen is a good way of keeping a young child out of potential danger. Make sure that it is at least 60 centimetres (2 feet) deep.

- Store toys and games within your child's reach so he doesn't have to stretch or climb to get them.

SAFETY MEASURES

Keep electric sockets covered

Fit coiled flexes to your kettle and iron

Ensure that strings on cot toys are less than 30 centimetres (1 foot)

SAFETY AT PLAY

The most common accidents that result from playing are cuts and bruises from falling over or off toys, or injuries from swallowing part of a toy or inserting it into a nostril. Sometimes an accident occurs because the child is not properly supervised, sometimes because the toy is broken or of a poor standard, and sometimes because the toy is simply too sophisticated for the child.

Many toys can injure a child in some way, but construction kits, toy cars and trains, and rocking and wheeled toys cause the most injuries. Even soft toys can cause choking and suffocation.

TOY SAFETY CHECKLIST

- Check packaging and labels to ensure the toy is appropriate to your child's age. In general, toys with small components are not suitable for children under the age of 36 months.

- Check warning labels for flammability or for any toxic ingredients.

- Don't stick pictures on the inside of your baby's cot as he may put them in his mouth.

- Cot toys should not be suspended on strings of more than 30 centimetres (1 foot) long.

- If your baby can stand up in his cot, remove toys from the side, as he can use them as a stepping stone to climb out.

- For a child under three, avoid toys with small detachable components, as these can be swallowed by very young children.

- If you have children of different ages, store each child's toys separately.

- Show your child how to use a toy.

- One- and two-year-olds can easily fall off rocking toys and trundle trucks, so keep an eye on your child, especially if he is playing on hard ground.

- Regularly check the batteries in battery-operated toys. Replace them if there's leakage.

- Make sure toys have no sharp or abrasive edges.

- Throw broken toys away rather than giving them to charity or to a jumble sale.

- Store toys safely away in a box with a lid that doesn't slam shut.

- If a toy comes wrapped in a plastic bag, unwrap it for your child, and dispose of the plastic bag.

CHOKE HAZARD TESTER

Once your baby acquires the pincer grasp he is in danger of picking up and swallowing small objects.

A choke hazard tester checks if an object is small enough to lodge in a child's windpipe. If the object slips into the tester, it's potentially dangerous.

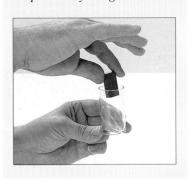

Toys
It's tempting to buy toys on impulse, but check for potential hazards first.

Ears should be firmly stitched on

The eyes should be firmly attached

The paint should be non-toxic

The fabric should be flame resistant

Check for splits or tears; loose stuffing might be eaten or inhaled

The edges should be curved or flexible, not sharp or rigid

The wheels should be non-detachable

OUTDOOR SAFETY

Your child will enjoy playing out of doors – he will be able to run around freely, get dirty, and explore a different environment. The main danger associated with playing outside is that he may run out of the garden or playground and into the road. Drowning is also possible if there is water or a pool in the garden. You can prevent this by making sure that your child always plays in an enclosed environment and that garden gates are locked with child-resistant locks. Drain or fence ponds, and empty paddling pools after use. The other main dangers include ingesting poisonous plants, animal faeces, and chemicals used in gardening.

GARDEN SAFETY CHECKLIST

- Make sure that any poisonous plants (see opposite) are removed and pull up all types of fungi as soon as they appear.

- Store garden tools and chemicals, such as weed-killer, in a locked garden shed.

- Make sure that garden chairs are always put up properly – injuries can be caused by unstable deck chairs and loungers.

- Check the safety of play equipment regularly.

- Put climbing toys on grass, not on paved areas.

- Make sure that your child cannot run out of the garden into the road – fit child-resistant locks.

- If you have a pond or a swimming pool and your child is under the age of two you should drain it, cover it, or fence it off.

- Fix broken glass in greenhouses straight away.

- Don't use power saws or mow the lawn if your child is running around. Always put power tools away after use.

- Cover sandpits to prevent fouling by animals.

- Don't allow animals to defecate in the garden.

- Cover up drains and water butts.

POISONOUS PLANTS

Although eating garden plants is rarely fatal they can cause unpleasant symptoms, ranging from irritation of the skin, mouth, throat, and stomach, to nausea and vomiting. Tell your child never to eat any plants or berries from the garden and remove plants that you know are poisonous. Daffodils, hyacinths, irises, buttercups, snowdrops, sweetpeas, and privet cause irritation of the gastro-intestinal tract, and rhubarb, many fungi, tomato leaves, willow, laurel, rhododendron, mistletoe, and lily of the valley cause general poisoning.

Playgrounds
Young children need challenging equipment to test their skills and use up energy, but make sure they're safe.

Young children should sit in box swings, not open ones

The play area should be surrounded by a fence so animals cannot get in

Climbing equipment should be situated on grass or sand

The sandpit should be too shallow for your child to bury himself

Equipment at ground level, like tubes and tyres, is safest for toddlers

Swings should be enclosed by a fence

Your child should not put his feet under a roundabout or jump off one when it's moving

The slide surface should have no joins in it

Slides constructed on an earth mound will break a fall

CAR AND ROAD SAFETY

The most basic rule of car safety is to make sure that your child is always strapped in. Rear-facing seats are best for infants and can be used in the front or back of the car. If there are no rear seat belts your baby should sit in the front, but she must sit in the back if a passenger airbag is fitted.

Until your child is six, use child locks on the rear doors of your car, and don't let your child lean out of the window, or stick her hands and arms out. Never take your eyes off the road to turn round and talk to your child when you are driving. If she is crying or needs your attention, stop the car first.

Accidents can happen when a car is stationary as well as when it is moving. A child can get her fingers stuck in car doors or windows as they are being closed, or get out of a car on the traffic side.

BABY SEATS

The safest way for your baby to travel by car is in a baby seat. A seat belt alone is not sufficient for a child under the age of ten because her pelvic bones are not strong enough to protect the pelvic organs from the pressure of the belt in the event of a crash. Baby seats are designed for babies from birth to nine months, and they can be used in the front or back seats of cars, although they are slightly safer in the back. The best design is a rear-facing seat

buckled into a seat belt. This means that in a crash the impact is against the baby's back, and not the delicate pelvic organs. Some models will convert to a forward-facing child seat.

CARRYCOTS

Although a proper baby seat is better, it is safe for your baby to travel in a carrycot in the back seat as long as restraints are used. The restraining straps should be secured to the back seat and bolted to the car frame. Keep the carrycot cover in place so that it is impossible for your baby to be thrown out.

CHILD SEATS

By the age of one year your baby will need a child seat. Some of these are fitted with a four-point anchorage kit, although these are not practical for all types of car. Other types are secured with the adult seat belt, and some have integral harnesses. Make sure you fit your child seat according to the manufacturer's instructions, since a badly fitted seat will not offer any protection in a crash.

When your child has grown out of a car seat – some types will last until she is six – she can use a booster cushion with an adult seat belt.

Child safety
Infants over the age of nine months need a child seat. This is forward facing and can be used in the front or back seat.

Baby safety
The best seats for babies from birth to nine months are rear-facing.

ROAD SAFETY

Road accidents are usually more serious and require longer hospitalization than any other childhood accidents, so this is an area where safety is of paramount importance. The responsibility for your child's safety when out in traffic lies with you, of course, not just when she is in her pram but when she reaches school age. Children do not develop the ability to judge the speed of traffic until they are about 10 or 11 years old and they are not good pedestrians until the age of 12. You can, however, instil the basics of road safety from an early age, by teaching her and, more importantly, by setting her a good example.

TEACHING YOUR CHILD

The first thing that your child must learn is that roads are dangerous places. It doesn't matter what the circumstances are – whether she has lost her ball or pet, or wants to greet someone – she must never run out into a road. Unless your road has no traffic don't let your child play on the pavement – encourage her to play in parks, playgrounds, or in the back garden instead, and make sure that these areas are secured with a fence or a locked gate. Tell your child that she must never play on a pedal bike or scooter near the road, that she shouldn't stand in between parked cars, and that if she loses a ball in the road, she should ask an adult to retrieve it.

SETTING AN EXAMPLE

The best way to teach your child road safety is to show her how you behave as a pedestrian. Most of us develop bad habits as adults, such as weaving through traffic, or crossing a road without allowing ourselves sufficient time. When you are with your child you should practise the Green Cross Code, even if it takes you longer to reach your destination. This way your child will learn by example.

When you cross the road with your child, hold her hand and explain what you are doing and why. Go to the kerb and tell your child that it is the safety line that must not be crossed without an adult. Look left and right and wait for a clear break in the traffic before you cross over. If you are pushing a pram, keep it on the pavement until you are ready to cross. Demonstrate to your child how to press the buttons at pelican crossings, and how to wait for the traffic to stop before you cross a zebra crossing. Never run across the road in front of traffic when you are with your child.

Your child's awareness of road safety is in part determined by the area she grows up in. A child who grows up in the country and only has to cross quiet country lanes may need extra supervision when she goes to a town or city because she has not made a strong association between roads, traffic, and danger. If this is the case with your child you can still teach her about road safety when you are driving in the car. When you stop at a pedestrian crossing point out what they are for and how pedestrians use them. Show your child sensible places to cross, such as straight stretches of road, and point out the dangers of crossing at places such as sharp bends or between parked cars, where you cannot see traffic coming. Point out pedestrians who are crossing well or badly, and explain why.

ENVIRONMENT

Make a careful assessment of the traffic and road conditions on your street. Although traffic speed is an important factor, recent research has shown that main roads pose six times as great a risk to pedestrians as residential or local roads. In other words, if you live on a main road you should never allow your child to go out of the house on her own.

If you live in a residential area you could try to increase the safety of roads by asking your local council to install speed ramps or to narrow the road at specific points. If possible, get together with other parents from your area and discuss a campaign for safe neighbourhood play. Your local authority can play an important role in helping you achieve this.

THE GREEN CROSS CODE

This simple road safety routine is really intended for children of eight years and upwards, but you should start to teach it as soon as your child is old enough to follow your example.

Repeat these steps to your child every time you cross the road together.

- *Find a safe place to cross the road, such as a zebra or pelican crossing.*

- *Stop, look, and listen for traffic.*

- *If there is any traffic, let it pass.*

- *Look in both directions, and when the road is clear, walk across. Keep looking and listening as you cross the road.*

PERSONAL RECORDS

Your baby's early milestones – her first smile, her first word – will seem unforgettable to you, but as time passes you'll find that your memory becomes hazy, not just about small details like when she first held her head up, but crucial ones like vaccination dates.

BIRTH RECORD: FIRST BABY

Name _____

Date and time _____

Place _____

Estimated date of delivery _____

Length _____

Weight _____

Blood group _____

Duration of labour _____

Type of deliver _____

Midwife/consultant _____

People present _____

DEVELOPMENT RECORD: FIRST BABY

First smile _____

Achieves head control _____

First tooth _____

Starts solids _____

Sits unsupported _____

Feeds self _____

Responds to own name _____

Uses mature "pincer" grip _____

Learns to "ungrasp" _____

First word _____

Understands "No" _____

Crawls _____

Fully weaned _____

Jargons _____

Stands _____

Bowel control _____

Bladder control _____

Walks _____

Makes simple statements _____

Dresses self _____

Obeys simple requests _____

Climbs stairs unsupported _____

Runs _____

Jumps _____

Counts to ten _____

Draws a circle _____

Starts nursery school _____

Starts school _____

The following pages will help you keep track of these important events. The medical records on pp.334–35 are particularly important. Use them to refresh your memory each time you take your child to the doctor; they may remind you of some forgotten detail that seems relevant. Fill in your own medical history, too, and that of your partner; these can often provide important clues to your child's state of health.

NOTES

BIRTH RECORD: SECOND BABY

Name _____

Date and time _____

Place _____

Estimated date of delivery _____

Length _____

Weight _____

Blood group _____

Duration of labour _____

Type of deliver _____

Midwife/consultant _____

People present _____

DEVELOPMENT RECORD: SECOND BABY

First smile _____

Achieves head control _____

First tooth _____

Starts solids _____

Sits unsupported _____

Feeds self _____

Responds to
own name _____

Uses mature
"pincer" grip _____

Learns to "ungrasp" _____

First word _____

Understands "No" _____

Crawls _____

Fully weaned _____

Jargons _____

Stands _____

Bowel control _____

Bladder control _____

Walks _____

Makes simple
statements _____

Dresses self _____

Obeys simple requests _____

Climbs stairs
unsupported _____

Runs _____

Jumps _____

Counts to ten _____

Draws a circle _____

Starts nursery school _____

Starts school _____

MOTHER'S MEDICAL HISTORY

Illnesses

_____

_____

_____

_____

_____

_____

_____

_____

_____

_____

Allergies

_____

_____

_____

Chronic conditions

_____

_____

MEDICAL RECORDS: FIRST BABY

Name _____

Illness	Date	Comments
_____	____	_____
_____	____	_____
_____	____	_____
_____	____	_____

Injuries

_____	____	_____
_____	____	_____
_____	____	_____

Allergies

_____	____	_____
_____	____	_____
_____	____	_____

IMMUNIZATIONS: FIRST BABY

Type	Date	Reaction
DTP: Diphtheria, tetanus, whooping cough (3 vaccinations, 1 booster)	____	_____
	____	_____
	____	_____
	____	_____
Polio (3 oral vaccinations, 1 booster)	____	_____
	____	_____
	____	_____
MMR: Measles, mumps, rubella (1 vaccination)	____	_____
Hib: see p.283 (3 vaccinations)	____	_____
	____	_____

MEDICAL RECORDS: SECOND BABY

Name _____

Illness	Date	Comments

Injuries		

Allergies		

IMMUNIZATIONS: SECOND BABY

Type	Date	Reaction
DTP: Diphtheria, tetanus, whooping cough (3 vaccinations, 1 booster)		
Polio (3 oral vaccinations, 1 booster)		
MMR: Measles, mumps, rubella (1 vaccination)		
Hib: see p.283 (3 vaccinations)		

FATHER'S MEDICAL HISTORY

Illnesses

_____
_____
_____
_____
_____
_____
_____
_____
_____

Allergies

_____
_____
_____

Chronic conditions

_____
_____

LENGTH, HEIGHT, AND WEIGHT

The most important criteria in assessing your baby's progress are happiness and general well-being. If these are apparent, there's no need for you to worry about his measurements; your local clinic can do that for you.

You may find it interesting to plot your baby's increasing height and weight on the following charts, but you should only become anxious about it if his growth pattern veers away from the centile line (see below). Don't compare your child to others of his age.

The range of "normal" heights or weights at a given age is very wide. A newborn boy may weigh anything from 2.5 to 4.5 kilograms (5 1/2 to 10 pounds) without giving cause for concern; a five-year-old boy from 13.5 to 26.5 kilograms (2 to 5 stone).

Each chart shows the range of heights or weights into which the vast majority of children will fall. The black line in the middle of each coloured band represents the 50th centile; that is, 50 per cent of children will fall below the line, and 50 per cent above it. The outer lines represent extremes beyond which very few children (fewer than 0.5 per cent) will fall. If your child does, you should consult your doctor.

A child's measurements, plotted regularly, should form a line roughly parallel to the central line. If not, the measurements may not have been correctly plotted or the correct chart may not have been used. If in doubt, consult your child welfare clinic.

GIRL'S LENGTH 0–6 MONTHS

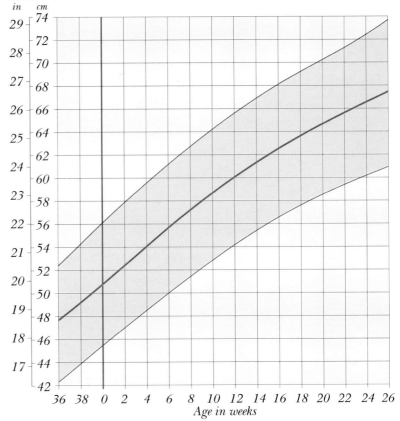

Age in weeks

GIRL'S WEIGHT 0–6 MONTHS

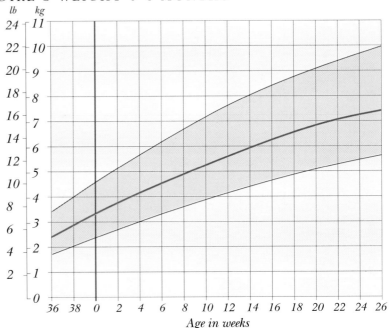

Age in weeks

BOY'S LENGTH 0–6 MONTHS

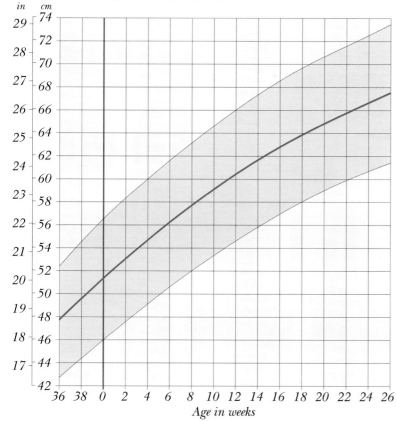

USING THE CHARTS

I believe that no baby needs weighing and measuring if she's thriving, but we've included charts for parents who are keen to follow their child's progress.

- *You will probably need to ask your midwife or hospital doctor for your baby's birth-weight and birth-length*

- *For a baby, you could fill in the charts using the measurements taken by your doctor or health visitor, or from readings done at the baby clinic*

- *For a preterm baby, you will have to adjust her age accordingly, at least until she is a year old. If, for example, your baby was born at 36 weeks, start recording her measurements at the appropriate point to the left of zero on the chart, and continue to subtract four weeks from her age each time you fill in the chart*

- *To measure your child's height, once she's three or four get her to stand against a wall with her feet together and her heels and shoulder-blades touching the wall. Make sure she holds her head up straight by gently tilting her chin upwards. If you like, measure her again at six-monthly intervals so she can see how she's growing*

- *To enter your child's measurements on the chart, find her age along the bottom axis and draw a straight line up from it. Now find her weight or height along the vertical axis, and draw a line across. Mark a solid dot where the two lines meet. The row of dots is your child's growth curve*

BOY'S WEIGHT 0–6 MONTHS

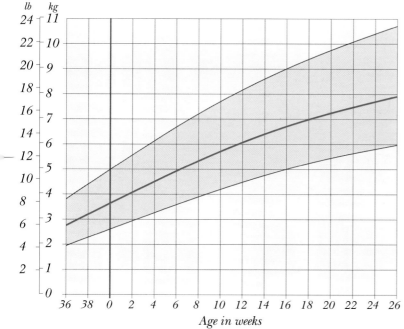

NOTES

GIRL'S LENGTH 6–18 MONTHS

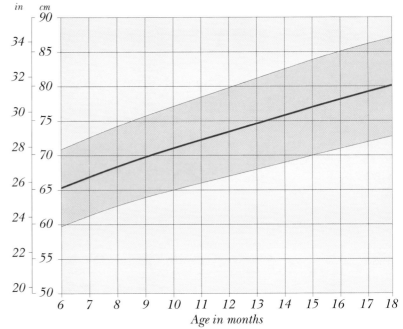

Age in months

GIRL'S WEIGHT 6–18 MONTHS

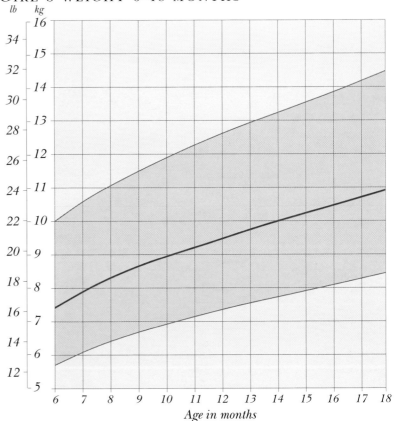

Age in months

BOY'S LENGTH 6–18 MONTHS

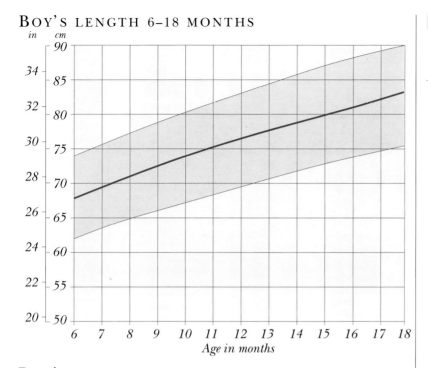

in — *cm*

Age in months

NOTES

BOY'S WEIGHT 6–18 MONTHS

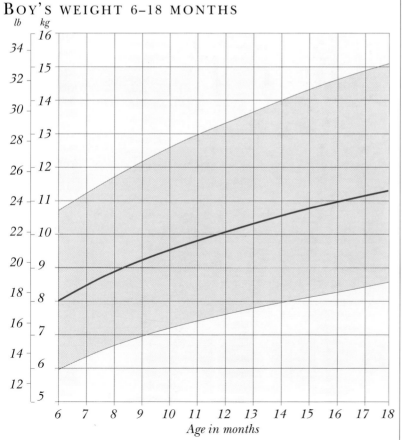

lb — *kg*

Age in months

GIRL'S HEIGHT 18–36 MONTHS

Age in months

GIRL'S WEIGHT 18–36 MONTHS

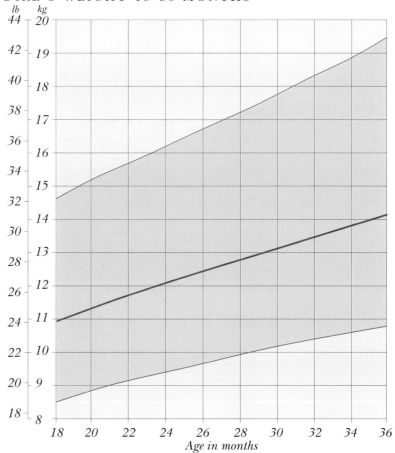

Age in months

BOY'S HEIGHT 18–36 MONTHS

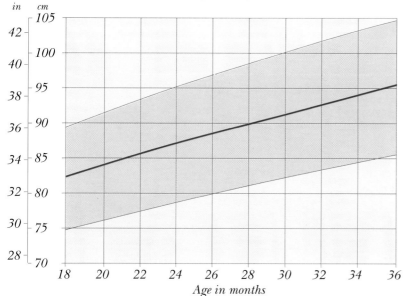

Age in months

BOY'S WEIGHT 18–36 MONTHS

Age in months

NOTES

NOTES

GIRL'S HEIGHT 3–5 YEARS

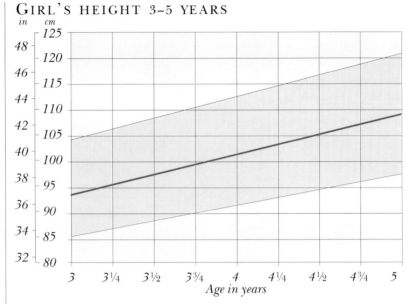

GIRL'S WEIGHT 3–5 YEARS

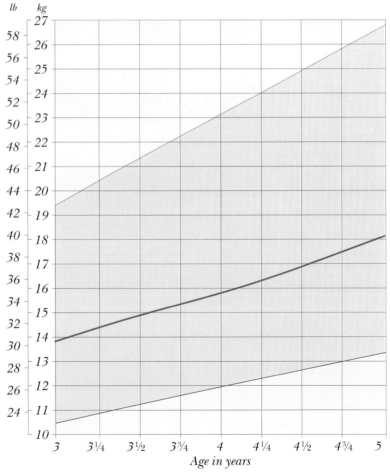

BOY'S HEIGHT 3–5 YEARS

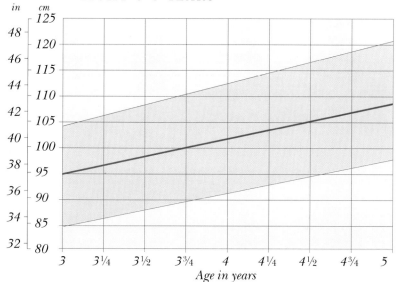

Age in years

BOY'S WEIGHT 3–5 YEARS

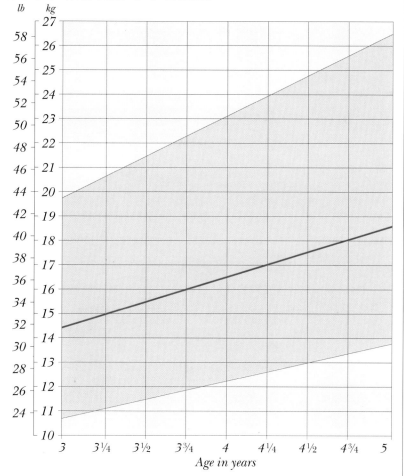

Age in years

FIRST AID

As a parent, you will inevitably have to cope with minor accidents as your child grows up. Most of the time these will be minor cuts and bruises, but you should be equipped to cope with major accidents or emergencies, should they occur. All parents should know the basic first aid techniques to deal with accidents quickly, effectively, and calmly. To give first aid effectively you need to understand and practise the techniques detailed on the following pages, and you should also keep a first aid kit in your home. This should be accessible in an emergency but stored out of reach of your child.

EMERGENCY FIRST AID

A severe accident with the loss of much blood or other body fluids may precipitate shock (see p.332), which is always serious. Other emergencies include choking (see p.333), a very severe respiratory tract infection that blocks the airways, drowning, and unconsciousness. Prompt action on your part can be lifesaving.

PRIORITIES

When your child has an accident you must get your priorities right. Tell any adult present to call an ambulance while you go through the checklist (right). Detailed instructions for the procedures involved are shown on pp.328–333. If there isn't anyone to help, you should go through the checklist before calling an ambulance.

Is your child in danger? If appropriate, remove your child from the danger or the danger from your child. Do not put yourself at risk, and do not move your child if you suspect a fracture.

Is he conscious? Shake your child gently by his shoulders and keep calling his name.

Is his airway blocked? Open your child's airway by supporting the chin and tilting the head back. Then clear any obstruction (see p.328–29).

Is he breathing? Lean close to your child's mouth to listen for breathing and feel it against your cheek. Look at his chest to see if it is rising and falling. If there are no signs of breathing after five seconds, give five breaths of ventilation (see p.330).

HOME FIRST AID KIT

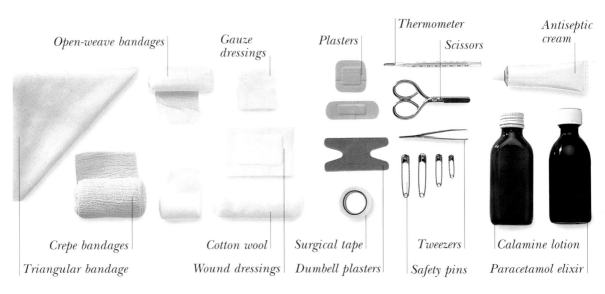

Open-weave bandages

Gauze dressings

Plasters

Thermometer

Scissors

Antiseptic cream

Crepe bandages

Triangular bandage

Cotton wool

Wound dressings

Surgical tape

Dumbell plasters

Tweezers

Safety pins

Calamine lotion

Paracetamol elixir

FIRST AID TRAINING

You must learn the procedures on these pages by heart in order to make use of them. If you have to waste time referring to this book to refresh your memory, your delay could be the difference between life and death.

This book cannot make you a "First Aider". To learn first aid properly you should complete a course of instruction and pass a professionally supervised examination. The Standard First Aid Certificate is awarded by the St. John Ambulance, St. Andrew's Ambulance Association, and the British Red Cross (see **Useful addresses, p.344**). It is valid for only three years, after which you should update your skills with further training.

Does he have a pulse? Check for a pulse in the arm or neck (see p.328–29), or place your hand on your baby's chest and count the beats. A normal pulse rate is about 120 beats per minute for a baby; less for an older child. If no pulse is present, or if the pulse is less than 60 beats per minute in a baby, give alternate chest compressions and ventilation (see pp.330–31) for one minute, call an ambulance, taking your child with you if you can, then continue resuscitation.

Call an ambulance If your child is having breathing difficulties or is unconscious, then call an ambulance, or get another adult to do so. Try not to leave your child unattended and be prepared to carry out resuscitation on him.

RESUSCITATION

In order for vital organs such as the brain to function they need a continuous supply of oxygen. If any part of the process by which oxygen is carried to body cells and tissues goes wrong, unconsciousness may result. Air must be inhaled to supply oxygen to the blood, and the oxygenated blood must be pumped around the body by the heart. If the brain is deprived of oxygen for more than three minutes, it will begin to fail. If the heart fails, death will occur unless emergency action is taken.

Resuscitation is necessary if, for whatever reason, your baby or child has stopped breathing or if his pulse has stopped (see p.328–29).

HOW RESUSCITATION WORKS

Oxygen supply
Three factors are involved in the transport of oxygen to the brain. The air passage, or airway, must be open so that oxygen can enter the body; breathing must occur so that oxygen can enter the bloodstream in the lungs; and the heart must be pumping so that the blood travels around the body (circulation) taking the oxygen to all the tissues, including those of the brain.

Air must be inhaled to provide oxygen

Oxygen enters the bloodstream via the lungs

The heart pumps the oxygenated blood round the body

Oxygenated blood reaches the tissues

THE ABC OF RESUSCITATION

In an emergency, when your child stops breathing or loses consciousness, you must remember to carry out the following checks in the order given:

A is for Airway *Open the airway, look in the mouth, and check for obstructions. Clear the airway if you can by tilting your child's head back (see p.326). Never sweep the back of the throat if your child is choking (see p.333).*

B is for Breathing *If your child shows no signs of breathing you will have to breathe for him with ventilations (see p.330).*

C is for Circulation *Check that your child has a pulse. If there is none or if it is very weak, you will have to give chest compressions combined with ventilation (see p.331).*

RESUSCITATION

If your child has lost consciousness and isn't breathing, she's at risk of brain damage and heart failure. You need to make a fast assessment of her condition in order to know what first aid treatment to give. If she is unconscious but still breathing and has a pulse, then you should call for help and place her in the recovery position (see p.329). If she's unconscious and not breathing but has a pulse, you will need to give artificial ventilation (see p.330). If she's not breathing and has no pulse, you must give chest compressions

combined with artificial ventilation immediately (see p.331). All of these procedures differ slightly for babies and children.

Tilt the head so that the tongue is clear of the windpipe

Tongue

ASSESSING A BABY

1 Check for consciousness
See if your baby is conscious by calling her name, gently shaking her, and tapping or scratching the sole of her foot. If she doesn't respond after about ten seconds, shout for help.

Run a finger along the sole of your child's foot

2 Clear the airway
Look in your baby's mouth. If you can see an obstruction, remove it with your finger, but be careful not to poke it further in. Open the airway by lifting the chin with one finger and tilting the head back very slightly.

Support the chin with one finger to keep the airway open

Look along your baby's chest and abdomen for signs of movement

Place the thumb on the outside of the arm and two fingers on the inside

3 Check for breathing
Look, listen, and feel for signs of breathing. Look along your baby's chest and abdomen to see if they are moving up and down. Listen closely for sounds of breathing and feel for her breath on your

cheek. If there are no signs of breathing after five seconds, you should give five breaths of artificial ventilation (see p.330), then check her pulse.

4 Check the pulse
Place two fingers on the inner side of the arm above the elbow and press gently. If you can't feel any pulse after five seconds, give chest compressions and ventilation (see p.331) for one minute, then call an ambulance and continue.

ASSESSING A CHILD

1 Check for consciousness
See if your child is conscious by shaking her gently and pinching her. Keep calling her name. If she doesn't respond, call for help.

2 Clear the airway
Look in the mouth to see if it is obstructed. If it is, clear it with your fingers, but take care that you don't push any obstruction further in. Open the airway by putting two fingers under your child's chin and lifting the jaw. Tilt the head back by placing your other hand on her forehead.

3 Check breathing
Look, listen and feel for signs of breathing. Look along your child's chest and abdomen for movements; listen for sounds of breathing; and feel for her breath on your cheek. If she is not breathing, give five breaths of artificial ventilation (see p.330), then check her pulse.

4 Check the pulse
See if your child's heart is still beating by checking her carotid pulse. You can find the pulse by placing your fingers just in front of the large muscle at the side of the neck under the angle of the jaw. If there's no pulse, you must give one minute of chest compressions combined with ventilation (see p.331), call an ambulance, then continue.

An unconscious child who is breathing and has a regular pulse should be placed in this position to keep the airway open and to allow liquids to drain from the mouth, provided there are no suspected fractures.

THE RECOVERY POSITION

The uppermost leg should be bent at a right angle so that the hip and knee act as a "prop"

Place the arm at right angles to the body with the elbow bent

For a baby
Cradle her in your arms, with her head tilted slightly back in order to keep the airway open.

1 If your child is lying on his back or side, kneel beside him. Straighten his legs and place the arm nearest you at right angles to his body with the elbow bent.

2 Bring the other arm across the chest and place the back of the hand against the cheek.

3 Still pressing your child's hand to his cheek, grasp the thigh that is furthest away from you and pull the knee up, keeping the foot flat on the ground and placing it next to the nearer knee.

4 Roll your child over into a resting position with his knee bent and his head resting on his hand.

VENTILATION FOR BABIES

1 Open the airway
If your baby has stopped breathing, lay her down on a firm surface and check her mouth. If you can see an obstruction, remove it with your fingers, but do not poke a finger down your baby's throat. Gently lift the chin with one finger and tilt the head back very slightly.

2 Give ventilation
Inhale, put your lips over the baby's nostrils and mouth making a complete seal, and breathe out gently into her mouth and nose so that her chest rises. Remove your lips and let the chest fall. Continue to give breaths at a rate of one every three seconds.

3 Check pulse
After one minute of ventilation, check for a pulse in the arm (see p.328). If there is none, or if it is less than 60 beats per minute, give chest compressions combined with ventilations (see opposite). After one minute of this send for an ambulance, taking the baby to the phone. If there's a pulse, continue to give ventilation, checking the pulse every minute.

VENTILATION FOR CHILDREN

1 Open the airway
If your child has stopped breathing lay him down on a firm surface. Check there is nothing obstructing the mouth or throat – if there is, remove it, but don't stick your finger down your child's throat. Place two fingers under his chin and tilt his head back.

2 Give ventilation
Using your finger and thumb, pinch your child's nostrils closed. Inhale, put your mouth over his mouth, making a complete seal, and breathe out until his chest rises. Remove your mouth and watch the chest fall. Continue to give one breath every three seconds.

3 Check pulse
After one minute of ventilation, check the pulse in your child's neck (see p.329). If there is no pulse, give chest compressions combined with ventilations (see opposite) for one minute, then call an ambulance. If there is, continue ventilation, checking the pulse every minute.

CHEST COMPRESSION FOR BABIES

1 Position the fingers
Chest compressions combined with ventilation, known as cardio-pulmonary resuscitation (CPR), are necessary when your baby has no pulse, or a pulse of less than 60 beats per minute, and is not breathing. Lay her down on a firm surface and position two fingers only in the middle of the chest just below an imaginary line between the nipples.

2 Give chest compressions
Press down sharply on the chest with the tips of your two fingers. You should give five compressions during a three-second period and you should push down to a depth of 2 centimetres ($^3/_4$ inch). Be careful not to thrust too vigorously or too deeply, or you could cause harm to your baby.

3 Give artificial ventilation
After five compressions give one breath of artificial ventilation (see opposite). Alternate chest compressions with artificial ventilation: for every five compressions over a three second period, give one breath. After one minute of this, send for an ambulance, taking the baby to the phone with you if necessary. Continue resuscitation until the ambulance arrives.

CHEST COMPRESSION FOR CHILDREN

1 Positioning the hand
Place your child on his back on a firm surface. Put the middle finger of one hand on the tip of the breastbone (the bone where the ribs meet in the middle) and the index finger above it. Position the heel of your other hand so that it rests just above the index finger.

2 Give chest compressions
Take your fingers away from the breastbone and, using the heel of the other hand, press down sharply to a depth of about 3 centimetres (1 $^1/_4$ inches). Give five compressions in three seconds.

3 Give artificial ventilation
After five compressions give one breath of ventilation (see opposite). Don't stop to take your child's pulse unless he shows signs of reviving. Alternate five compressions every three seconds with one breath of ventilation. After one minute, call an ambulance, then continue.

SHOCK

Although shock is commonly thought of as an emotional response to a distressing event, in a medical context 'shock' refers to a perilous drop in blood pressure resulting in insufficient blood reaching the body tissues. If it is not dealt with quickly the vital organs can stop functioning and the child can die. Shock is made worse by fear and pain, both of which are likely to accompany any accident.

Dealing with shock
Lay your child down with his legs higher than his chest.

Symptoms Initially, the body responds with a flow of adrenalin. This gives rise to a rapid pulse, pale, greyish-looking skin, especially around the lips, sweating, and clamminess. As shock progresses your child may be thirsty, she may feel sick, and she may vomit. She is likely to be weak and dizzy, her breathing will be shallow and fast, and her pulse (see p.328) will be fast and irregular.

As shock progresses, the body withdraws the blood supply from the surface of the body to its core, and the oxygen supply to the brain weakens. In very severe cases, when the oxygen supply to the brain is insufficient, your child may become restless and anxious, and she may be yawning and gasping for air ("air hunger"). Eventually she will lose consciousness and the heart will cease functioning.

WHAT TO DO

If you suspect that your child is suffering from shock you should call an ambulance as soon as possible. If she's lost a lot of blood, try to stop the bleeding (see p.335), and deal with any burns (see p.336) or any other obvious cause of shock. Move her as little as possible but get her to lie down with her legs raised on some pillows so that her legs are higher than her chest; this makes it easier for blood to flow back to the heart. Undo any fastenings around the neck, chest, and waist, and turn her head to one side in case she vomits.

Your child will be very anxious so it is important to stay with her and keep reassuring and talking to her. Fear and pain both tend to worsen shock, so keep your child as calm and as comfortable as you can under the circumstances. Make sure that she is warm, but not too hot. A blanket on top of her and around her head will keep her insulated. (In a very young child, the blanket should be wrapped right round the body.) If your child is suffering from shock as a result of an injury, she may need surgery when she gets to hospital, so don't give her anything to eat or drink. If she is thirsty wet her lips with some water. Keep checking her breathing and pulse rates, and be prepared to give resuscitation (see pp.330–31) if necessary.

CAUSES OF SHOCK

There are two main causes of shock: a sudden drop in blood pressure due to paralysis of the nerves, as in electric shock, or a loss of blood or body fluid, as in severe burns.

An accident may lead to profuse bleeding, either internally or externally (see p.335), resulting in a reduced volume of blood circulating round the body. Severe untreated dehydration can lead to shock, especially if your child has a fever, vomiting, or diarrhoea, and the lost fluids are not replaced.

Your child's blood pressure will drop rapidly if she has a severe allergic reaction to, say, a wasp or bee sting, a food, or a drug. The allergens cause the blood vessels to dilate, tissues to swell and the air passages to constrict. Insufficient oxygen reaches the tissues and she will be in danger of suffocation. This is known as anaphylactic shock.

Other causes of shock include peritonitis (inflammation of the abdominal lining), spinal injury, and some types of poisoning.

CHOKING

If your child's airway becomes completely blocked or she is unable to get sufficient oxygen into her lungs, she may lose consciousness. Normal breathing may return when your child loses consciousness and the muscles relax. If she doesn't breathe, you must commence resuscitation (see pp.328–31).

You must remove the blockage to restore normal breathing. Encourage a baby to cough out the foreign body by patting her back. If this doesn't work, follow the steps outlined below. (For a baby under one year, or for any small child, you should follow the sequence for a baby; abdominal thrusts can injure small children.) If the procedure doesn't work immediately, repeat it until help arrives or the obstruction is cleared.

FOR A BABY

1 Back blows
Lay your baby face down along your forearm, keeping her head low and supporting her head and shoulders on your hand. Slap her sharply five times between the shoulder blades.

2 Chest thrusts
If slaps haven't worked, turn your baby face up and lay her along your other arm. Place two fingers on the lower half of her breastbone (in the centre of her chest just below the nipples), and give five sharp downward thrusts of about 2 centimetres (³/4 inch).

3 Check the mouth
Look in your baby's mouth, placing your finger on her tongue. If you can see the obstruction, use a finger to hook it out, but do not put your finger down her throat. If the blockage hasn't cleared, call an ambulance. Repeat this sequence until help arrives.

FOR A CHILD

1 Back slaps
Encourage your child to cough up the obstruction. If he can't, lay his face down across your knees and slap him sharply five times between the shoulder blades. If slaps haven't worked continue with chest thrusts.

2 Chest thrusts
Lay your child face up on the floor. Place the heel of one hand in the centre of his chest just below the nipples and give five sharp downward thrusts of about 3 centimetres (1¹/4 inches). See if the blockage is visible, but don't stick your finger down his throat.

3 Abdominal thrusts
If the blockage hasn't cleared, place the heel of one hand in the middle of the abdomen just below the rib cage and thrust firmly back and up five times. Check his mouth again. If the blockage hasn't cleared, call an ambulance. Repeat this sequence until help arrives.

ELECTRIC SHOCK

Your child may get an electric shock from frayed flexes or wires, light switches, defective electrical appliances, or from touching an appliance with wet hands. It is important to warn your child about the hazards of electricity from an early age and stress that water and electricity are a dangerous combination. Replace frayed wires and put dummy plugs in any electrical sockets not in use.

Symptoms In severe cases your child may lose consciousness and his heartbeat may stop. In mild-cases he may have slight burns.

WHAT TO DO

Before you go to help your child, you must break the contact between him and the source of electricity. Either switch the current off at the mains or pull the plug out. If you have to break the contact manually make sure you do it safely: push your child away using an object made of a non-conducting material such as wood or plastic and stand on an insulating material while you do it. If there is no alternative, drag your child away by his clothes. This can be very dangerous, however, as if you touch his skin or if his clothes are damp, you will receive a shock too.

Once the contact has been broken, you should examine your child for burns. If burns are severe or your child is unconscious you should call an ambulance. In the meantime treat the burns by pouring on cold water and then placing a sterile dressing on them (see p.336). Monitor your child's condition closely; if he starts to suffer from shock (see p.332) you may have to resuscitate him. If he is unconscious but breathing, place him in the recovery position (see p.329).

Use a wooden object to break contact with the source

A telephone directory makes a good insulator

POISONING

Common poisons include bleach, weedkiller, and plants such as berries, irises, daffodils, and fungi. You should leave medicines and chemicals in their original containers, which should be tamper-proof where possible, and lock them away. Always call your doctor if you suspect poisoning.

Symptoms A corrosive chemical often burns around the mouth and it's usual for the child to feel nauseous and vomit or have diarrhoea. With very poisonous chemicals your child may lose consciousness or he may have convulsions. There may be a poisonous substance such as berries, pills, or a bottle containing household chemicals lying around – keep this to show to your doctor as evidence of what your child has swallowed.

Breaking contact
Stand on a dry insulating material while you push your child's limbs away from the source with a non-conductive object of wood or plastic. Do not touch your child's skin with your hands.

WHAT TO DO

Try to identify the poison. Call your doctor or an ambulance. Keep a sample of the poison to show to the doctor, and, if you can, tell him how much your child took and when.

If you suspect or know that your child has swallowed a poison, don't try to induce vomiting. If the chemical is regurgitated it will cause as much damage on the way back up as it did when it was first swallowed. Instead, give your child sips of milk or water. Traces of poison on hands or face should be washed away with water.

If your child has lost consciousness, check her pulse and breathing and, if necessary, resuscitate her (see pp.330–31). When she is breathing lie her in the recovery position (see p.329).

DROWNING

A child can drown in as little as 5 centimetres (2 inches) of water and so it's very important not to leave your child alone near a paddling pool, a bath, or even a bucket of water. If a drowning child is not rescued quickly he will be asphyxiated.

RESCUE

Drowning in a large body of water is a hazard to you as well as your child, so first attempt to rescue him without entering the water. Try to reach him with your hand or a pole, or throw him a lifebelt. Get into the water only if there is no alternative. In shallow water carry your child to land by wading through the water; tow him only if he is already unconscious. While you are carrying him make sure that his head is lower than his chest – if he vomits there will be less risk of his inhaling vomit.

WHAT TO DO

Take your child to the nearest warm, dry place and, without undressing him, lay him down on blankets or a coat. Check his airway, breathing, and pulse (see pp. 328–29), and give resuscitation if necessary (see pp. 330–31). If he is unconscious but still breathing, put him in the recovery position (see p.329) and monitor his breathing all the time. Replace his wet clothing and insulate him from the cold.

Your child should receive medical attention as soon as possible; either call an ambulance or take him to hospital yourself, because even if he appears to recover there is a chance that he may suffer from a condition known as "secondary drowning" in which the air passages swell up. Your child may also need treatment for hypothermia.

BLEEDING

Cuts and grazes (see p.342) are rarely serious and, unless infected, can be dealt with at home. Severe external bleeding or internal bleeding, however, can lead to shock and eventually loss of consciousness. These should be treated as emergencies.

WHAT TO DO

Profuse bleeding is both serious and distressing. It should be dealt with quickly before your child goes into a severe state of shock.

Severe external bleeding Expose the wound if it is covered – cut away clothing if necessary – and apply pressure to the wound with a clean dressing or cloth. If there is glass sticking out of the wound don't remove it. Instead, apply pressure on either side; this will compress the ends of the damaged blood vessels. Lay your child down, keeping the injured part of the body in a position above the heart to slow down the flow of blood to the wound.

Do not use a tourniquet to stem bleeding, but do apply a dressing to the wound and secure it with bandages after applying pressure to the wound. If blood appears through the bandage put another one on top. If there is glass sticking out of the wound build up the bandages on either side until you can bandage over the top without pushing the glass deeper into the wound. Call an ambulance or take your child to hospital.

Internal bleeding If your child is showing signs of shock (see p.332), if there is pattern bruising (bruising that follows the pattern of the object that crushed against the body), or, if there is bleeding from the ears, nose, mouth, or vagina, you should suspect internal bleeding. Treat your child for shock (see p.332) and call an ambulance.

BURNS AND SCALDS

Burns are usually described in terms of the amount of damage to the skin. Superficial burns are the least serious and can result from a minor spillage, or touching a very hot surface. Partial-thickness burns are more serious and fluid-filled blisters form on the skin. Full-thickness burns are very serious since all layers of the skin are damaged, fluid loss is high due to weeping of the skin, and the nerves and muscles may be damaged. Unless a burn is very minor you should always seek medical help.

WHAT TO DO

If the burn is minor run cold water over the affected part of the body for about ten minutes. Cover it with a sterile dressing to protect it from bacteria. A clean plastic bag will make a good temporary dressing if you have nothing else suitable.

If the burn is major call an ambulance, then lay your child down and pour water over the affected area for ten minutes or until the ambulance arrives. Check that your child is breathing and take his pulse. You may need to treat him for shock (see p.332). If he loses consciousness be prepared to resuscitate him (see pp.330–31). Unless your child's clothes are sticking to the burnt area, you should gently take or cut them off him.

Do not

- Touch the affected area or attempt to burst any blisters that form.

- Apply lotion or fat to the area.

- Stick a plaster or adhesive dressing to the burn.

- Cover the burn with a "fluffy" dressing or any cloth that sheds lint.

- Remove anything that is sticking to the burn: you may cause further damage to the skin or tissue and introduce infection.

- Overcool your child if he has severe burns; this could lead to hypothermia (see p.340).

CLOTHES ON FIRE

Douse with water
Make your child lie down as quickly as possible with the burning side of his body facing upwards. Put the flames out with water. Do not pour water on your child if he has been burnt by an electrical object that is near by. Throw water downwards along the body to stop flames reaching the face.

Smother flames
If there is no water near by, wrap your child in blankets or a thick coat or rug to deprive the flames of oxygen. Do not use a flammable fabric to smother the flames.

TAKE CARE

Severe burns are dangerous: a child can rapidly go into shock (see p.332) because of the loss of body fluids. Untreated shock leads quickly to unconsciousness. The larger the area of the burn the greater the likelihood of severe shock. If more than one-tenth of your child's body is burned he will need immediate treatment for shock; you should call an ambulance urgently.

HEAD INJURIES

If your child bangs or knocks his head he will normally have recovered within minutes. If he bangs his head quite hard he may have some temporary swelling. Head injuries that should give cause for concern are those that produce severe bleeding, or those that give rise to the symptoms of concussion, even several hours after the injury. Look out for drowsiness, headaches, and nausea.

Symptoms Mild symptoms resulting from a slight knock include a headache and a bump or swelling where the impact occurred. If the injury is more severe, your child may lose consciousness and the symptoms of concussion may follow (see below right). He may be drowsy, stunned, or dazed, and he may suffer nausea and vomiting. Disturbances in vision and headaches are common. If the skin of the scalp is cut, bleeding may be profuse.

Straw-coloured fluid or watery blood leaking from the ears or the nose may indicate a skull fracture. Other symptoms include a depression of the scalp and unconsciousness. A suspected skull fracture should be treated as an emergency.

WHAT TO DO

If your child is unconscious, call an ambulance and place him in the recovery position (see p.329). Keep checking his pulse and his level of response (see pp.328–29) and be prepared to give resuscitation if necessary (see pp.330–31). If he comes round after a short time, keep checking his level of consciousness by getting him to respond to his name. Do not leave him alone.

If there is bleeding from the scalp, nose, or ears, press a clean pad firmly to the area to stop the flow. If there is a wound, do not touch it with your fingers. If the bleeding stops, clean and dress the wound, though not if this causes the bleeding to start again. If the wound if long or jagged, take your child to the hospital to have it stitched. If bleeding results from a small cut, clean it with soap and water and place a dressing on it. Any discharge from the ear should be allowed to drain away. If your child is conscious and you think that he may be concussed take him to see your doctor.

If you don't have a sterile dressing, any clean fabric pad will do

Scalp wounds
Apply firm, steady pressure to the wound with a sterile dressing or clean pad for ten minutes or until the bleeding stops. The pad should be larger than the wound.

CONCUSSION

A child who has suffered a blow to the head may show symptoms of concussion, which is a temporary disturbance of the brain.

Your child will lose consciousness for a short time and then recover completely. He may feel dizzy or nauseous and have a slight headache, and may even be unable to remember what led up to his injury. Concussion can occur several hours after a blow to the head so you should monitor your child closely for 24 hours for these symptoms. If the symptoms persist for more than a few days or if they recur, consult your doctor.

Cause of concussion
Because the brain is not fixed rigidly inside the skull it is free to move around a little. This means that if there is a blow to the head the brain is shaken or knocked against the skull, giving rise to the symptoms of concussion.

SEIZURES AND CONVULSIONS

The most common causes of convulsions are fever (see p.281), epilepsy (see p.270), head injuries, diseases that damage the brain, and poisoning. Convulsions may also occur for no apparent reason. During a convulsion there is a disturbance in the normal electrical impulses in the brain, causing muscles to jerk involuntarily. It is important that the child is not restrained in any way. Convulsions usually occur on isolated occasions, but children with epilepsy suffer repeated attacks.

Symptoms Children with epilepsy may suffer from minor fits (known as "petit mal") which appear as a lapse of concentration or daydreaming, or from major fits ("grand mal"), which are seizures. In a mild seizure your child may experience a tingling or twitching in some part of his body, such as his arm or leg. In a grand mal convulsion your child may cry out and then lose consciousness and fall to the floor. His body will become stiff and he will hold his breath. This "stiff" phase is followed by rhythmic jerking movements of the arms and legs and arching of the back. Your child has no control over his bodily functions and he may become incontinent. He may clench his teeth and bite his tongue, or froth at the mouth.

After the convulsion your child's muscles will relax and he will begin to breathe normally again. When he regains consciousness he is likely to be dazed or confused and he will want to sleep.

WHAT TO DO

It's very important that you don't try to intervene while your child is having a convulsion. Even if you think he is at risk of biting his tongue you should not try to open his mouth or put anything in it. Clear a space around your child so that he cannot hurt himself, call a doctor, and stay with your child all the time. If your child remains unconscious put him in the recovery position (see p.329). You should make a note of the duration and the symptoms of your child's convulsion to tell the doctor as it will help her diagnose the cause.

EYE INJURIES

Any injury to the eye should be taken seriously. Common injuries include a foreign body or chemical in the eye, a blow to the eye causing bruising or a black eye, and a cut in or near the eye.

Symptoms These vary according to the type of injury, but may include bruising around the eye socket, pain, inability to open the eye fully, or spasms of the eyelid. There might be impaired vision, a bloodshot appearance, and, if the eyeball has been punctured, blood or fluid leaking from the eyeball.

WHAT TO DO

Treatment will depend on the type of injury, but in all cases it should be prompt. Your child will probably need to be taken to casualty.

- If your child has a foreign body in his eye try to remove it using the corner of a handkerchief, or by flushing out his eye (see below). If it is embedded in the eye or is on the iris, tape a pad over his eye and take him to casualty.

Flushing out the eye
Lay your child down with his head tilted in the direction of the affected eye and pour water across the open eye, from the inner corner away from the nose.

- For a blow to the eye place a pad soaked in cold water over the eye to minimize bruising.

- If your child has a chemical in his eye take him to casualty, but first try to flush out the eye with water from a jug (see picture) or by getting your child to lean under a running tap, affected eye lowermost. Do this for about 15 minutes.

- If your child cuts his eye, hold a sterile pad against the wound and take him to casualty.

FRACTURES AND DISLOCATIONS

The most common type of childhood fracture is a greenstick fracture, in which the bone bends and splits. Other types of fracture include simple fractures (a clean break) and compound fractures (the bone breaks through the skin). A dislocation is a bone that is displaced from its joint, usually after a wrenching force.

Symptoms Typically, there is difficulty moving and a limb may look oddly shaped. There will be pain, swelling, bruising, and possibly a wound at the site of the injury. With a dislocation, your child may experience a "sickening" pain.

WHAT TO DO

All fractures and dislocations should be treated promptly in hospital. You should keep your child as still as possible until an ambulance arrives and don't let him have anything to eat or drink. You can prevent the worsening of an injury by immobilizing the joints above and below a fracture.

TYING A SLING

Support the injured arm

1 Positioning the bandage
Bend the injured arm across the chest. Place the bandage (use a triangular bandage or a square or cloth folded diagonally) between the arm and the chest. Pull one corner around the neck to reach the shoulder of the injured arm.

Secure with a reef knot

2 Tying the bandage
Bring the bottom of the bandage up over the child's forearm and tie the bottom corner of the triangle with a reef knot to the corner resting at the injured shoulder. Tuck in the ends of the knot.

The fingers should protrude from the sling

3 Fastening the corner
Using a safety pin, secure the loose point of the bandage at the front of the elbow. If you don't have a safety pin, tuck the point into the sling. The hand should be left exposed.

LEG BANDAGE

1 Improvising a splint
Lay your child down and place padding between his legs. Use newspaper, rolled blankets, or a pillow.

A rolled newspaper makes a good splint

2 Tying the bandages
Using the broadest bandages you can find, tie the broken leg to the uninjured leg at the knee, calf, and ankle. Make a figure-of-eight at the ankles. All the knots should be on the side of the uninjured leg.

TAKE CARE

If you suspect that your child has fractured his spine or his neck there may also be damage to the delicate spinal cord carried by the vertebrae, so it is essential that you don't move your child until an ambulance arrives and don't let him move his head. If there is spinal cord injury, your child will experience burning, tingling, or even a loss of sensation in his limbs.

HEATSTROKE

When the body overheats as a result of exposure to extreme heat the temperature control mechanism in the brain fails and the sweat glands stop working. Your child cannot lower his temperature in the adult way. This is a relatively common occurrence among children who go out in strong sun before they have the chance to acclimatize. Your child's temperature may rise above 40°C (104°F) and in extreme cases he may lose consciousness and stop breathing. Most cases however, are mild.

Symptoms Although the skin looks and feels hot, it remains dry. Your child will seem drowsy and lethargic, and he may have a rapid pulse rate. In severe cases your child may become confused, start to lose consciousness, and stop breathing.

WHAT TO DO

Take your child's clothes off and lay him down in a cool place. Call a doctor if your child's temperature is as high as 40°C (104°F) and, while you are

Lowering body temperature
Take your child out of the sun, and sponge her with tepid water or play a fan on her skin.

waiting, sponge him with tepid water or wrap him in a cool wet sheet. Place a covered icepack on his forehead, give him lots of cool drinks, and play a fan on his body. Monitor his pulse rate and temperature closely. Check his temperature every minute until it lowers to 37.2°C (99°F), then stop cooling but continue to monitor his temperature.

If he begins to lose consciousness you should place him in the recovery position (see p.329) and check his breathing. If he has stopped breathing, give ventilation (see p.330) and call an ambulance.

HYPOTHERMIA

If your child gets cold as a result of being exposed to cold, wet, and windy weather, a near-drowning, or simply being in a room that is too cold, he may suffer from hypothermia. Clinically, hypothermia is defined as a body temperature of below 35°C (95°F). Deep hypothermia occurs when the body temperature drops to below 26°C (79°F) and this can be fatal since the heart, liver, lungs, and intestines may slow down and cease functioning.

Symptoms Your child may be shivering and his skin will feel cold and dry. He may look pale and blue (although babies may look pink) and his breathing may be slow and shallow. He will be lethargic and there might be behavioural signs such as apathy, confusion, and quietness. In severe cases of hypothermia your child may start to lose consciousness.

WHAT TO DO

Take off any wet clothing, wrap your child in warm, dry clothes and blankets, and hold him close to your body. Call a doctor urgently.

Older children can be warmed up with a warm bath and warm (not hot) sweet drinks. Monitor your child's temperature constantly with a thermometer or by feeling his skin. If your attempts to warm him up are not working, or if he loses consciousness, call an ambulance. If he seems to be warming up, put him in a warm bed and stay with him until the doctor arrives or you are sure his temperature is back to normal. Never place a direct source of heat, such as a hot water bottle, on your child's skin.

EVERYDAY FIRST AID

As your child grows up he will inevitably experience some commonplace accidents such as cuts, bruises, blisters, bites, and stings. Most of the time they are not serious and can be treated at home with comfort and some simple first aid techniques.

ANIMAL BITES

Animal bites can happen if your child is teasing or playing boisterously with a domestic pet, usually a dog or a cat. Although being bitten can be traumatic for your child, bites are not usually serious. The main danger is that if the animal bites deep into the flesh, bacteria will be lodged in the wound, making your child vulnerable to infection. If your child is bitten by a dog or other animal while you are travelling abroad seek medical treatment immediately, since anti-rabies injections may be needed.

The first thing you should do is reassure your child, as he will probably be quite frightened. If he was bitten because he was teasing the animal you should explain this to him and emphasize that it is an isolated incident.

What to do

Wash the wound thoroughly with warm water. Apply an antiseptic cream and cover the bite with a dressing. If the bite is severe, try to control the bleeding with direct pressure and by raising the wounded part of the body and wrapping it tightly with a bandage. Cover the wound with a dressing and take your child to hospital. He may need a tetanus injection if he hasn't been immunized.

SNAKE BITES

The adder is the only venomous snake in the UK and its bite is rarely fatal. If your child is bitten while you are abroad you should make a note of the snake's appearance so that the appropriate antidote can be given. Depending on the snake, the symptoms of a snake bite can include puncture marks in the skin, pain, redness, and swelling around the bite, and, in very severe cases, impaired breathing, sweating, vomiting, and impaired vision.

What to do

It is important to keep your child calm, since if he panics this can speed the spread of venom around the body. Wash the area of the bite with water, immobilize the affected part of the body with bandages, and take your child straight to hospital.

INSECT BITES AND STINGS

Stings and insect bites are not usually serious unless there is an allergic reaction. Stings in the mouth or throat, however, are serious, as the swelling they cause can obstruct the airway. Stinging insects include bees, wasps, and hornets; biting insects include fleas, mosquitoes, and ticks. A sting is felt as a sudden, sharp pain and appears as a raised, white area on an inflamed patch of skin. A bite is less painful and normally causes mild discomfort and inflammation.

What to do

Apply a cold compress and, later, calamine lotion to the bite or sting to relieve discomfort. If you can see the sting sticking out of your child's flesh, scrape it off gently with a fairly blunt knife.

If your child is bitten by fleas, have your family pet treated and your house disinfected. Mosquito bites can be avoided with insect repellent. When abroad, always use malaria prophylaxis medicine. Tick bites are painless but can cause infection and disease, so you should seek medical treatment.

If your child is stung in the mouth give him an ice cube to suck (unless he is under one year old) and seek medical help at once since swelling can restrict breathing. If your child has an allergic reaction to a sting you should treat it as an emergency. Symptoms of an allergic reaction include swelling of the face and neck, puffy eyes, impaired breathing, red blotchy skin, wheezing, and gasping.

Gently scrape across the skin to loosen the sting.

Removing a sting
Use a fairly blunt knife rather than tweezers, since tweezers may squeeze the sac of poison at the top of the sting

JELLYFISH STINGS

If your child steps on a jellyfish she may experience a severe local reaction – jellyfish have stinging cells that discharge venom when touched. The severity depends on the type of jellyfish. Those in the UK are not very toxic and are unlikely to produce severe symptoms – just a rash that may itch or be slightly painful. Rare jellyfish found overseas are more poisonous, and in extreme cases can cause vomiting, shock, breathing difficulties and unconsciousness, and can lead to death.

What to do

The stinging cells that stick to your child's skin release their poison gradually as they burst. You can help by inactivating the cells or preventing them from bursting. Alcohol or vinegar will do this, and any fine powder, like talcum powder, will make the cells stick together. If your child experiences a severe reaction to any sting or wound caused by a marine creature take her to hospital.

BLISTERS

When the skin is burnt or subjected to pressure or friction a blister may form as a protective cushion. Blisters are bubbles of skin with tissue fluid underneath. They are common on the heels of the feet if your child's shoes don't fit correctly or if she wears shoes without socks. Blisters are not usually serious unless they are the result of bad sunburn, they burst and become infected, or they are very large and painful, when you should consult your doctor.

What to do

Do not burst a blister. In a day or two new skin will form underneath the blister, the tissue fluid will be reabsorbed, and the blistered skin will dry and peel off. To aid this healing process you should cover the blister with a clean dressing (not a plaster, since this can burst the blister when you peel it off) and keep it dry. If your child's blister is very large your doctor may decide to burst it.

CUTS AND GRAZES

As long as a cut is superficial and is not infected (this is a risk with cuts by fingernails, plants, or animals), it should not require treatment other than a smear of antiseptic cream. A graze is simply an abrasion of the skin that leaves the surface raw and tender. A cut that bleeds profusely can lead to shock (see p.332) so treat it as an emergency. A very jagged cut may require stitches, and with a deep or dirty cut there is a risk of tetanus (see p.283).

What to do

Run cold water over the wounded area, and wash with soap. Dry by patting with a clean tissue, apply an antiseptic cream, and cover with a sterile dressing or a plaster. If your child has an incision wound where the cut has two straight edges you can hold them together using skin closure tape. If the wound is dirty or deep there is a risk of infection and you should take your child to hospital to see if she needs a tetanus injection.

If a cut is very deep or bleeds profusely you should take your child to hospital straight away, as she may need stitches. Before she gets to hospital, apply pressure to the wound using a clean handkerchief or pad (or your hand if you have nothing suitable) and make sure that the wounded part of the body is raised to slow the flow of blood.

SPLINTERS

Small shards of wood, glass, metal, or a thorn or spine from a plant can easily become embedded in your child's skin, particularly if she is playing out of doors. Unless splinters are embedded in the flesh or they prove too painful to remove, they can be dealt with very easily at home.

What to do

First try to find out from your child what kind of splinter it is. If it is glass, you should not try to remove it yourself as you could cut your child. Seek help from your doctor. Look for the end of the splinter. Take a pair of sterilized tweezers (you can sterilize them by holding them over a flame; then let them cool) and gently pull the protruding end

Pull the splinter out in the same direction it went in

Removing a splinter
If the end of the splinter is visible, use sterilized tweezers to pull it out gently. Don't try to remove a glass splinter yourself, as you could cut your child.

of the splinter out. Squeeze the area to make it bleed a little, since this will help clean it. When you have removed the splinter, clean the skin with soap and water, then apply a little antiseptic cream. If the splinter is completely embedded in your child's skin it may need to be removed by your doctor under local anaesthetic – don't poke or probe the area with a needle. If you think that there may be dirt in the wound your child may need a tetanus injection (see p.283).

BRUISES

Active children often get bruises from falls and knocks, and they are rarely serious; they usually take 10–14 days to disappear completely.

What to do

Minor bruises need no treatment, just a cuddle if your child is upset. If the bruise is large, apply a cold compress for half an hour or so to contain the bruising. Consult your doctor immediately if pain on the site of a bruise gets worse after 24 hours (this could indicate a fracture) or if your child repeatedly has bruises with no apparent cause (this could indicate a serious condition).

CRUSHED FINGERS

This is a fairly common accident in very young children who don't understand how door, windows, and drawers operate. A crush injury can be serious so it is vital to release the trapped hand as quickly as possible and to comfort your child.

What to do

If the skin is not broken, then once the finger or fingers have been released, hold your child's hand under a cold running tap or hold a bag of crushed ice or frozen food against it. When the pain has subsided a little, wrap the hand in a bandage. If the crush is very severe and there is internal bleeding or swelling, call an ambulance.

FOREIGN BODY IN THE EAR

The commonest objects for children to push into their ears are small beads, bits of crayon, and small components from construction toys. Occasionally an insect can fly into the ear, or cotton wool can be left behind after cleaning. A foreign body in the ear may cause temporary deafness, it may result in an ear infection, and it may damage the eardrum.

What to do

If your child has an insect in her ear canal, lay her on her side with the affected ear uppermost and pour tepid water from a jug into the ear. The insect should float out. Any other type of foreign body needs to be treated by a doctor. If you attempt to remove it yourself you may cause more damage. Your doctor can remove it and treat any resulting infection or damage to the skin. You can reduce the risk of foreign bodies in the ear by making sure your child isn't given toys with small parts, particularly if she is under three years old.

FOREIGN BODY IN THE NOSE

If your child has pushed something into her nose you may not notice, though she will probably complain of pain. Occasionally it takes several days for symptoms to become apparent. Your child might develop a blood-stained discharge from the nose, she may find it difficult to breathe, and there may be swelling, inflammation, and bruising around the bridge of the nose. A foreign body in the nose is rarely serious, but there is a risk that your child will inhale the object, so it requires hospital treatment.

What to do

Do not try to remove the object, as you could cause your child an injury, or push the object in further. Keep her calm, get her to breathe through her mouth, and take her to hospital.

At hospital a doctor will remove the foreign body using a pair of forceps; if your child is very young she may need a general anaesthetic beforehand.

PENIS CAUGHT IN ZIP

This can happen if your child is careless when doing up his zip. The tip of the penis gets caught between the teeth of the zip, and, although there should be no long-term damage, it is very painful.

What to do

You should not attempt to undo the zip. Instead, take your child to hospital and relieve the pain in the meantime by placing wrapped ice cubes over the zip and penis. A doctor will undo the zip after giving your child a local anaesthetic. Aftercare includes applying antiseptic to the penis and giving paracetamol elixir to relieve pain. Your child should pour warm water over his penis as he urinates, to dilute the urine and prevent stinging.

USEFUL ADDRESSES

POSTNATAL SUPPORT

Association of Breastfeeding Mothers
26 Holmshaw Close
London SE26 4TH
Tel: 0181 778 4769

Association for Postnatal Illness
25 Jerdan Place
Fulham
London SW6 1BE
Tel: 0171 386 0868

Family Planning Association
27–35 Mortimer Street
London W1N 7RJ
Tel: 0171 636 7866

Health Visitors Association
50 Southwark Street
London SE1 1UN
Tel: 0171 378 7255

MAMA (Meet-a-Mum Association)
Cornerstone House
14 Willis Road
Croydon CR0 2XX
Tel: 0181 665 0357
For isolated or depressed mothers

National Childbirth Trust
Alexandra House
Oldham Terrace
Acton
London W3 6NH
Tel: 0181 992 8637

PARENTS' GROUPS

BLISS (Baby Life Support Systems)
17–21 Emerald Street
London WC1N 3QL
Tel: 0934 713630 (freephone)
For parents of special care babies

CRY-SIS Support Group
BM Cry-Sis
London WC1N 3XX
Tel: 0171 404 5011
Advice on babies who cry excessively

Exploring Parenthood
Latimer Education Centre
194 Freston Road
London W10 6TT
Tel: 0181 960 1678
Advice on parenting problems from newborn to adult

Foundation for the Study of Infant Death
35 Belgrave Square
London SW1X 8QB
Helpline: 0171 235 1721
(24 hours)

Gingerbread Association for One-Parent Families
49 Wellington Street
London WC2E 7BN
Tel: 0171 240 0953

Multiple Births Foundation
Queen Charlotte and Chelsea Hospital
Goldhawk Road
London W6 0XG
Tel: 0181 740 3519

National Council for One-Parent Families
255 Kentish Town Road
London NW5 2LX
Tel: 0171 267 1361

Parentline
Westbury House
57 Hart Road
Thundersley
Essex
Tel: 01268 757077
Helpline for all ages

Stepfamily
72 Willesden Lane
London NW6 7TA
Tel: 0171 372 0844

TAMBA (Twins and Multiple Birth Association)
PO Box 30
Little Sutton
South Wirral L66 1TH
Tel: 0151 348 0020
Tamba twin line: 0732 868000

Vegetarian Society
Parkdale
Dunham Road
Altrincham
Cheshire WA14 4QG
Tel: 0161 928 0793

CARE AND EDUCATION

British Association for Early Childhood Education (BAECE)
111 City View House
463 Bethnal Green Road
London E2 9QY
Tel: 0171 739 7594

National Childminding Association
8 Masons Hill
Bromley
Kent BR2 9EY
Tel: 0181 464 6164

Preschool Playgroups Association
61–63 King's Cross Road
London WC1X 9LL
Tel: 0171 833 0991I

FIRST AID AND SAFETY

British Red Cross
9 Grosvenor Crescent
London SW1X 7EJ
Tel: 0171 235 5454

British Standards Institute
Linford Wood
Milton Keynes MK14 6LE
Tel: 01908 22022
Information on safety standards

Child Accident Prevention Trust
18–20 Farringdon Lane
London EC1R 3AU
Tel: 0171 608 3828

Royal Society for the Prevention of Accidents (RoSPA)
Cannon House
The Priory Queensway
Birmingham B4 6BS
Tel: 0121 200 2461

St. Andrew's Ambulance Association
St. Andrew's House
Milton Street
Cowcaddans
Glasgow G4 0HR
Tel: 0141 332 4031

St. John Ambulance
1 Grosvenor Crescent
London SW1X 7EF
Tel: 0171 235 5231

CHILDREN WITH SPECIAL NEEDS

Association for Spina Bifida and Hydrocephalus (ASBAH)
Asbah House
42 Park Road
Peterborough PE1 2UQ
Tel: 01733 555988

The Association for Stammerers
15 Old Ford Road
Bethnal Green
London E2 9PJ
Helpline; 0181 981 8818

British Diabetic Association
10 Queen Anne Street
London W1M 0BD
Tel: 0171 323 1531

British Dyslexia Association
98 London Road
Reading
Berks RG1 5AU
Tel: 01734 668271

British Epilepsy Association
Anstey House
40 Hanover Square
Leeds LS3 1BE
Tel: 0113 2439393
Helpline: 0345 089599
Support from local groups

Child Growth Foundation
2 Mayfield Avenue
London W4 1PW
Counselling and advice for parents of children with growth problems

Coeliac Society of UK
PO Box 220
High Wycombe
Buckinghamshire HP11 2HY
Tel: 01494 437278
(weekdays, 9.30 a.m.–3 p.m.)

Contact-a-Family
170 Tottenham Court Road
London W1P OHA
Tel: 0171 383 3555
Supports parents of children with special needs

Cystic Fibrosis Trust
Alexandra House
5 Blyth Road
Bromley
Kent BR1 3RS
Tel: 0181 464 7211

Down's Syndrome Association
155 Mitcham Road
London SW17 9PG
Tel: 0181 682 4001

Federation of Multiple Sclerosis Therapy Centres
Unit 4
Murdock Road
Bedford MK41 7PD
Tel: 01234 32578

Hyperactive Children's Support Group
71 Whyke Lane
Chichester
West Sussex PO19 2LD
Tel: 01903 725182
(9.30 a.m.–3.30 p.m., Tues–Fri)

MENCAP (The Royal Society for Mentally Handicapped Children and Adults)
Mencap National Centre
123 Golden Lane
London EC1Y 0RT
Tel: 0171 454 0454
For people with learning disabilities

The Muscular Dystrophy Group of Great Britain and Northern Ireland
7–11 Prescott Place
Clapham
London SW4 6BS
Tel: 0171 720 8055

The National Association for Gifted Children (NAGC)
Park Campus
Boughton Green Road
Northampton NN2 7AL
Tel: 01604 792300

The National Asthma Campaign
Providence House
Providence Place
London N1 0NT
Tel: 0171 226 2260

National Autistic Society
276 Willesden Lane
London NW2 5RB
Tel: 0181 451 1114

The National Deaf Children's Society
Family Services Centre
24 Wakefield Road
Rothwell
Haigh
Leeds LS26 0SF
Tel: 0113 2823458

The National Eczema Society
4 Tavistock Place
London WC1H 9RA
Tel: 0171 388 4097

Royal National Institute for the Blind (RNIB)
224 Great Portland Street
London W1N 6AA
Tel: 0171 388 1266

Scope (formerly The Spastics Society)
Library and Information Unit
12 Park Crescent
London W1N 4EQ
Tel: 0171 636 5020
Helpline: 0800 626216
(weekdays, 11 a.m.–9 p.m.; weekends, 2–6 p.m.)
Support, assessment, and education for people with cerebral palsy

The Sickle Cell Society
54 Station Road
Harlesden
London NW10 4UA
Tel: 0181 961 7795
Send SAE for information leaflets

INDEX

ACKNOWLEDGEMENTS

Carroll & Brown Limited would like to thank:

Photography
Jules Selmes

Illustration
Aziz Khan: 33, 40, 50, 87, 104, 105, 109, 175, 262, 265, 266 (right), 267, 271, 273, 278 (bottom), 279, 285, 291, 295, 298, 299, 300, 301, 306, 308, 309, 310, 311, 312, 327, 337, 338; Coral Mula: 29, 290, 296, 297, 305, 336; Howard Pemberton: 103, 179, 266, 269; Ian Thompson: 25, 278, 286

Medical consultants
Dr Margaret Lawson; Dr Frances Williams

Advice and assistance
Association for Spina Bifida and Hydrocephalus; Child Accident Prevention Trust; Child Growth Foundation (height and weight charts); Cleft Lip and Palate Association; National Childbirth Trust; The Vegetarian Society. The first aid information on pp.326–343 has been validated by Joe Mulligan, Training Officer, British Red Cross.

Typesetting
Debbie Lelliott; Rowena Feeny; Axis Design

Film output
Disc To Print (UK) Ltd

Equipment
Boots the Chemist; Children's World; Debenhams; Freeman's Mail Order

Models
Julia Alcock; Milo Baraclough; Cassie-Ella Bernard; Gertrud Blomberg; Lena Larsson Blomberg and Fredrik; Zoë Bothamley; Georgina and Elliot Bourke; Alison Briegel, Alice, and Charlie; Jayde Caines; Niyazi Caykara; Oliver Clarke; Ricardo Cohen; George Cooper; Hannah and Charlotte Coster; Ella Crawley; Cora Eugene and Kairone; Emily Fogarty; Keitel and Stone Frankle; Joseph Gavshon; Julia Gibbon; Candy Gummer; Hannah Heyes; Katie Hogben; Natalie Joseph; Elliott Kenton; Sami Khan; William King; Beverley Lagna; Malcolm Langton; Lee Lawer; Angela Loveday and Jack; Georgina McCooke; Ursula Macfarlane and Josiah Ackerman; Kelly MacNabb; Joan Marcello and Marco; Antonio Marcello; Joseph Milner Sweeney; Cordelia Nelson; Reiss Ng;

Stephanie Parker and Daniel; Jordan Raymond; Temuera Reefman; Millie Satow; Kuba Shand; Caroline Sims and Michael; Alice Smith; Jayde, Mairéad, and Michael Snell; Aisling Walsh; Tess Watson; Mark Weegmann; Beresford Williams; Jessica Williams; Albert Wood

Additional editorial assistance
Kesta Desmond; Richard Emerson; Steve McGrath; Cathy Meeus; Jennifer Rylaarsdam

Index
Anne McCarthy

Additional design assistance
Juanita Grout, Richard Horsford

Picture credits
Collections/Anthea Sieveking, 26; Mike Good/Zartec Studios, 114; Taeke Henstra, Petit Format/Science Photo Library, 12; John Radcliffe Hospital/Science Photo Library, 292; Dr H.C. Robinson/Science Photo Library, 291; Science Photo Library, 302; Ron Sutherland/Science Photo Library, 15; Katrina Thomas/Science Photo Library, 13